D0934853

Our
American
Weather

Books by George H. T. Kimble

GEOGRAPHY IN THE MIDDLE AGES
THE WORLD'S OPEN SPACES
THE WEATHER
THE WAY OF THE WORLD
OUR AMERICAN WEATHER

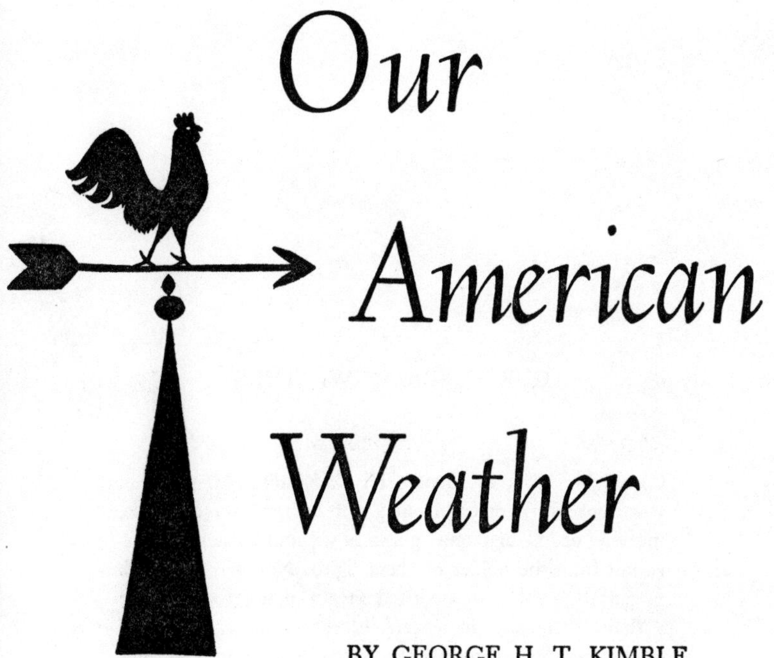

Our American Weather

BY GEORGE H. T. KIMBLE

Maps and charts by Jean Paul Tremblay

McGraw-Hill Book Company, Inc.

New York Toronto London

OUR AMERICAN WEATHER

Library of Congress Catalog Card Number: 54-9711

Published by the McGraw-Hill Book Company, Inc.
Printed in the United States of America

EIGHTH PRINTING

34560

Designed and illustrated by Herschel Wartik

Preface

THERE IS nothing quite like American weather anywhere else in the world. To be sure, its ingredients are common enough—sunshine and cloud: cold and heat: wind, rain, and snow—the same as those of every country from China to Peru: and the compounding of them is done no differently in Kansas than in Kurdistan, and to a "normal-minded" statistician the amounts compounded in the course of a cycle of Cathay are hardly distinguishable from those compounded in the cycle of California. But the Topekan does not live with normals: what he *feels* is not the 54°F. annual mean temperature, but the blizzard that descends out of the north in February, the soft south wind that blows in May, the heat that overwhelms him on a July day, and the chill that refreshes him on a September night. What the Pasadenan knows is not the average rainfall for the year, but the long summer drought with its desiccating days and airless nights; the tentative rains of autumn and the scent of the grateful earth that accompanies them; and the occasional frosting of winter snow on the hills behind him.

It is in the shuffling of such sharply accented weather sequences, rather than in the compounding of their elemental ingredients, that American weather comes by its unrivaled individuality.

This individuality expresses itself in many ways. Here it is a predisposition to go to extremes: have not all of us marveled at the abandon with which Dame Nature juggles her winter winds, today coaxing the mercury up into the 50s, tomorrow thrusting it down to zero? There it is a liking for getting things done in a hurry, whether it be the transforming of spring mud into summer dust, or of summer dews into autumn frosts. Elsewhere it is an impatience with authority—not least, seemingly, the meteorologist's authority, for where else in the world do so many well-conceived forecasts bring forth so many ill-nourished explanations of their failure? And everywhere and all the time it is a love of originality (we have yet to see two consecutive days that are atmospherically identical) and a flair for flamboyance. Hailstones the size of baseballs, winds that flatten a house to the ground as easily as they can lift it into the air, heat that can fry an egg, and cold that can freeze a cow dead in her tracks—what are these if not the work of a prima donna?

The main causes of this individuality are two in number. First, the constant assailing of the American skies by well-matched "air forces" of contrasted temperaments. These air forces, or air masses to give them their more usual name, are recruited from no less than six different quarters: from the North Pacific; the Canadian Far North; the North Atlantic; the Central Pacific; the American Southwest and adjacent Mexican plateau, and the Central Atlantic–Caribbean area. From the North Pacific comes maritime air, known to meteorologists as Pacific polar maritime air, characterized the year round by good visibility, broken skies, low temperatures, and a showery disposition when it moves inland over the western Sierras. From the Central Pacific in wintertime comes another breed of sea air—Pacific tropical maritime air. This is conspicuous for its cloudy to overcast skies, its high humidities, warmth, and at times its rather indifferent visibility. In summer this air mass shifts its sphere of operation and seldom affects the American mainland. From the high arctic comes air—polar continental by name—that, in winter, is very dry and cold and consequently marked by almost cloudless skies and exceptional visibility, and not infrequently by high winds; and in summer is cool and dry, but capable of producing plenty of afternoon cloud by the time it has reached our northernmost tier of states. From the semi-arid plateaus of Mexico and the Southwest there come in summer (in winter the necessary supply of heat is missing) occasional forays of tropical continental air that is dry, cloudless, and immoderately hot, especially during the day. The Atlantic breeds a third pair of air masses—Atlantic polar maritime and Atlantic tropical maritime. The former is generally content to stay offshore, but when it does come inland you can quickly tell, for in winter it is raw and cloudy and in summer clammy and cool. Atlantic tropical maritime air, unlike its Pacific equivalent, forms part of the country's permanent "air strength": if anything, it is more active in summer than in winter. But like its Pacific equivalent, it is warm and moist, a most agreeable air in winter, though in summer more enemy than friend of perspiring mortals.

On almost any given day one or more of these air forces will be in evidence over large parts of the Union: the rest will be skirmishing around the continental flanks, re-forming either offshore or north of the 49th parallel for a new assault, or temporarily *hors de combat* in their polar and tropical supply zones. How first one and then another of these massive powers is in the ascendant: how occasionally all of them are ousted from our continental battleground to be superseded temporarily by air forces of more local origin and less impressive ability is the story of a campaign that seemingly has no beginning, no end, and sometimes no discernible plan. But at least the story is never twice the same.

In the second place, the individuality of American weather

reflects and, indeed, is fortified by the individuality of the American terrain. We would have to go far to find a stretch of land more strongly articulated structurally and physically, let alone one wielding a greater weather-modifying influence.

The sensitivity of the atmosphere to changes of elevation, aspect, exposure, even of soil and vegetation, is common knowledge, and to its effects we can all bear testimony. Quite small ponds, bays, hills, and dales have the power to change the feel of the wind, the daily march of temperature, and the intensity of a rainstorm: how much more mountains of the magnitude of the Sierras, the Great Lakes, and the great valleys of the Appalachians? Even the great American city adds its tally, as we shall later see, to the variegation of American weather.

But the terrain plays another and bigger role than this. Because the main mountain systems run north-south rather than east-west, the heart of the continent has no defense (as India has, for instance) against the periodic incursions of south-moving polar air. In winter cold "northers" are felt on the Gulf coast and beyond, and the snow line swings farther south in the central lowlands than it does, level for level, in any other country of the world. By way of partial compensation, higher summer temperatures are registered along the international border, level for level, than in similar latitudes of Europe and Asia—and for the same reason: there are no Alps or Himalayas to block the poleward advance of tropical air. And because the western Cordilleras run the entire length of the country—and beyond—they constitute a stiff obstacle to the inland penetration of Pacific air, whether polar maritime or tropical maritime. Nowhere else in the world do mountain systems stand in the way of so much clouded air so consistently.

In other words, the grain of the country is such that it facilitates the flow of heat and cold, while restraining the flow of moisture. In so doing, it makes a monumental contribution to the style—good, bad and indifferent—that stamps the fashion of "the varied year."

Our American Weather is an attempt to catch something of this "style" as it alters from season to season and from place to place, and to portray the changing, yet recurring, patterns of weather that are woven into the fabric of the American landscape. For notwithstanding her eccentricities and extravagances, Dame Nature is no slouch of fashion. Each season, if not each month, has its dominant motif: each mountain and valley, each shore and plain its characteristic "custom-made" mantle. There may have been springs in Maine that were strangers to ethereal mildness: summer suns in Oregon that were anything but fantastic: falls in Wisconsin that were far from mellow, and winters in Arkansas that were more bitter than sullen; but all of us, whether blessed with a poet's insight or not, recognize in the very act of striving for the fitting word that seasons, like landscapes, have their "wonted liveries."

Our concern is with these liveries and the "cloth" of which they are made. In each chapter we shall try to describe those spectacles of the weather parade that are most widely associated with specific times of the year. We readily admit that the association is, in many instances, poorly founded and that, in many more, it is only evident if we make a generation rather than a season our measuring rod: but we think it unlikely that even the Miami Chamber of Commerce would deny the existence of cold waves in winter and their greater frequency in January than in December or February, or the existence of summer thunderstorms and their greater frequency in July than in June or August.

Wayward as the course of weather undoubtedly is and inscrutable as some of its processes may seem to be, the fact is that it has a code of behavior and respects it. We may not like the code, but as the chances are it is a good one (after all, the weather has managed to keep things going an unconscionably long time), the least we can do is to strive to understand it. Our exertions may not make us very wise, but they could make us humble.

George H.T. Kimble

Acknowledgments

MANY FRIENDS have contributed to the making of this book. They are, of course, in no way responsible for the propriety, or otherwise, of the author's opinions: they may well be dismayed by some of them.

Special thanks are due to Raymond Bush, upon whose wealth of weather wisdom substantial demands have been made; to Nordis Felland and her colleagues on the staff of the library of the American Geographical Society, who, given even the faintest scent, never failed to run their quarry to earth; to Phyllis Horwitz, who, given the most illegible script, never lost her way, or her patience; and to Arline Holden, who, amid the preoccupations of family life, found time to compile the index.

Also gratefully acknowledged is the permission, readily granted, of the following gentlemen to use illustrative material for which they hold the copyright: Dr. H. E. Landsberg, Chief of the Climatological Services Division of the U.S. Weather Bureau; Dr. Kenneth C. Spengler, Executive Secretary of the American Meteorological Society; Professor F. Kenneth Hare of McGill University; Professor S. S. Visher of Indiana University, Dr. I. R. Tannehill of the U.S. Weather Bureau, and the directors of the American Telephone and Telegraph Company.

I am no less indebted to Mr. Robert Frost, Sir Alan Herbert, and the proprietors of *Punch* for their courtesy in allowing me to draw upon their publications.

Contents

January

Unseasonable weather

THERE ARE at least three things about any American winter you can be pretty sure of: it will be different from what you, and the forecasters, expected; it will be more given to extremes than means; and it will be the most popular topic of conversation.

Some parts of the continent are, it is true, less given to meteorological aberrations than others. Southern California is more likely to have a heat wave in January than a snowstorm: the Florida "Gold Coast" can bank on seeing the sun shine five days out of seven, while Mount Washington in New Hampshire will probably be in the teeth of a gale just about as often. But weather is more than snow, sunshine, and storm. It is a compound of a score of physical ingredients: it is a mosaic of contrasted moods, and a fabric of many colors, and it is nothing if not quixotic. One of its commonest habits is to break its habits, for it is no respecter of "the dotted line" or the table of normals. Winter's sun may caress, but seldom long enough to weary its suitors: its cold may kill, but nobody, not even the Eskimo, dies of monotony. Upon occasion it can reshuffle the months, with results almost as dramatic as those described by Shakespeare in *A Midsummer Night's Dream:*

. . . hoary-headed frosts
Fall in the fresh lap of the crimson rose;
And on old Hiems' thin and icy crown
An odorous chaplet of sweet summer buds
Is, as in mockery, set; the spring, the summer,
The childing autumn, angry winter, change
Their wonted liveries; and the mazed world,
By their increase, now knows not which is which.

Of course Shakespeare lived in England, where it is perfectly possible for a day in June to be colder than a day in January. On this continent the weather also has its eccentricities, but that is not one of them. All the same, sharp, even violent fluctuations of temperature giving rise to "unseasonable" warmth, or cold, are common enough. In Montreal, for instance, the thermometer is likely to stand above freezing point for a period of at least 12 hours two or three times during the month of January. Just how unseasonable such conditions are can be appreciated when we point out that the mean January temperature there is nearly 20 degrees below freezing level. By way of contrast, however, Montreal is almost equally likely to experience days in January when the temperature is 20 degrees or more *below* the mean figure: these, in the view of the inhabitants, are even more unseasonable. New Yorkers must be prepared for anything from zero to 60 degrees above, in spite of the fact that their mean January temperature is just about freezing point. Middle Westerners are even worse off. They have to contend with a thermometer that may rise and fall all of 80 degrees during the month. Even holidaymakers on the Florida "Gold Coast" must take a chance of shivering occasionally, for while 80 degrees in the shade is nothing unusual at places like Palm Beach and Miami, ground frosts are not unknown at night. The truth of the matter is that very few parts of continental North America are immune to violent temperature oscillations, in winter at all events.

For, as we might expect, unseasonable weather is very largely a winter phenomenon. At Montreal during the past thirty-five to forty years there have been nearly six times as many warm days, that is, days on which the temperature was 10 degrees or more above the seasonal average, and more than sixteen times as many cold days, that is, days on which the temperature was 10 degrees or more below the seasonal average, in January as there were in July. Not dissimilar ratios apply to places as far flung as Calgary, Chicago, Cleveland, and Chattanooga. The reason why this should be so is that in winter the continental interior is never very far removed from vast reservoirs of extremely cold air and warm air, whereas in summer the only cold-air repository is found over the polar seas, and even there the temperature does not sink much below freezing point. To reach the St. Lawrence or the Mississippi Valley, this cool air must cross many hundreds of miles of heated land surface. At the other end of the temperature scale, conditions favoring exceptionally high daytime maxima in summer are ordinarily such—clear skies, little wind, and low relative humidity—as to make for rapid nocturnal radiation. This usually has the effect of pulling down the mean temperature, that is, the average of the daytime maximum and the nighttime minimum, to a figure falling within the 10°F. "plus-departure" zone.

January thaw

The most striking thing about unseasonable winter weather is that it is more likely to occur at some times than others. For instance, a mild spell—that is, a spell in which the temperatures are at least 10°F. above the seasonal average—is more than six times as likely to occur in the New York area between January 19 and 24 as it is between December 4 and 12 or between February 7 and 12. The chances that at least one day between January 19 and 24 will be unseasonably mild are about four to three—which, in our capricious climate, is saying something. The temperature in New York on the afternoon of January 19, 1954 was in the 40s: the following evening it was 56°F. Two days earlier it had registered zero at the author's back door. Nor is New York by any means alone in this respect. The existence of a comparable positive temperature anomaly during the period of January 20–23 has been established beyond cavil for Washington, Montreal, Boston, and many other stations in the Northeast. An analysis of the January temperature normals for Boston shows that in five years out of ten the temperature on January 22 is higher than on either January 19 or 25. This may not strike the casual reader as anything more than a chance distribution, but to the meteorologist it is, for the atmosphere is an incredibly poor timekeeper, being wont to count time more by months than days. It is equally striking, to the meteorologist, to find that on January 22 there is almost as high a probability of temperatures around 38°F. as there is of "normal values" around 30°F. A week later, on the other hand, temperatures around 38°F. are rare—far more rare, in fact, than temperatures around 20°F.

The conviction that we are dealing with a recurring atmospheric anomaly—or "singularity" as it is sometimes called—and not merely with a statistical pattern is strengthened when we discover that the mean pressure pattern for January 22 is quite distinct from the mean pressure pattern for the month and, for that matter, from the mean pattern for the period immediately before and after the twenty-second. The usually assumed picture of winter circulation over the United States—with its high-pressure center over the Deep South and trough of low pressure off the east coast—becomes distorted around the seventeenth and eighteenth by a northward shift of the high and the formation of a trough in the Great Lakes region, which then moves eastward and, by the twenty-second to twenty-third, restores and intensifies the normal picture. According to Dr. E. W. Wahl, who has investigated this phenomenon in great detail, "This strongly suggests the association of the singularity with other changes in the weather in other regions and it might very well be that the whole hemispheric behavior of the general circulation shows some definite change during this time."

So there really does appear to be something in this idea of a January thaw: which, to say the least, is surprising, since it started life in Europe which has a very different kind of winter from that in New England whither it was imported by the early Pilgrims.

Cold waves

Our cold waves, it seems, likewise have a marked preference for certain dates. Thus, an analysis of the lengthy temperature records of McGill Observatory in Montreal shows that temperatures averaging at least 10°F. below the seasonal norm are more than twice as likely to be reported in the last week of January as they are in Christmas week. A similar analysis for New York shows that comparable temperatures are more than twice as likely to occur during the first week of February (that is, a little later than in the Montreal area, which is reasonable enough when you remember that it takes time for cold air to travel south) as they are during Christmas week. But this is not to say that a cold wave will strike the Northeast on the twenty-eighth of next January. You might have a warm wave instead. However, there is this to be said about cold waves. Although they may not keep track of the calendar, they give due notice of their arrival, and they are among the easier phenomena to forecast. The atmospheric circumstances that favor their advent are as follows:

1. A strong high-pressure system located in the general vicinity of the Northwest Territories and the Yukon. The clear skies, snow-covered ground, long nights, and absence of wind characteristic of such a pressure system make for rapid radiative cooling.

2. A fast-moving low in the Great Lakes region—the faster it is moving eastward, or northeastward, the better.

3. A steep pressure gradient between the two: this increases the isobaric slope down which the cold air will move, and speed of air movement is really more important than its starting temperature in deciding whether a given outbreak of polar air will qualify as a cold wave by the time it blows across the stockyards of Chicago. Even so, the full impact of the wave can be cushioned considerably if the nights which the wave spends en route

Fig. 1. Daily maximum and minimum temperatures, Chicago, Illinois, November, 1952–March, 1953.

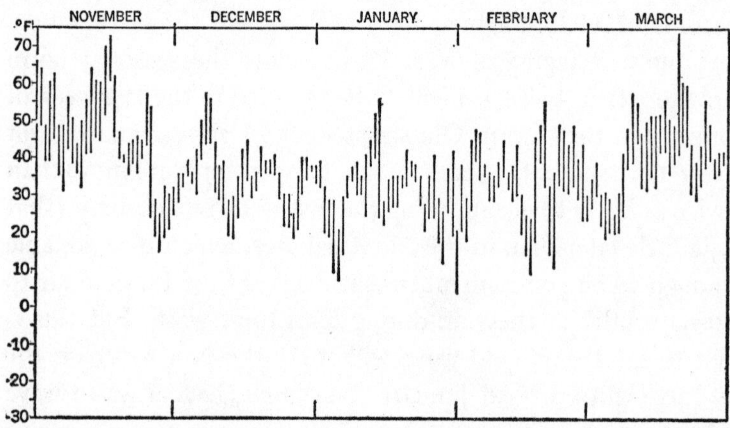

are cloudy, for clouds are first-class blanketers of heat; the cold can also be tempered if the wave spends any length of time over open water, as, for instance, over the larger of the Great Lakes which never entirely freeze.

In the Iowa-Illinois-Indiana region, the sudden plummeting of the mercury to very low readings is experienced on the average only two or three times a winter. Along the Canadian border in Manitoba, Minnesota, North Dakota, Saskatchewan, and Montana the frequency is much greater. Fortunately, as can be seen by these graphs, most of the waves do not last long, though, admittedly, they last long enough for the fancy of the folk who live with them. In Montana and the Canadian prairies, they may persist for a fortnight. In the Chicago area they are unlikely to last more than three or four days; in the middle Mississippi Valley, the mean period is nearer two days than four. And the farther south you go, the shorter their expectation of life and the greater the chance that they will be succeeded by a warm wave of comparable intensity. In fact, alternating warm spells and cold spells are the chief ingredi-

Fig. 2. Daily maximum and minimum temperatures, Butte, Montana, November, 1952–March, 1953.

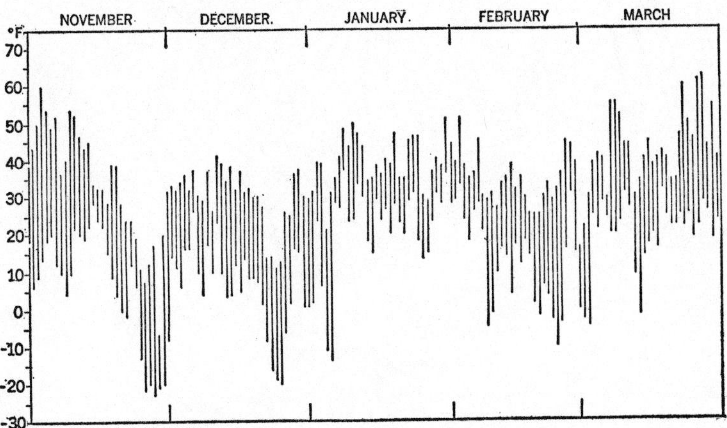

ents of the witches' brew which is the winter of the Middle West. There is nothing very "temperate" about it—notwithstanding that the region falls in the so-called temperate belt. For that matter, there is nothing very temperate about the winter weather of nine-tenths of the entire continent, and to portray winter conditions through the medium of monthly averages is no more likely to recreate the real "personality" of the winters of those nine parts than the alternate use of blue and yellow paints is likely to suggest green.

Even the most equable parts of the continent, like Vancouver Island, the San Francisco Bay region, Southern California, and Florida, are subject to day-to-day temperature fluctuations sizable enough to be embarrassing to their respective chambers of commerce and, much worse, ruinous to their economies. Upon occasion a cold wave originating in the Mackenzie Valley may not only advance as far south as Mexico,

Fig. 3. Departure of mean temperature from normal over the United States for week ending January 25, 1949. (Courtesy of the Weather Bureau, U.S. Department of Commerce)

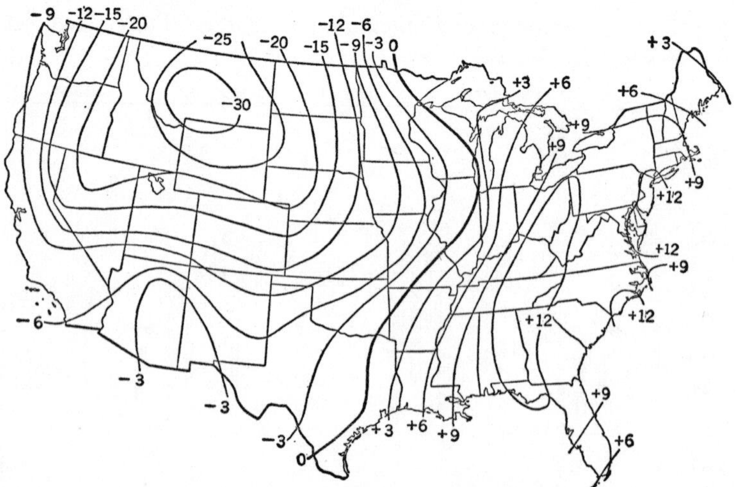

but spill across the passes and plateaus of the western Cordilleras to the Pacific coast. The thermal results of such a wave are reflected in the accompanying map, which shows the departure of mean temperature from the normal for the week ending January 25, 1949, over the United States. It will be seen that the entire western half of the country was in the grip of subnormal temperatures: the temperatures in several of the northern Mountain states were 20°F. below normal, and the entire California coast was more than 6°F. below normal. And this was not the first cold wave to sweep the West that month. There had, in fact, already been three. During one of these the temperature at Los Angeles dropped to 27.9°F.—the lowest on record—and citrus growers in the Riverside area sustained a 20-million-dollar crop loss: in another, San Diego had its first snowfall within the span of its records.

And yet during that same January the eastern half of the continent experienced a heat wave. Florida was reporting temperatures from 5 to 10°F. above normal; Washington, D.C., reported a record 73°F. one day and Newark, New Jersey, a record 60°F., and there was so little snow at some of the winter resorts that hoteliers were seriously thinking of importing some from Quebec for appearances—only Quebec didn't have enough either!

How cold can it get?

When it comes to extreme cold, there is a world of difference between one part of the Union and another. In Montana, temperatures of −60°F. have been recorded at no less than four stations, and temperatures of below −50°F. at many more. In Massachusetts the lowest recorded temperatures are in the minus 20s, and in Mississippi, the minus 10s. And the spread of winter extremes in North America as a whole is even bigger than this, for a temperature of —81°F. has been recorded in Yukon Territory (at Snag Airport, February 3, 1947), and down in the Florida Keys the Weather Bureau men have yet to see their first frost.

From the infrequency of their occurrence in the United States—there were only ten observations up to 1951—temperatures of —60°F. or below appear to require a very special combination of local circumstances. On all these ten occasions the ground was snow-covered—deeply in most cases—the atmosphere was dry and calm, the sky was clear, and the station was located well above sea level and had a basin-like exposure that encouraged the drainage of cold air in contact with the snow to the point of observation. Five of the ten reports came from valleys in the Yellowstone Park region, more than a mile above sea level.

Low as these temperatures are, the chances are that lower ones will be registered before the century is out, always assuming, that is, that the climate of the continent as a whole does not change materially. It is, so the statisticians tell us, in the nature of things for the magnitude of recorded extremes, whether minima or maxima, to depend on the length of the record. According to their informed guesses, a temperature of —64°F. will sooner or later be recorded at Havre, Montana, notwithstanding the fact that the lowest temperature reported there to date is only —57°F. (On second thought, the "only" is superfluous.) Again, Chicago is likely, one of these days, to experience a low of —28°F., which would be 5°F. lower than the existing record. Miami may wake up one January morning to find the mercury down in the low 20s—the present low is 27°F., and even San Diego may some day get 6 degrees of frost, as against the existing record of 5 degrees.

It's not the cold, it's the windchill!

As every reader of *Annapurna* knows, the real enemy Maurice Herzog and his companions were up against was not the near-zero temperatures but the wind which whipped those temperatures into a body-paralyzing potion. Until a few years ago, however, there was no precise measure of the body-cooling power of the atmosphere. Thanks to the experimental work of men like Paul A. Siple, who ever since he went south with Admiral Richard Byrd in 1928 has devoted himself to antarctic and arctic research, we now have a means of expressing quantitatively the fact that any normally clothed person feels much colder when the wind is blowing than when the air is calm. This cooling power is commonly, and appropriately, referred to as "windchill" and, for those who are interested in such things, is expressed in kilogram-calories of heat lost per hour per square meter of water. What it does is to combine wind speed and air temperature, and so produce a linear scale that yields absolute values of body-cooling rates and, more important perhaps, numerical comparisons between the characteristic windchill values of one locality and another.

Much of the research done since 1942 in the field of arctic survival, environmental protection, acclimatization rates, and maintenance of basal metabolism has been centered around the windchill concept. Though it has its critics (and it takes account of only one way in which the body may lose heat under cold wind conditions, and no account at all of atmospheric humidity which is certainly a factor in the equation of body comfort *), the concept of physiological chill through heat loss by convective exchange with the air is a considerable ad-

* Below about 15°F. it makes little difference whether the air is dry or damp. Over the range from 35 to 50°F., or so, dry air cools the skin more rapidly than moist air: hence the cutting qualities of the dry "norther" of spring even though its temperature may approach 50°F.

vance on the use of ordinary air-temperature statistics in assessing arctic cold.

Of course, we all have a pretty general idea of the difference a little breeze makes to the *feel* of the air on a cold day. Even zero weather is not hard to take when the air is calm. I once saw a kilted commanding officer of a Canadian arctic establishment conduct a visiting general on an outdoor tour of inspection when the temperature was hovering around zero. The C.O. looked quite comfortable, and the general was duly impressed—rather more so than the attendant Eskimos, I fancy.* They think nothing of running out of their snowhouses naked to stop a dogfight or kill a prowling bear, so long as there is no wind. But once let the wind start to blow and the arctic winter is no place for fancy dress. The "feel" of air 20°F. below zero moving at 5 miles per hour is about the same as that of air 20°F. above zero moving at 45 miles per hour. In both, exposed parts of the body of a normally healthy person are likely to freeze. So important is the wind factor that calm air at 40°F. below zero is less likely to cause frostbite than air just below freezing point blowing at gale force.

When is midwinter?

The answer to this question, like many another in the climate category, depends on where you happen to live. As you can see from the accompanying table, the incidence of the lowest temperatures varies widely from one part of the country to another.

* As a matter of fact, the Scotsman's kilt is by no means as silly as it seems (to Sassenachs, that is). The chilling of the knees which it permits not merely cools the Scotsman off in general, but also tends to stop perspiration on that part of the body where, in a very cold climate, it is most dangerous, namely, the feet. If the feet perspire, they are that much more likely to freeze later, because the moisture gets into the air chambers of the footgear, and the sock or boot ceases to be a good insulator and becomes instead a good conductor, permitting the loss of body heat.

In the Deep South midwinter occurs around the winter solstice, and the cold there, contrary to the general rule, does not grow stronger as the days get longer. On the Atlantic coast the lag between the solstice and midwinter tends to get bigger the farther north you go, at least as far as New Jersey, Connecticut, and Rhode Island, where it is all of six to seven weeks. At first thought this is rather baffling, for in both regions the sea-tem-

COLDEST WEEK OF THE YEAR *

* (As measured by the average weekly mean temperatures of selected stations in each area)

Eastern U.S.A.	
Maine	Jan. 22–28
Vermont	Jan. 22–28
Massachusetts	Jan. 22–28
Rhode Island	Feb. 5–11
Connecticut	Jan. 29–Feb. 4 Feb. 5–11
New Jersey	Jan. 29–Feb. 4 Feb. 5–11
Delaware	Dec. 24–30 Jan. 29–Feb. 4
E. Pennsylvania	Jan. 22–28
C. Virginia	Dec. 24–30
W. South Carolina	Dec. 17–23
N. Alabama	Jan. 1–7
C. Georgia	Dec. 17–22 24–30
N. Florida	Dec. 17–23
S. Florida	Dec. 24–30
E. New York	Jan. 22–28

Central U.S.A.	
N. Mississippi	Jan. 1–7
E. Tennessee	Dec. 24–30
S. Ohio	Dec. 24–30
Texas	Dec. 17–23
North Dakota	Jan. 15–21
W. Nebraska	Jan. 15–21
E. Kansas	Jan. 15–21

Central U.S.A. (*cont.*)	
W. Oklahoma	Jan. 8–14 15–21
N. Minnesota	Jan. 15–21
C. Wisconsin	Jan. 15–21
Iowa	Jan. 15–21
SW. Missouri	Jan. 8–14
C. Illinois	Jan. 15–21
S. Arkansas	Jan. 8–14
S. Louisiana	Dec. 17–23
Upper Michigan	Jan. 22–28
N. Indiana	Jan. 15–21
N. Ohio	Jan. 22–28

Western U.S.A.	
W. Washington	Jan. 15–21
E. Oregon	Jan. 15–21
SE. Idaho	Jan. 15–21
W. Montana	Jan. 15–21
NE. Wyoming	Jan. 15–21
NW. California	Jan. 8–14
C. California	Jan. 8–14
S. California	Jan. 15–21
Nevada	Jan. 15–21
SE. Utah	Jan. 8–14
SE. Colorado	Jan. 15–21
S. Arizona	Jan. 8–14
NE. New Mexico	Jan. 8–14 15–21

perature graph reveals a well-retarded minimum, as is only to be expected, bearing in mind the heat-conserving properties of a large water body. Possibly the South's early winter is the product of a combination of factors, including the comparative warmth of the coastal waters (even in January and February the sea temperatures off the "Gold Coast" are quite likely to be in the low 70s), the predominance over the same region of on-shore winds which are continually counterattacking the cold-air forces infiltrating from the north, and the substantial heating power of the southern sun (Key West is, after all, only a stone's throw from the Tropic of Cancer). On the other hand, the late midwinter of the northeast coast is probably a function of the coolness of the offshore waters which owe more to the Labrador current than the Gulf Stream, the offshore, and so cold, prevailing winds, and the curtailment of the power of the returning sun to warm the earth on account of the presence of snow and ice, and the smaller angle of incidence of the sun's rays.

The march of temperature at individual stations is frequently out of phase with that for the surrounding region, and stations less than 100 miles apart can show wider divergences than those exhibited by stations 1,000 miles and more apart. In California the delay in the arrival of the minimum ranges from eight days in the central San Joaquin Valley to thirty-six days in the High Sierras immediately to the northeast, at the head of the Yosemite Valley: there is a similar spread between the southern San Joaquin Valley and the Santa Monica–Long Beach region. Professor John Leighley of the University of California, Berkeley, who made a most detailed study of these climatic idiosyncrasies, found that the shortest delays between solstice and minimum temperatures are characteristic of protected localities, "either small valleys surrounded by high country, as at the stations in the northern third of the state . . . or . . . the edges of the large interior valleys." He also found that the higher up the station is, the longer the delay. In places it would look as though the time lag was also a function of proximity to the sea, for, taking the California coast as a whole, the minimum occurs between ten and twenty days later than it does fifty miles inland.

Of course, in a given year the lag between the shortest day and the coldest day may be considerably longer or shorter than the mean value, but the chances are that the coldest *spell* will fall within a week or so of the specified times.

The coldest *day* may fall as early as November or as late as April: however in the majority of the forty-eight states it shows a distinct tendency to occur sometime after midwinter, generally in early February. This seems to be especially true of the northeastern half of the country, and is possibly related to the fact that the snow cover is then at its maximum and cold waves advancing out of the northlands are kept "on ice" for a greater distance than at any other time of the winter. February also seems to be the favorite month for record low, that is, absolute minimum, temperatures. Of the ten lowest readings made in the United States, seven date from the first fortnight of February, six between February 8 and 15.

By contrast, the lowest winter maxima are rarely recorded in February and only about as frequently in January as in December. Why this should be is not entirely clear: one contributory cause may be that, whereas minimum thermometer readings tend to reflect opportunities for radiation which are governed as much by the state of the ground, that is, whether snow-covered or not, as by length of night and origin of air mass, maximum thermometer readings tend to reflect more closely the warming power of the sun, which is at its lowest ebb at the time of the winter solstice.

The ice storm

Nothing is so likely to make weather news in winter as an ice storm. For two reasons: first, it dislocates traffic and communications worse than almost any other atmospheric phenomenon; and second, it has a habit of arriving unannounced—to the mortification oftentimes of the forecaster. The trouble, from the meteorologist's point of view, is that the dividing line between the conditions which make for a snowstorm and those which make for an ice storm is drawn so fine that he might as well toss a coin as go through with all his abracadabra. Differences of temperature as small as 1°F. and of elevation of no more than 100 feet can be very critical. In the January, 1953, ice storm that wrought so much havoc in the outer suburbs of New York, the New Jersey village of Alpine in which I live was completely encased in ice—up to 1½ inches in diameter. The neighboring village of Closter, 150 feet or so lower in elevation, didn't know there was a storm. The difference in temperature between the two villages could not have been more than 2°F. at the most. The divide between the affected and nonaffected zones was as sharp as a contour line: as a matter of fact it followed, very closely, the 200-foot contour line.

The main ingredients of an ice storm are simple enough. All you need is either supercooled rain with a temperature just below freezing point, falling onto a surface with about the same temperature, or ordinary rain, preferably on the cold side, falling onto a surface very much below freezing point. The ideal locale for such a storm is in advance of a really warm front moving across a cold, frost-bound surface. Here the precipitation will almost certainly take the form of rain (if it starts as snow, it won't do the trick at all), and the surface-air temperature will be subfreezing. If the rain has to fall a very long way through cold air, the drops will probably freeze into solid balls before contact is made with the ground. Such a storm will be unlikely to cause any great inconvenience or damage. But if the raindrops have to fall only a short distance, the chances are that they will not begin to solidify until the moment of contact with a cold surface. In this latter case, every exposed object gets coated with a layer of ice, or glaze. If the rain is heavy, only a small part of the water is immediately transformed into ice: the rest runs over the frozen surface of the object in question, but sooner or later it too becomes converted into a coating of ice. Exceptionally, this coating may grow to be 3 inches thick. In this event, serious damage will be done to trees and overhead transmission lines. When we realize that the weight of ice adhering to telegraph wires and twigs in such circumstances can be twenty times the weight of the wires and twigs themselves, the capacity of an ice storm for working devastation is readily understood. In the unprecedentedly severe storm experienced in England at the end of January, 1940, it was found that 11 tons of ice was being supported by some of the telegraph poles before they finally snapped; individual wires carried as much as 1,000 pounds of ice. The effect of that particular storm on animal life was pathetic. Birds had their feet frozen to branches of trees and consequently died of starvation; pheasants could not fly because their wings were frozen solid; starlings, deprived of food, turned cannibals; and even cats became immobilized during their nocturnal wanderings, and had to have their feet thawed out.

On this continent ice storms represent a winter hazard in all but six of the forty-eight states and in most of the provinces of Canada. In the United States only Florida, New Mexico, Arizona, Utah, Nevada, and the southern part of California are habitually free from their attentions, and in Canada, only the Yukon, Northwest Territories, and the high arctic north of the timber line. The reasons for their immunity from glaze are as different as the areas concerned. Florida is too warm, the Southwest and intermountain regions are too dry, and northern Canada is too cold for the necessary frontal situations to arise.

The favorite haunt of the ice storm is an L-shaped belt extending from central Texas northward to Kansas, then eastward across the Ohio Valley and the lower lakes to New England and the Middle Atlantic states. Throughout this belt there is at least a one-in-three chance of a serious storm occurring every winter. Ice storms also frequent the Pacific Northwest and the southern Appalachian country: here their favorite predisposing causes are not so much fronts as cool, near-saturated maritime air masses, coupled with enough forced ascent to bring about condensation on an already snow-covered surface.

Fig. 4. Frequency of ice storms. (*Courtesy of American Telephone and Telegraph Co.*) *

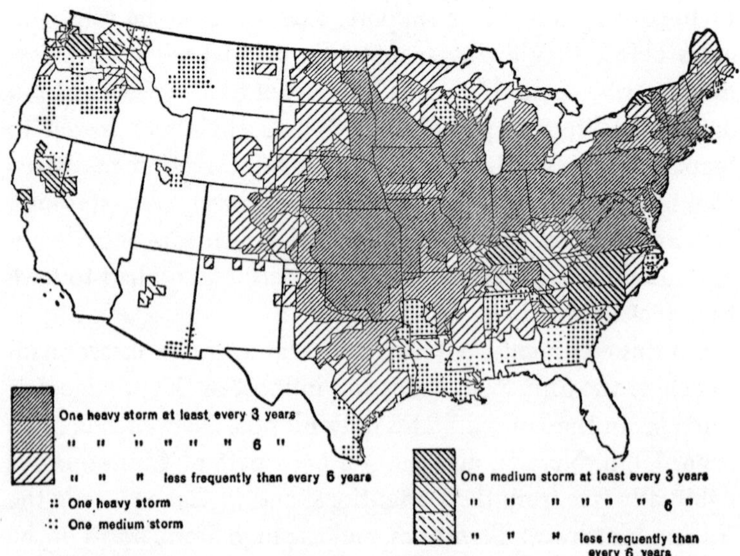

* This map has been adapted from one published in 1934. Since then no further studies have been undertaken by the company.

As far as the United States is concerned, the most destructive ice storm of recent years was almost certainly the one that paralyzed a 100-mile-wide swathe of country stretching from Louisiana and northern Alabama northeastward to West Virginia in January of 1951. Meteorologically it was triggered by a great outbreak of polar air that swept down the Mississippi Valley nearly to the Gulf of Mexico before meeting any real resistance. The resistance, when it came, was, however, fierce, for along the southern margin of this polar front there developed a string of militant lows, one of which advanced on the "polar" stronghold carrying all, almost literally, before it. Between January 28 and February 1, 1951, more than 5 inches of water, most of it in the form of freezing rain, fell on western and central Tennessee, Kentucky, and parts of West Virginia. On the morning of February 1, when the storm finally subsided, another 3 inches of frozen precipitation covered the ground—and not the ground only, but power lines, telephone lines, and trees which, by then, were lying in a wild disorder across the countryside. The resulting dislocation of the region's economy will be remembered long after talk of the blizzard of '88 has been forgotten. Thousands of homes dependent upon electricity were without fuel for more than a week; tourists were stranded, up to five days in some cases; many householders found themselves faced with major repair bills (roofs caved in frequently); commuters were unable to get to work—even worse, to get home from work. Only the children had fun!

The storm damage was estimated by the U.S. Weather Bureau to be of the following order:

Forests	$56,000,000
Communications and power lines	10,000,000
Fruit and nut trees	4,000,000
Buildings and plumbing	4,300,000
Livestock	3,000,000
Truck and grain crops	1,600,000, and several millions losses to transportation, other businesses

The glaze resistance of trees

Some trees can take a lot more punishment from an ice storm than others. By an unfortunate coincidence, as I write the New Jersey countryside around me is in the grip of an ice storm—"the worst ice storm in a generation" so the papers tell me, and a look at my garden suffices to convince me. A 150-year-old tulip tree has already lost enough limbs to keep us in firewood for the rest of the winter; a number of black locusts stand beheaded; the silver birches are bent double to the ground; and almost every twig of every bush and tree is encased in a translucent cylinder of ice between 1 and 2 inches in diameter. There is beauty in the sight, to be sure, for the sun has momentarily transmuted the virginal whites and grays into liquid gold. And there is hope, too, for some of the trees are still unbowed and look as though they had every intention of living to tell the tale.

In recent years a great deal of attention has been paid to the ability of trees to withstand heavy ice accretion, and some highly interesting differences between species have been established.

Other things being equal, the species with the highest chances of survival are: ailanthus (tree of heaven), yellow birch, American hornbeam, shagbark hickory, northern catalpa, hawthorn, common horse chestnut, beech (American and European), white ash, ginkgo, Kentucky coffee tree, butternut, American hophornbeam, Norway spruce, oak (except the pin variety), and eastern arborvitae.

Those with the lowest chances are: box elder, silver maple, speckled alder, poplar (white, eastern, southern, Lombardy), aspen (big tooth, quaking), apricot, cherry (pin, black), peach, black locust, willow (all varieties), Japanese pagoda tree, linden (American, silver), and elm (all varieties).

Possessing fair resistance to ice damage are maple (all varieties except silver), birch (all except yellow), flowering dogwood, black ash, common honey locust, eastern red cedar, American sweet gum, tulip, common apple, red mulberry, pine (Austrian, white, Scots), plane (London and American), common pear, and Canadian hemlock.

As a general rule, old trees tend to suffer more damage than young trees, and tall trees more than small trees of the same species. Trees with conspicuous V-shaped forks are liable to split badly at the forks unless cabled or braced in advance. Dense low-branching evergreens have a knack of safeguarding their existence by developing icicles downward from branch to branch and finally to the ground in such a way that all are supported by a skeleton ice structure.

Life begins at forty below—for those that like it!

Weather is a global affair—almost the only truly global phenomenon there is. And to forecast it with any degree of accuracy it is necessary to have a continuous flow of data—synoptic, that is, simultaneously observed data at that—from all parts of the world. Some parts, admittedly, are more important to the meteorologist than others: these are the air-mass source regions, the world's weather manufactories. One such place is, as we have seen, the high arctic, for it is here that our cold waves are born and, indirectly, our so-called "polar" fronts. Because human activity, military and civil, has come to depend to an increasing extent upon meteorological intelligence, and will come to do so even more as polar and subpolar flying develops, it has been found necessary to establish weather-observing stations in the extreme north of this continent, beyond the limit of permanent settlement, even of Eskimos. One of these stations, located at Alert Bay near the northern extremity of Ellesmere Island, is within 500 miles of the North Pole; several others are nearer to the Pole, and to Russia for that matter, than they are to any North American outposts of civilization.

In such an environment life begins at about 40 degrees below. It isn't always 40 degrees below, of course: frequently it's lower, and there are some warm winter days when the thermometer may climb to zero. During July and August, in which spring, summer, and fall are telescoped, it may occasionally rise to almost 60°F. Doubtless the smart thing to do is not to poke your head out-of-doors in such conditions, but almost everything a meteorologist is concerned with lies out-of-doors. Though he has devised self-recording instruments for almost everything, he hasn't yet devised self-servicing self-recording instruments, nor has he found any that will read cloud amount, identify cloud types and motion, measure horizontal and vertical visibility—let alone keep the snow from drifting into his instrument screen. So anybody who goes to Resolute Bay, Isachsen, Eureka Sound, Alert Bay, or Thule had better like the cold, and be able to take at least a couple of years of it without a break. And it would be just as well for him to take along a few books, for the man who has learned to lean heavily on the chromium-plated bars of Main Street is liable to run out of ideas about the end of the first week. But those who can take it are loud in its praises, and have even been known to volunteer for a second term of duty. Certainly it's a pretty healthy life: the cold makes short work of most ordinary germs, though it usually happens that a man returning from one of these stations succumbs to the first streptococcus he meets. It is also a challenging life: if you haven't got what you need, you must either do without it, or improvise. And some of the improvisations are, to say the least, ingenious. A mechanic at one of the stations was once caught by his C.O. watching a coffeepot come to the boil, only the brew wasn't coffee. A long coil of copper tubing extended from the top of the pot, and a clear liquid was dripping from the end of the tube into a glass. The mechanic's father, it transpired, had spent a good deal of his life outwitting the Arkansas revenuers. More seriously, it is a significant life. As R. W. Rae, one of the men who has really begun to live, put it when asked whether the scientific results obtained were sufficient to justify the cost, "The chief function of these stations is to provide basic data from a hitherto unknown region. This information will permit research to be carried out on the large-scale motions of the earth's atmosphere as a whole. This is the only way to improve our understanding of atmospheric processes, which in turn is the only way to improve our forecasting—and to extend the forecast periods. The research cannot be done without the observational data and the data cannot be obtained without the stations." * Let us hope there will always be men like Mr. Rae to man the stations.

* "Arctic Experiences," a paper presented at the regular monthly meeting of the Royal Meteorological Society, Canadian Branch, Toronto, February 23, 1950.

Skiers' month

If you are prepared to go far enough, you can ski somewhere or other in North America in any month of the year—even in July and August. According to a friend of mine (who is by way of being an authority on the subject, having skied in three continents) some of the best skiing in the world is to be had on the Juneau ice field in southeast Alaska in midsummer. You just have to be rather careful about the crevasses, but once you know where they are, apparently they present no more of an obstacle than a half-concealed side of a barn or a gravel pit does in midwinter.

But most folks either have other things to do in midsummer or are not scientific enough to be given glacier-top assignments as geologists. They have to do their skiing nearer home, and in winter.

If you happen to live in the northern and central Sierras, you will usually be able to start your ski season by the end of October and go on skiing till the following May or even June. If you live in the Laurentians, you may in a good season be able to start by mid-November and continue through to May, at least in the Mont Tremblant region; in a poor season, on the other hand, you may not get going before the end of December, even early January, and you may be compelled to stow your gear by the end of March. In northern New England and the Adirondacks the possibilities are much the same, but the mean duration of "skiable" snow is two to three weeks shorter than in central and eastern Quebec. Farther south, in the Catskills and the northern Appalachians, you will be lucky to get more than a month of good skiing, and the chances are that the month will be February rather than January or March.

February is likely to be the best month for skiing almost everywhere throughout the Northeast and over much of the West, for the following reasons. Firstly, because it is, on the average, one of the snowiest months of the winter. In many localities, for example, Gander, Newfoundland; Blue Hill, Massachusetts; Lake Tahoe, California; and Mesa Verde Park, Colorado, it is the snowiest month of all, and over much of the rest of the country it is second only to January—and this notwithstanding that it is a short month. This means that on the higher ground there are usually three or four good falls during the month to cover the existing snow base. Secondly, by February the snow accumulation is at or near its seasonal maximum. Over southern and eastern Quebec, where good snowfalls can usually be reckoned on in both December and January, there may be as much as 5 feet of pack by then, and in northern New England and the Adirondacks, perhaps as much as 4 feet. In some of the western Sierras, there may be as much as 20 feet. This means that the inequalities of the terrain are then masked to their maximum amount and that the penalty of a fall is less serious than at other times. Thirdly, although a thaw can occur in any, and all, of the winter months, there is rather less chance of the skier being discommoded by one in February than either in December or March. Over most of the Northeast, in fact, he stands more chance of running into a prolonged cold wave than a prolonged warm spell. Fourthly, heavy rainfalls, which can quickly convert a skier's paradise into a place of another name, are less likely to occur in this area in February than in any other month of the year. Lastly, the days are drawing out by then, the sun is gathering power, and the sunshine prospects are distinctly brighter than in either December or January. True, in March they are brighter still, but so are the chances of an early spring thaw, heavy rains, treacherous going —and a broken neck.

White magic

Although the "treasures of the snow" have engaged the thoughts and inspired the tongues of wise men since before the time of Job, it is only in recent years, as a result largely of laboratory study, that they have begun to understand the manner of its making; and there is still much they do not know about it.

Contrary to what we might be inclined to think, it takes more than the marriage of cold air and cloud to make a snowflake. The ordinary child of such a marriage is so small and light that it finds less difficulty in floating than in falling, and when it does fall, its rate of descent is so slow that it requires two days to reach the ground from a height of 10,000 feet—theoretically at least, since, in all likelihood, it would waste away before the end of the journey.

For moisture to be precipitated from a cloud in such a form that it will reach the earth as recognizable snow, a vast amount of "snowballing" has to take place—or, more technically, coalescence of the component ice particles. Even a small snow crystal represents the coalescence of a million or more such particles. How is it done?

The ice elements found in ordinary winter clouds, so the

scientists tell us, are of three main kinds: ice crystals or groups of crystals having a common nucleus, snowflakes, and hailstones. Every ice particle originates from a nucleus which may consist of a frozen cloud droplet or a solid particle such as a speck of dust, covered by a thin film of water which subsequently freezes. After nucleation (a process about which not too much is known as yet), the ice crystals continue to grow, provided their cloudy environment is supersaturated relative to ice, by the diffusion of water vapor to their growing surfaces. In shape these crystals will vary from simple hexagonal plates and prisms to complicated groupings of a stellar sort.

They further tell us that there is a close relationship between the shape of the crystals and the characteristics of the parent cloud. In clouds where the temperature is below approximately —13°F., that is, in clouds of the cirrus and altocumulus-altostratus types, the dominant shape is the hexagonal prism. In clouds with higher temperatures, that is, in clouds for the most part of a stratiform and cumuliform kind, prisms give way to thin hexagonal plates. Because these plates and prisms, though roughly of the same weight to begin with, are subject to collision, they become differentiated in weight as time goes by and so acquire different velocities, with the result that their chances of further collision and growth are increased. In a dense cloud of mixed water and ice particles, collisions are so frequent that the crystals are likely to develop into sizable aggregates of soft hail ("graupel" is its technical name) or multiple branchlike crystals, the branches of which may propagate secondary branches to produce intricate patterns of astonishing loveliness. This secondary growth may continue until the spaces between the branches become filled (except perhaps for some small enclosed hollows), so forming a large platelike structure in the center of which the original hexagonal crystal may still be identified.

To get most of these crystals down to the ground, it is necessary for further collisions to take place. Inspection of an ordinary snowflake will, in fact, show that it consists of "a rather haphazard agglomeration of loosely interlocking crystals." (Sometimes it is even possible to separate the individual components.) And you will usually find that the wetter the crystals, the more ready they are to stick together; which is another way of saying that large snowflakes are most likely to fall from the base of "warm" clouds of high vapor content. Actually, it is now believed that the biggest snowflakes are those which start life as small crystals in clouds where the temperatures are above 5°F. and which subsequently fall through warmer, moister air, where most of the "snowballing" occurs.

But the scientists have still to tell us what causes the amazing variety of forms assumed by the snow crystal. Mr. Wilson A. Bentley, of Jericho, Vermont, spent fifty years examining snow crystals under a microscope without ever finding two exactly alike!

The measurement of snow

Since a good percentage of the annual precipitation of Canada, the northern third of the Union, and the high Sierras falls in the form of snow, which subsequently helps to feed the spring floods and spring crops, its measurement is a matter of more than academic interest. Unfortunately it is difficult to measure snowfall accurately. What is needed is a careful determination both of the depth of snow as it falls and also of the water equivalent of the snow. Many folk will tell you that there is no difficulty whatever about the second part of the determination: that all you have to do is to divide the depth of newly fallen snow by 10 and read off the answer. However, there is snow and snow: depth for depth, light fluffy snow may have less than half the water content of fine, crystalline snow or sleet. The only proper thing to do in the circumstances is to melt the snow down. But this is where the trouble is likely to start, especially if a wind was blowing when the snow fell; for then it is practically certain that the amount of snow caught in the standard rain gauge does not represent conditions over the surrounding open country. Generally, the gauge gives you short measure; and the stronger the wind, the shorter the measure. Only in calm weather is the gauge method likely to yield satisfactory results. At all other times it is advisable to rely upon measurements made with the help of graduated vertical stakes placed at intervals over the open ground. By using a hollow sampling rod, cores of snow, equal to the depth of snow that has fallen, can be taken from the vicinity of these stakes: melted down, these will give a pretty fair approximation of the water content of the latest snowfall.

Where the snow lies

There are very few parts of North America which never see snow. At the same time, at least one-fifth of the United States is not subject to regular snowfalls. South of a line running approximately from Cape Hatteras, North Carolina, through Birmingham, Alabama, to San Antonio, Texas, and thence close to the Mexican border and the Pacific coast northward as far as Oregon, there are unlikely to be more than two days in any winter when the ground is snow-covered: and even north of this line there are areas which may go two or three seasons without getting a measurable snowfall.

Generally speaking, however, the mean duration of the snow cover increases steadily north of this limit, especially over the interior. Thus, the average number of days with snow cover (of one inch depth or more) goes from less than one at New

Orleans to more than 140 at Fort William, Ontario, near the United States–Canadian border. The corresponding increase on the Atlantic coast is from one at Savannah, Georgia, to approximately fifty at the Maine–New Brunswick border. On the Pacific coast the increase is from one at Cape Mendocino to approximately ten at the Washington–British Columbia border.

Mountain peaks apart, the area in the United States likely to be snowbound longest is located in the region of Yellowstone Park: here the snow lies on the ground for a full six months in the year. Northern Canada, needless to say, can show still more impressive figures: on Baffin Island even at sea level the ground is sometimes clear of snow only for a bare six weeks, and it is often difficult to tell when the snows of one season have ended and those of the next have begun.

Fig. 5. Average annual number of days with snow cover (1 inch or more). (Courtesy of the Weather Bureau, U.S. Department of Commerce)

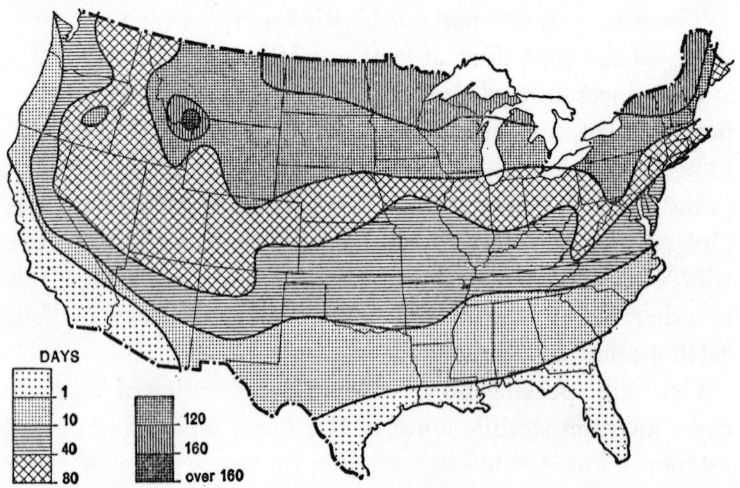

Snowstorms to beat the plow

One of the stock arguments advanced by elderly folk who are persuaded that the winters in this country are not what they were is that there was a whale of a lot more snow around town when they were children. And they are probably right, notwithstanding the fact that a snowfall remembered as being waist-high in one's childhood is unlikely to have been more than knee-high to an adult! For as we shall see, the statistical evidence in favor of a warming up of the winters over the eastern half of the continent and, with it, a falling off of the snowfall is, in the aggregate, quite impressive. At the same time, when Nature is so minded, she can still produce from her treasury as fine and prodigal a blizzard as ever stirred the imagination of Paul Bunyan. As a matter of fact, some of the best (for talking about afterward, that is) continue to prey on one of Paul Bunyan's favorite stamping grounds—the Keweenaw Peninsula of Upper Michigan. Indeed we suspect that even a Paul Bunyan would have had no reason to alter the dimensions of the snowstorms that swept along the Calumet area of the Keweenaw Peninsula in January, 1950. Together they yielded no less than 115 inches of snow, 46 of which fell in the six-day period January 15–20. In one of the blizzards (January 15–16) 22 inches of snow fell in 12 hours to the accompaniment of a 60-mile-an-hour wind. There was so much snow on one of the roads that snowplows crawled past a snow-covered automobile without seeing it!

Even these figures have been exceeded in the hill country to the southeast of Lakes Erie and Ontario. Here the average winter total is still well over 150 inches, and single falls of 30 inches and upward are not unheard of. A 37-inch fall was reported from the Buffalo area in December (14–16), 1945, and a 40-inch fall (from the Watertown, New York, area) as recently as March, 1947. At the turn of the present century (November 14–15, 1900) there was even a bigger one—of 49 inches.* This you might well think would make upper New York State the snowiest place east of the Rockies. And so it is, as far as the Union is concerned, but not for the continent, since heavier snowfalls are annually reported from parts of eastern Canada. The Mont Tremblant district of the Laurentian Mountains of Quebec averages 175 inches (I have known seasons when there was still enough snow on the northern flank of Tremblant to tempt skiers as late as June), while the exposed ramparts of southeasternmost Labrador—from Cartwright to Harrington Harbor—get all of 200 inches. Farther north the seasonal expectation falls off until, by the time the shores of the Arctic Ocean are reached, it is no more than 40 to 50 inches.

For the biggest falls of all, of course, we must go to the western Sierras. On their windward slopes seasonal aggregates in excess of 400 inches are commonplace; aggregates of 600 inches are not unknown, and at Tamarack, Alpine County, California, there is at least one well-authenticated seasonal fall of over 800 inches: at the height of the 1906–1907 season, the one in question, there was a snow pack of 348 inches—or 29 feet!

Igloos, Eskimos, and insulation

Air is an excellent insulator. whether it is the air held captive between double windows, in the mesh of a woolen blanket, or in the interstices of a snowflake. Newly fallen snow is one of the best insulating materials in the world, for it seldom con-

* These heavy lakeshore snowfalls result chiefly from the fact that the prevailing westerly winds, in crossing the comparatively warm waters of the Great Lakes in early winter before they have started to freeze up (most of them never freeze up solid), acquire considerable water vapor and heat. This frequently has the effect of making the air mass unstable and ready to precipitate as soon as it encounters high land. It may even start "unloading" before it leaves the Lakes, if there is a large temperature differential between the air and the water.

tains less than 10 parts of air to 1 part of ice, and may contain as many as 35 parts to 1. Even an old snow cover is rarely less than half air. It is because of this that snow is so good at keeping the warmth of the soil in and the cold surface air out.* The contrast between the top and bottom of a snow layer is often very striking. Thanks to radiation and evaporation, the top of a clean snow surface is subject to almost continuous loss of heat, and becomes particularly cold on clear nights. Even on sunny days the presence of snow results in lower air temperatures than if the ground were bare, for the crust can never rise above a temperature of 32°F., which means that the snow cannot warm the layer of air that is in contact with it to any extent. On the other hand, because the underlying soil is protected by its snow cover from comparable radiation, its temperature remains fairly steady, usually some little way below freezing point.

The extent to which a deep snow cover can keep the heat in is seen in the following temperatures simultaneously recorded during a very cold snap in the Middle West:

Temperature 3 ft. above snow surface	—19°F.
Temperature of snow surface	—27°F.
Temperature of snow 7 in. below surface	24°F.

That is, there was a difference of 51 degrees between top and bottom of the blanket, a difference, incidentally, greater than that between the average summer and winter temperatures of places like Chicago and New York.

Eskimos and *coureurs de bois* have long made use of this "blanket" effect in the building of winter houses. The inside of a well-made snow igloo can be maintained at comfort level, say 60°F., with the aid of a quite small fire, even though the temperature of the air outside is around —50°F.

* This helps to explain why sheep buried in deep snowdrifts have been found alive after several days.

In the St. Lawrence–Great Lakes region the deep and prolonged snow cover saves the soil from being frozen to great depths. Early in December, severe frosts may harden the soil down to 20 inches or more, since in most years not much snow has fallen at that time. By the end of the month, however, 12 to 15 inches of snow have usually accumulated over the open country, and the "blanket" has been spread. The freezing of the soil then ceases, and the bottom of the frozen layer remains about 20 inches or so below the ground surface for the rest of the winter, despite the often very severe cold spells of January and February. When the spring thaw sets in, the depressing period during which the topsoil is liquid and the subsoil still frozen solid is consequently shorter than would otherwise be the case. In Manchuria, where the winters are just about as hard as they are in the St. Lawrence–Great Lakes region and the normal snowfall is small, the ground freezes down to a depth of 6 feet or more. The ensuing thaw takes longer and is proportionately more depressing.

The trail of the blizzard

It's an ill wind that blows nobody any good, but there are, alas, many such winds. Consider, for example, the blizzard of the prairies and the northern plains. While no coldly factual recital of its life history can begin to do justice to the havoc it wreaks upon its domain, it may not be a bad thing to start with one, if only to restrain the glib use of the word by millions of folk who are inclined to call any personally inconvenient snowstorm by that name.

The place is Huron, South Dakota: the time, January 22, 1952: the storm, strictly run of the mill, and occasioning very little notice outside the Middle West.

"Winds reached the high velocities of 60 to 70 miles an hour in the western part of the State, but very little snow fell in that section. The winds reached velocities of 40 to 50 m.p.h. in the middle and southern parts of the eastern section. Snow formed 10- to 15-foot drifts, and mail service was delayed for about five days. The low temperature and drifting snow claimed eight lives. Twenty-five hundred cattle were lost. Many people suffered from frostbite when cars became stalled, or when persons were forced to be out in the storm for various other reasons. The snow and drifting caused all roads to be blocked for three days, after which the side roads remained closed and air-lift operations were necessary in the middle section. This area extended from the southern border in a northerly direction to the northern border of South Dakota, making an area 100 miles wide at the southern border to 50 miles wide at the northern border. . . . The average windspeed (at Huron) on the 22nd was greater than 30 m.p.h. for the period 4:05 A.M. to 11:07 A.M., with gusts up to 45 m.p.h. The temperature fell (from a high of 21°F.) to zero by 7:00 A.M. of the 22nd, to −5°F. by 10:30 A.M. and −11°F. by midnight. Prior to the storm, there was an eight-inch snow cover on the ground. The storm itself gave an additional 4.1 inches of snow." *

To qualify among meteorologists for the name of blizzard, a snowstorm must be characterized by low (or rapidly falling) temperatures, winds of gale force (or above), and driving snow. The snow may be precipitated from the clouds or whipped into the air from a surface cover of snow left over from a previous storm.

On this continent, blizzards occur most frequently in the eastern arctic, the Prairie Provinces, the northern Great Plains, and the upper Mississippi Valley. Occasionally, severe blizzard conditions may penetrate southward as far as Texas, west-

* Roy L. Fox, "Blizzards of the Northern Plains," *Weatherwise*, Vol. 5, No. 6 (1952), p. 126.

ward to the high Sierras, and eastward to the Great Lakes and New England. The most blizzard-ridden part of the continent extends north and west of the upper Great Lakes; the seasonal incidence here is of the order of one a month from December to April.

The home of the blizzard is in the Canadian northlands—in those great high-pressure reservoirs of cold air that periodically, during the winter half of the year, break through their "retaining walls" of inert atmosphere and advance, streamlike, southward across the ice- and snow-covered lowlands of central Canada. However, these outbreaks alone do not automatically produce blizzards—what is needed equally is a lively little low-pressure system, or "disturbance," along the southern perimeter of the cold-air mass. When this low, which frequently forms in the lee of the Rockies, moves out onto the high plains, the cold polar air swings southward behind it, that is, to west of it, uplifting the warmer, moister air lying in its path and so providing the incipient storm with the "raw material" for its snow. At the same time, the pressure gradient steepens, with consequent strengthening of the wind, especially in the cold air behind the low, and its snow-lifting capacity. By the time the wind has reached gale force, say, 30 miles per hour, the chances are that, even if no snow is actually falling from the heavens, enough is being whipped up off the ground to reduce visibility to a few yards—possibly even to nothing.

Is it ever too cold to snow?

Flurries of snow are likely to occur whenever a current of cold polar air invades the middle latitudes, or when air that has been drifting around for some time over a cold land surface gets wafted across a comparatively warm water surface. In its pristine condition, polar air is very cold, and so contains very little moisture: saturated air at zero contains only one-third as much moisture as saturated air at freezing level, while saturated air at 30 degrees below zero contains only one-fifth as much moisture as saturated air at zero. Consequently, no matter how hard it tried, it would take a very long time for subzero air to produce a heavy fall of snow.

As a matter of fact, really heavy falls of snow over a wide area require tropical rather than polar air for their manufacture; and even then they only occur in association with well-marked fronts. If we examine the weather map on the occasion of a severe state-wide snowstorm, we are almost sure to find that the heaviest falls occurred on the poleward or continental side of a well-marked warm front. Here the surface air temperature may be anything from 37°F. downward.* Theoretically there is no reason why the temperature of the air through which the snow is falling from the tropical air current aloft should not be, let us say, 20 to 30 degrees below zero. Before now, 2 inches of snow have fallen from such a warm upper wind with the surface thermometer standing at 24 degrees below zero. However, as a general rule, we can assume that the lower the surface temperature is, (1) the farther aloft does the warm, snow-carrying air current lie, (2) the shallower that current is, and (3) the less likely it is on that account to release a large amount of snow. The nearer the front approaches, the warmer the surface air tends to become—there is always a certain amount of air-mass mixing going on in the vicinity of the front, enough at least to take the keen edge off the polar air—and the thicker grows the cloud layer from which the snow will fall; in other words, the greater is the expectation of snow.

So it comes to this: while it is seldom, if ever, too cold for snow, there is more chance of a heavy fall with a comparatively

* If it is above this figure, the precipitation most probably will be in the form of rain.

high temperature than with a comparatively low one. In the United States the heaviest falls have a habit of occurring when the temperature is between 24 and 30°F.

Snow rollers

Dame Nature has many moods, most of them serious. From time to time, however, she delights to remind her children that though she is old and none may count her years, she is capable of having fun—even of playing with "toys." The snow roller is one of her toys.

The initial reaction of those who see the phenomenon for the first time is likely to be one of incredulity: it cannot be the work of children (there are no attendant footprints), and by what conceivable combination of agencies can Nature produce such an oddly assorted array of mobile forms, varying in shape as they do from spheres to cones and cylinders and in size from hen's eggs to 40-gallon drums?

Reliable eyewitness accounts of snow-roller formation are few and far between and are at variance on certain points. Three things are agreed at least: snow rollers will not form unless there is a newly fallen layer of wet snow on an old and crusted snow layer, unless the temperature is around freezing point (preferably a degree or two above), and unless there is a strong breeze. But clearly something else is needed, for, whereas these conditions are common enough, snow rollers are rare. What this something is is uncertain. There are observers who think it is turbulence, and who claim that without a strongly accented downward component the wind could not possibly scoop enough snow off the surface to start the "ball rolling." However, once the ball has begun to roll, a bumpy wind of this kind would surely be more of a hindrance than a wind of a more laminar kind. Another possible starting mechanism is suggested by the following eyewitness account. In Queen's County, Nova Scotia, in the early spring of 1948, there was a prolonged period of light snowfall with temperatures slightly above the freezing point. The snow had reached a depth of 3 to 4 inches on the ground when large composite flakes of 1 to 2 inches in diameter began falling. A brisk northwesterly wind was blowing, and many of the flakes hit the snow surface at a sharp angle; it was noticed that immediately upon contact with the earth the undersurfaces of some of the newly fallen flakes were caught by the wind and tipped over, thereby forming the nascent snow rollers. As the land sloped gently to the southeast, the wind continued to push this small mass downhill until sizable rollers developed.*

The snow-eater

Several times each winter the eastern foothill country of the Rockies from Alberta to Colorado is set upon by strong westerly winds that come, quite literally, out of a clear blue sky. These are the chinooks, named for the Chinook Indians who used to inhabit the country to the west of the Northern Rockies from which many of these winds come.

During a typical chinook, the sky immediately in the lee of the mountains is likely to be cloudless, but a few miles to the east of them it may well be darkened by a narrow arc of boiling, roll-like clouds that retain their position for hours on end—even though the air in them is traveling at a speed of anything up to 50 miles per hour. In this respect they are very similar to the "standing clouds" which sailplane pilots occasionally encounter to the lee of high ground. Such winds may blow only for an hour or so, or for as much as two or three days on end. They frequently raise the temperature by 40°F.; and rises of

* Quoted by R. A. Hornstein, "Snow-rollers," *Weather*, June, 1951.

50°F. in a day are not uncommon. Occasionally they give rise to electrical disturbances of sufficient intensity to stall a car and "kill" the radio.

The physics of a chinook wind are essentially those of the bicycle pump. As everybody knows, a bicycle pump gets uncomfortably hot when it is exercised vigorously; the air in it is warmed by compression. The opposite happens when air is suddenly released from the pump: it expands rapidly and becomes sensibly cooler. This dual process of dynamic cooling and dynamic warming takes place when air is first made to rise up one side of a mountain and descend the other. Normally it does not descend quickly enough, or operate on a sufficiently wide scale, to produce apparent results, but it does so in the case of the chinook, which involves speedy transport of large quantities of mild moist air landward from the Pacific. This air loses some of its water vapor load every time it encounters one of the high transverse cordilleran systems, and the drier it becomes, the higher it has to be pushed before it will again condense into visible cloud. By the time it reaches the last of the great barriers, the Rocky Mountains proper, the air is frequently so "dehydrated" that it does not get cooled down to its dew point, that is, the condensation level, in the course of its ascent of the windward slope, but only in the still higher crest of the standing cloud which, in a strong current, may develop to the east of the mountains.*

During each of the several ascents which this Pacific air must make in the course of its rugged trip to the high plains, the temperature of the air falls off with height, because of the expansion it undergoes. The rate at which it cools will depend for the most part on its relative humidity. All the time the air re-

* Anybody who has watched the behavior of running water at a rapids will know that the stationary wave forming downstream from a large rock can easily exceed in height the elevation of the rock itself.

mains above its dew point, it will cool at a rate of approximately 5.4°F. for every 1,000 feet of ascent (this rate being known as the dry adiabatic lapse rate): but as soon as the dew point is reached—and it is probably reached three or four times during its undulating journey—the rate of cooling with height declines on account of the heat released to the atmosphere from the condensing particles of water vapor.* But once the last "crest" has been passed, whether it be the crest of the standing wave or the mountains that lie back of it, and the current of air falls below the condensation level, it begins to warm up at the greater rate, namely, 5.4°F. per 1,000 feet of descent, appropriate to dry, or unsaturated, air.

This means, of course, that the temperatures in such an eastward-moving air mass will be higher, level for level, on the leeward side of the Rocky Mountains than on the windward, cloud-covered slopes of the ranges nearer the coast.

It also means that, by the time this air has descended to the level of the high plains, its relative humidity will have fallen from approximately 100 per cent at the cloud level to around 40 per cent—perhaps lower. Such air is greedy of moisture in any form: it can evaporate a 6-inch snow cover in almost as many hours. The Blackfoot Indian name for it—snow-eater—could hardly be bettered.

A year of snow—a year of plenty

The folklore of Europe and North America is full of sayings that attribute tremendous significance to abnormality, or subnormality for that matter, in a single meteorological element. For reasons which we shall have frequent occasion to refer to

* The precise lapse rate above the condensation level depends on the amount of water vapor condensed, but it is always less than the rate in unsaturated air, and usually of the order of 3.5°F. per 1,000 feet.

in the course of our calendar survey, we do not often find it possible to endorse the popular opinion. However, here is one for which it would not be too difficult to make a case, for a cover of snow and a well-frozen ground incident to a cold winter prevent that alternate thawing and freezing so damaging to wheat and other autumn-sown grains. Conversely, an unseasonably early show of growth is likely to be injured by later frosts—a principle variously expressed in the following sayings:

January warm, the Lord have mercy.

If you see grass in January,
Lock your grain in your granary.

January blossoms fill no man's cellar.

All the months of the year
Curse a fair Februeer.

A February spring
Is worth nothing.

ESP and the groundhog

In the hall of meteorological fame, no animal is held in more honor—we might almost call it awe—than the groundhog. The sky may be full of high-flying swallows, and nobody will think of fine weather; peacocks may bawl and owls screech all night long, and nobody will talk of rain; an entire convocation of cats may promenade past you with their tails up and their hair bristling, and you will not so much as dream of wind; but let a solitary groundhog be seen by a cub reporter in the Poconos looking at his shadow on February 2, and it is news of the first magnitude, for does it not most assuredly signify a long winter—at least six more weeks of it? And if it isn't so seen, it is still news, for does it not give promise of an early spring?

While we are well aware that it is impossible to slay a pretty myth with a plain fact, and while we have as high a regard for the groundhog as the reporter, we feel it incumbent upon us to point out two things. First, that the groundhog (alias woodchuck) legend was imported into North America from Germany, where, incidentally, a bear or a badger plays the role of prophet instead of the woodchuck, and where—even more important—the winters bear no great resemblance to those of continental United States and Canada either in regard to severity or duration. Second, in its original form, the legend makes no reference to the habits of *any* animal, but merely ascribes prognostic significance to the weather of Candlemas Day, namely, February 2, just as other weather legends ascribe significance to the weather of St. Joseph's Day (March 19), Lady Day (March 25), St. Barnabas' Day (June 11), St. Swithin's Day (July 15), and many another saint's day.*

What of the prognostic powers attributed to other living things? The "berries for a hard winter" kind of forecast we can dismiss straight away, because the size of any berry crop, or any crop for that matter, is determined by past, and not future, conditions. The same applies, *mutatis mutandis*, to the abnormally thick coat the mule deer is supposed to grow in preparation for severe weather (a precaution he frequently fails to take, to his undoing). As for the squirrel and its alleged prescience in storing up a larger supply of food in expectation of a long, hard winter, would it not be more logical to attribute this activity to a better-than-average nut season? And what of the migratory birds? Do not they possess the power to tell what sort of weather is coming? Frankly we are skeptical, the lore of the weatherwise notwithstanding. For two rea-

* It was natural enough that the weather of saints' days, when people were in the habit of forsaking their usual occupations in favor of out-of-door celebrations, should become a subject of unusual meteorological interest and speculation.

sons. If they have this sixth sense, it seems to desert them when they need it most: for how often have we read of flocks of exhausted migrants taking refuge on board a stormbound ship or, even worse, of the mass destruction of such birds as they have headed straight into the heart of a storm? In the second place, if they have it, it is odd that they seldom seem to know what to do in face of a temporary relapse from one season to another. A late snowfall will occasionally catch the nesting woodcock unawares, and compel it to incubate its eggs under arctic conditions. In Europe in early spring the redwing, one of the first birds to go north, is sometimes driven southward again from a snowbound Scandinavia, only to die from hunger on the equally snowbound fields of England and France.

The sorry fact is that the lower orders are no better at foretelling the weather long periods ahead than man has hitherto been. And even in regard to impending changes, it is doubtful whether they are more knowledgeable than the meteorologist blessed with the gift of extrasensory perception.

March

". . . in the mad March days"

March is proverbially a windy month, and North American records show that it lives up to its reputation. At stations as widely spread as Montreal, Chicago, and Key West, March tops all other months for wind, though it must be admitted that April runs it a close second.

It is not difficult to see why March, or April, should be so windy. At that time of the year, the Canadian arctic has scarcely begun to see the sun, so that its temperatures are still hovering around the minimum, and high pressure prevails over most of the area. On the other hand, in the south of the United States the midday sun is already high in the heavens, the earth is warming up rapidly, and pressures are generally low. This means that, on the average, there is a fairly steep barometric gradient from north to south, a state of affairs that promotes the meridional transport of air *—not to mention active fronts and their associated storm centers.

* The late Sir Napier Shaw, in his day Britain's leading meteorologist, once estimated that in late winter and early spring 3½ trillion tons of cold air is transported southward from the arctic.

But another factor should also be taken into account, namely, the density of the air masses involved in this movement. Gradient for gradient, an air mass moves faster when it is cold than when it is warm: very cold air may move up to 20 per cent faster than very warm air.

But let us not exaggerate the storminess of the month. Except for mountaintops like Mount Washington and well-exposed promontories and islands, like Anticosti Island in the Gulf of St. Lawrence where gales are likely to be recorded on about half the days of the month, wind velocities are more likely to average 10 miles per hour than 40. Inland and away from mountains, gale-force winds are infrequent: Chicago (the "windy city") is unlucky if it gets more than three such winds during the month, and Winnipeg if it gets more than one. In Denver the frequency of gale-force winds is even lower: there they only occur in about two out of every three years.

The wind—"whence it cometh and whither it goeth"

If the earth consisted wholly of land or of water, and if it were uniformly heated and at rest, there would be very little wind. What there was we should be more likely to feel on our heads than on our faces, since air movement would be almost entirely confined to vertical exchanges of hot surface air and cold upper air, that is, convective currents.* However, the earth is not uniformly hot. Much more solar energy is received in low latitudes than near the poles. It is this inequality in terrestrial heating that drives the gigantic thermodynamic engine which is our atmosphere. Between the equator and about 30 to 35°N (and S) there is a net annual surplus of solar energy: poleward from about the 35th parallel there is a net deficit, the loss of radiant heat to space by the earth and its atmosphere exceeding

* See June, pp. 123 to 127, for a discussion of the convective process.

the gain from the sun. This deficit is largest at the poles. If this unbalanced condition were incapable of periodic correction, the temperature of middle and high latitudes would fall steadily until equilibrium between export and import of heat was achieved at a very low temperature: since, however, there is plenty of evidence to show that the mean temperature along a given latitude varies but little from year to year, it is plain that some compensating mechanism must operate. This mechanism is the atmospheric circulation.

At the equator the heated air makes its way aloft: at the poles the cold air sinks toward the ground. There is therefore a smaller volume of air, and so lower pressure, in the upper atmosphere at the poles than at the equator, but since gases always strive to move from an area of greater pressure to an area of less pressure, an equalizing poleward flow of air of equatorial origin tends to be set up in the upper levels of the atmosphere. As a result, the surface pressure of the polar regions increases, becoming greater, temporarily, than the surface pressure of the equatorial regions, and so inducing an equatorward flow of air at the surface.

On a stationary uniform planet, this meridional circulation would prevail in all places at all times. But our planet is neither stationary nor uniform: it spins from west to east, dragging the atmosphere with it, and it is divided into water bodies and land bodies which respond very differently to the sun's wooing.

Because the earth spins, we would expect, on purely dynamic grounds, the upper, poleward-flowing stream of air to acquire a westerly component and the lower, equatorward-flowing stream to acquire an easterly component. As a matter of fact, over most of the globe the upper winds are predominantly westerly. The surface-wind systems, however, show much more variety, and easterly winds are, for the most part, confined to the trade-wind belt, which comprises no more than a third of the earth's surface. The dynamic reasons for the nonconformity of the other two-thirds of the earth have long puzzled the pundits, and they are still far from clear. However, for our immediate purpose it is probably enough that we should be aware of the broad climatic consequences of the general circulation, for it is the circulation rather than local radiative and geographical circumstances—important though these can be—that fixes the weather patterns of a given continent.

In the accompanying schematic drawing we attempt to show, in much generalized form, both "plan" and "elevation" views of the circulation of the Northern Hemisphere. The elevation is really a north-south cross section of the atmosphere on a typical March day along, let us say, the 100th west meridian. The plan gives the areal disposition of the major pressure systems likely to be encountered during the same month, or, for that matter, in any other winter month. The following features should be observed:

First, the globe-encircling trough of low pressure in the vicinity of the equatorial belt of high temperatures and rising air.

Fig. 6. Schematic representation of general circulation of the Northern Hemisphere. (Courtesy of Professor F. K. Hare: "The Restless Atmosphere")

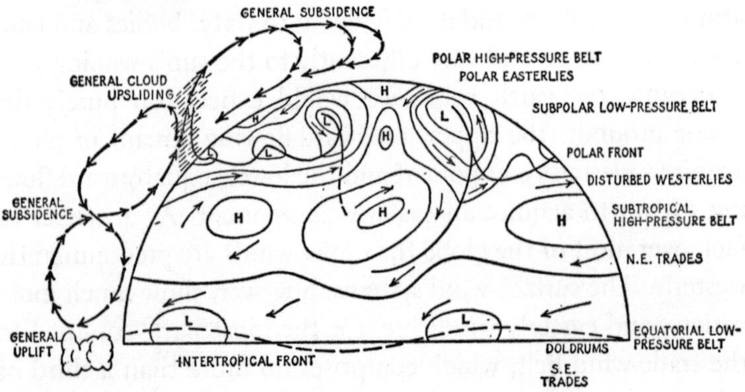

Into this trough flow the easterly trades (northeasterly in the Northern Hemisphere, southeasterly in the Southern): where they converge is located the intertropical front, or, as it is more commonly styled, the doldrum belt. It is here that the continually manufactured heat surpluses are drawn aloft into the upper air, to the accompaniment oftentimes of heavy rains and squalls: once aloft, they separate, part of them going north, part south. The presence of these poleward-moving streams in low latitudes can often be detected by observing the motion of high clouds of the cirriform type. The farther toward the poles these "countertrades" are found (they seldom persist beyond the 35th parallel), the stronger their westerly component. Since, with the single exception of the summer monsoons of southeast Asia and northern Australia, they are the only currents that leave the equatorial belt, it is clear that they are chiefly responsible for maintaining the thermal equilibrium of the earth.

Second, the series of high-pressure "cells," or anticyclones, located in the subtropical belt of generally high pressure. On their equatorial side these anticyclones are flanked by the easterly trades; on their polar sides, by winds that are westerly. Along the western margin of each separate cell, the prevailing winds are southerly; on the eastern margin, northerly. It is in these intercellular troughs, or "cols," with their directionally opposed winds—winds, too, that are often strongly contrasted in their physical properties—that many of our Northern Hemisphere cyclones are bred. The prospects of such "cyclogenesis" tend to be greatest when the air moving toward the equator, that is, along the eastern margin of the cell, has come down from high latitudes which, as we have already seen, it is quite likely to do toward the end of winter. It is chiefly by such outbreaks of cold heavy air that the high-pressure cells of the subtropics are supported: the subsiding air of the countertrades above them provides the balance of their support. The cells that contribute most to the articulation of our North American weather are the Bermuda (or Azores) high and the Central Pacific (or Hawaiian) high.

Third, the polar and subpolar anticyclone. This is perhaps the easiest belt to explain since it is the direct product of the radiative cooling that takes place in high latitudes. Even in the long summer day, the region's intake of solar energy does not begin to compare with that of middle and low latitudes, with the result that there is a year-round equalizing poleward flow of upper air to make good the surface deficit. The periodic "topping up" of the polar high with surplus air from lower latitudes ensures that high pressures are maintained summer and winter alike. There are times, of course, when the pressure is less high than at others, as, for instance, at the end of an exceptionally vigorous outbreak of polar air, but the loss is soon made good.

Fourth, and most important of all in our weather economy, is the middle- and high-latitude belt of cyclonic storms, indicated on the plan as irregularly shaped low-pressure centers linked together by the polar front. Where southward-moving air from the polar high comes in contact with northward-moving air from the subtropical pressure cells, there the so-called polar front is found. Sometimes it lies much farther south than others: on some days it may be inactive, while on others it may prove a veritable storm dispenser. However, throughout the winter half of the year it is the scene of almost constant atmospheric skirmishing, and may be held responsible for fully three-quarters of all our dirty cyclonic weather, including almost all our gales.

By and large, it begins to look as though the anonymous French author of the thirteenth-century *Image du monde* had just about the right idea when he said that air

. . . that is . . . lyft and taken from his place remeveth other ayer in suche facion that it reterneth as it were afterward, and gooth cryeng and brazeng [*i.e.*, braying] as water rennyng; for wynde is none other thyng but ayer that is meuyd [*i.e.*, moved] so longe tyl his force be beten down with the stroke. Thus come ofte clowdes, raynes, thondres and lygthnyngs . . .*

At any rate, it is much simpler than our modern explanations.

How strong is the wind?

The job of estimating the speed of the wind is one that calls for considerable objectivity. This, for most of us, is a quality hard to come by, for wind is something we *feel*—something which one day may hurt, the next day may help us—and which, in consequence, makes its impact upon us more by what it does than what it is. If we are caught out-of-doors in a 25-mile-an-hour wind on a dark and snowy night, we are much more likely to insist on calling it a "howling gale" than if we encounter it at the seashore on a sizzling summer afternoon. And, of course, much will depend on the frequency with which we are exposed to winds of that strength: a sailor, for instance, is less likely to parlay a "strong breeze" into a "whole gale" than a city dweller.

As with many another meteorological problem, it was a sailor —Captain (later Rear Admiral Sir Francis) Beaufort—who devised the first widely accepted, objective wind scale. Because the strength of the wind is arrived at on this scale inferentially rather than instrumentally, no attempt was made by Beaufort to give it numerical precision. He was content to deal in "forces," and because he lived at a time (early nineteenth century) when all ships carried sail, he chose to base his scale, which he arbitrarily divided into thirteen divisions, on the varying amounts of sail a full-rigged ship could carry. To take two

* Part II, Chap. 29 (Caxton's translation).

examples: a "strong breeze"—force 6 on his scale—is "that to which she could just carry in chase full and by, royals, etc., and topgallant sails"; while a "whole gale"—force 10 on his scale—is "that with which she could scarcely bear lower main topsail and reefed foresail."

Such phraseology is meaningless to the vast majority of people today and was fast becoming so when Dr. (later Sir) George C. Simpson brought out a simple landlubber's version of the scale, complete with equivalent speeds. This scale was adopted by the International Meteorological Committee at its meeting in Vienna in 1926. We reproduce it, together with a set of more meaningful but still very approximate equivalents for the modern seaman.

Beaufort number	Limits of velocity in m.p.h. at 33 ft. above level ground	Description of wind in forecasts	Noticeable effect of wind	
			On land	At sea
0	Less than 1	Calm	Smoke rises vertically	Sea is mirror-smooth
1	1–3	Light air	Direction shown by smoke drift, but not by vanes	Small wavelets like scales, but no foam crests
2	4–7	Light breeze	Wind felt on face; leaves rustle; wind vanes moved	Waves are short and more pronounced
3	8–12	Gentle breeze	Leaves and twigs in motion. Wind extends a light flag	Crests begin to break. Foam has glassy appearance, not as yet white
4	13–18	Moderate breeze	Raises dust and loose pages and moves small branches	Waves are longer. Many whitecaps
5	19–24	Fresh breeze	Small trees in leaf begin to sway	Waves are more pronounced. White foaming crests seen everywhere

Beaufort number	Limits of velocity in m.p.h. at 33 ft. above level ground	Description of wind in forecasts	Noticeable effect of wind	
			On land	At sea
6	25–31	Strong breeze	Large branches begin to move. Telephone wires whistle	Larger waves form. Foaming crests more extensive
7	32–38	Moderate gale	Whole trees in motion	Sea heaps up. Foam begins to blow in streaks
8	39–46	Fresh gale	Twigs break off. Progress generally impeded	Waves increase visibly. Foam is blown in dense streaks
9	47–54	Strong gale	Slight structural damage occurs. Chimney pots removed	As for Force 8
10	55–63	Whole gale	Trees uprooted. Considerable structural damage	High waves with long overhanging crests. Great foam patches
11	64–75	Storm	Damage is widespread. Experienced round the edge of hurricanes and tornadoes	Waves so high that ships are hidden in the troughs. Sea covered with streaking foam. Air filled with spray
12	Above 75	Hurricane	Countryside is devastated. Winds of this force are encountered only near the center of hurricanes, typhoons, etc.	

Mechanical wind finders

While approximations of this kind are good enough for most of us most of the time, they have long since ceased to satisfy the meteorologist who today may be required to make a frost forecast for an orange grower (for the difference between a 4- and a 7-mile-an-hour wind can be the difference between unsatisfactory and satisfactory conditions for the operation of his orchard heaters), tomorrow may be asked to calculate the rate of advance of a forest fire, and the day after may brief a pilot on the winds he is likely to encounter in the course of a 3,000-mile flight.

As far as the wind at or near the surface is concerned, any one of a number of anemometers will give the required precision. The familiar cup variety, invented by an Irish clergyman in the mid-nineteenth century, consists of a horizontally rotated windmill in which the "sails" are hemispherical cups: these are carried on arms attached to a vertical spindle. As there is very nearly a constant ratio between the travel of the wind and of the cups, it is quite easy to arrange for a train of geared wheels to indicate the flow of air in miles an hour, knots, or any other unit. Various electrical versions of the cup anemometer have been put on the market in recent years. One of the commonest employs reduction gears that produce an electrical contact every time one of the gears makes a complete rotation. By counting the number of contacts through a period of, say, one minute, the velocity in miles an hour can be obtained. The counting operation is usually facilitated by a light or a buzzer. The direction of the wind also can be found electrically by having contacts for the various cardinal compass points mounted on a small shaft that rotates with the wind vane. These can be made to light small lamps mounted on a board fashioned in the manner of a compass.

The chief drawback to the cup anemometer is that it fails to respond instantaneously to change of velocity, because of the momentum of the windmill. To record such changes, an anemometer of quite another type is employed. This makes use of the difference of pressure set up between two pipes, one of which is kept facing the wind, while the other is connected to a system of suction holes on a vertical tube. The difference of pressure so produced is utilized to operate a float carrying a pen, the height of the pen above the zero position being made proportional to the wind speed. In this way every gust and lull may be shown on the record.

So much for the ground wind, which, after all, is the only wind most of us are concerned about, unless we happen to live on a mountain or in the penthouse of a thirty-story apartment building. In such an event, as all will know who have stood on Pike's Peak or the parapet of any of the midtown Manhattan skyscrapers, it is a very different wind that we experience. For one thing, it will almost certainly be much stronger —perhaps as much as three times stronger,* and for another, it will probably blow from a different direction—anything up to 40 degrees different, the differences in both cases being the work of surface friction.

To the aviator, this upper wind really matters far more than the surface wind, though he is interested enough in this when it comes to taking off and landing. And he wants this wind, whether it is the wind at 2,000 or 20,000 feet, not to the nearest compass point, but to the nearest degree or two, and its speed to the nearest couple of knots or miles an hour. Wind drift can be a big thing when the machine is large and the journey long, and no navigator wants to find himself over the Atlantic when he should be over Idlewild. How is this wind found for him? Up to about 2,000 feet its speed and direction can be estimated with fair accuracy from the distance apart of the isobars on an ordinary surface weather chart. But when it comes to estimating the wind at 20,000 feet the surface isobars do

* If you cannot bring yourself to believe that a pleasant surface breeze of, let us say, 15 miles an hour is represented by a 30-mile-an-hour wind at 1,000 feet and a 45-mile-an-hour gale at 2,000 feet, take a look at the clouds the next time you feel like lying on your back.

not give the forecaster very much assistance, since the chances are that the wind will be much stronger than it is at 2,000 feet, and blowing from a quite different direction. Accordingly, he has to use other wind-finding devices.

One of the earliest employed devices, and still one of the most widely used, is the balloon-and-theodolite device. A rubber balloon, somewhat larger than the usual toy variety and inflated with hydrogen or helium, is released from the ground, and is carried along with the wind as it rises. With the aid of a theodolite, which is not so very different from a surveyor's transit, the ascent is followed, and the bearing of the balloon in degrees from true north and the inclination of the telescope to the horizon are read off directly from horizontal and vertical scales. If the height of the balloon is known, it is merely a matter of trigonometry to calculate the speed of the air stream in which it is moving. What usually happens is that the balloon is assumed to rise at a uniform rate, for example, 400, 500, or 1,000 feet a minute. Although there are several factors working against the maintenance of a steady rate of ascent, as, for instance, the up-and-down currents in the air, this method can generally be relied on to give an answer that is not more than 10 per cent wide of the mark. If two theodolites are used, one at each end of a measured base line, the speed and direction of the balloon can be measured very precisely, for in this case there is no need to make any assumptions about the rate of ascent. The big snag about this device, whether you use one or two theodolites, is that you are dependent on your ability to keep the balloon in view. In a cloudy climate like that of Newfoundland or the Pacific Northwest, most balloons get lost en route for high heaven: this means that ascents above 10,000 to 15,000 feet in those parts of the world are comparatively rare. Furthermore, the theodolite method is essentially a daytime one. Yet it is precisely in bad weather and during the hours of darkness, when navigation is difficult, that the aviator is most in need of accurate wind information. The darkness difficulty can be got over, provided there is no troublesome cloud cover, by attaching a small Chinese lantern or electric torch to the balloon, but on a bright night it is uncommonly easy to hitch one's theodolite to a star! The cloud difficulty is less amenable to solution, or, rather, it was until radiosondes came to be used for the purpose.

The first successful attempt to transmit radio signals from apparatus carried by a small balloon dates back to 1927. Since then, many forms of apparatus designed to regulate such signals and report the weather elements of the upper atmosphere have been invented. In essence, the modern radiosonde is a lightweight, highly compact instrument designed to measure the pressure, temperature, and relative humidity of the upper air, and to transmit those measurements automatically by radio to ground stations. Tied to the tail of a large balloon some six feet or more in diameter, the radiosonde is ordinarily able to reach an elevation of between 50,000 and 80,000 feet before bursting. Throughout its ascent, signals are continually being transmitted by ultrahigh radio frequency. But the radiosonde provides more than a detailed cross section of temperature, pressure, and humidity conditions. Since the balloon to which it is attached is free, it is carried by the wind as it rises, which means that, with the help of a direction finder, an operator can measure the speed and direction of the wind at any desired level above the ground. And, needless to say, these radio waves have no difficulty in penetrating either cloud or darkness.

With the application of radar to meteorological techniques, wind finding has become even simpler: for a free balloon carrying a metallic "target" that will receive and return the propagated radio signals can be tracked in all weathers and at all times of the day and night by direction- and range-finding equipment; the computed wind directions and speeds are generally as accurate as, if not more so than, those taken by the single-theodolite method—and it can all be done from a comfortable chair in an office.

". . . *high tempestuous gusts*"

If you have ever observed the trace of a recording anemometer of the pressure-tube type, you will know that it is in the form of a sharply serrated ribbon of variable width. The upper edge of the trace represents the gusts and the lower edge the lulls. These oscillations arise from the fact that the air movement, which we call wind, is not steady. Irregularities in the surface, such as humps, hollows, trees, buildings and, over the sea, waves, set up eddies in the same sort of way as stones in the bed of a stream set up eddies in flowing water. It is these eddies which are responsible for the oscillations of the trace, that is, for the gustiness of the wind.

This gustiness factor, which is, of course, of considerable practical importance where aircraft are concerned (especially in taking off and landing), and in such professions as architecture and engineering (no suspension-bridge builder would dream of calculating his stresses on the basis of mean velocities alone), varies with several things. In the first place, it varies with the exposure of the instrument: because of this, anemometers used at regular reporting stations are normally placed between 60 and 100 feet above their surroundings. It varies, too, with the wind speed: as a rough rule, you can take it that the gustiness of a wind decreases with increase in mean wind velocity. Thus, whereas it is not unusual to find a 30-mile-an-hour wind gusting up to 50 miles an hour (that is, more than 50 per cent above its mean speed), a 60-mile-an-hour wind blowing over the same surface will be unlikely to gust higher than 80 miles an hour (that is, approximately one-third more than its mean speed). Then, again, it varies with the time of day, being worse generally in the early afternoon than during the night. It is further affected by elevation, becoming steadily less significant with height above the ground. There is also some justification for saying that it varies with the origin of the wind in question. Thus, air of maritime polar origin arriving in the United States via the Pacific is frequently more gusty than maritime air of tropical or subtropical origin reaching the continent from the Caribbean.

One important result of all this is that winds over the sea and at well-exposed places round our shores tend to be much less gusty than winds over the land. At Key West, for instance, the gusts in a 30-mile-an-hour wind are seldom likely to exceed 37 miles an hour; along the open Gulf Coast, they will probably touch 45 miles an hour in the same mean wind; while at a place like Fifth Avenue in New York, they will fall not far short of 60 miles an hour. Expressed in another way, a mean wind of 20 miles an hour may produce gusts of greater velocity in a built-up area than a 30-mile-an-hour wind at a coastal station.

Why it's windier at the shore

If there's one thing you can be more certain about than another, especially in winter, it is that, no matter how hard the wind is blowing inland, it is blowing harder still at the shore. This applies not only to ocean shores, but lake and river shores as well: even Battery Place, facing the Hudson River in downtown Manhattan, has about 50 per cent more wind than Central Park in midtown Manhattan.

Why should this be? As we have just seen, air moving over the surface of the globe is continually meeting obstacles that cause some of its momentum to be lost to the surface, and part of the residue to be dissipated in the resulting turbulence. The momentum lost in this way is supplied by the layer affected by the turbulence, the thickness of which depends on a number of factors, but which on the average is between 1,500 and 2,000 feet in depth. Over the sea, where friction is small, the loss of momentum, with the reduction of wind velocity it involves, is small: over the land, particularly over wooded or built-up areas, the loss is large. A wind passing from sea to land experiences, then, a decrease of velocity on account of increase of friction. This friction can be very considerable, enough, in theory, to bring the air to rest, and the only reason why there is any wind over the land at all below about 1,500 to 2,000 feet is that the wind at that height exerts a dragging effect on the air below it.

The difference in the frictional effect of land and water is expressed in the rule of thumb that the relation between the wind velocity at 1,500 to 2,000 feet, sometimes called the gradient wind, and at the surface is approximately 3:2 over the sea and 3:1 over the land. So when it is blowing half a gale outside your house, spare a prayer for the poor fellows on the high seas who are almost certainly battling against a *whole* gale. And remember the rule the next time *you* go sailing. If you don't, you may finish up with the epitaph Isidorus of Aegea wrote for a landsman whose greed of gain tempted him to make a voyage at the wrong time of year:

The wind does not blow the same upon threshing floors and sails.

When winds bring their own weather

Ask any ten town dwellers which way the wind is blowing, and you will probably find that eight of them don't know, that the ninth is as much as 90 degrees out, and that the tenth knows because he heard it on the radio an hour ago. "And why should they?" you may ask. "What does it matter anyway? An east wind is surely much about the same as a west wind, and a gale is a gale from any quarter of the compass." To the cliff dwellers in Manhattan, perhaps; but not to the shepherds in the hills of Wyoming, the fishermen off the Grand Banks, and the citrus-fruit growers in Southern California. Nor, for that matter, to the poet.

It's a warm wind, the west wind, full of birds' cries;
I never hear the west wind but tears are in my eyes.
For it comes from the west lands, the old brown hills,
*And April's in the west wind, and daffodils.**

You don't need to be an Englishman, or a John Masefield, to know that *that* sort of a wind never blows out of the east, least of all in early spring. And, equally, you don't need to live in Boston to know that the harsh sentiments of James Russell Lowell's line—"The only argument available with an east wind is to put on your overcoat" †—could apply to no other wind.

On this continent it would no doubt be a gross oversimplification to speak, as Francis Bacon used to do, apropos of England, of every wind having its own weather. Drought as well as rain may attend a southerly wind over the prairies; heat waves in New York have before now come in the wake of a northerly wind; and while some west winds bring muggy, overcast, and drizzly weather to the British Columbia coast, others bring fresh, showery weather. But there are places and seasons where the relationship holds. Along the Malabar coast of India a southwesterly wind has the sound of rain in it all summer long. In the Aegean Sea a northerly wind blows with reason-

* John Masefield, "The West Wind," *Collected Poems*, 1953, The Macmillan Company.

† *Democracy and Addresses.*

able regularity throughout July and August, bringing clear skies, low humidity, and refreshment to the islanders if not to the earth. Along the coast of Algeria a southerly wind at any time of the year is searing, and a powerful irritant to both mind and body.

While we have few, if any, winds in the United States or Canada of the caliber of the monsoon, the etesian, or the sirocco, marked wind-weather relationships can be observed temporarily whenever a part of either country becomes subject to anticyclonic control. It is quite true that anticyclones can and do mix up their weather with the greatest of ease, despite the popular belief, enshrined upon the face of most hall barometers, that they are invariably fair-weather systems; but once give them a chance to settle down, and you can rely upon the wind turning up with much the same kind of weather for days on end. Exactly what the kind of weather is depends to some extent on the size of the system, and even more on its geographical location. Small ones are usually short-lived, and we need not bother with them, because until an anticyclone has been going two or three days it has not had time, as a rule, to give its winds "exclusive" properties. For instance, when in winter the subtropical Pacific high reaches out northeastward to join forces with the continental high located over Idaho and Nevada, thereby setting up a one-way flow of air between the Hawaiian Islands and Washington and British Columbia, the air which reaches the west coast during the first 24 hours of this pressure regime may be almost anything from tropical maritime air left over from an earlier anticyclonic regime to polar continental air that has spilled seaward over the Rockies. By the time the high has been established three or four days, all this residual air will, with any luck, have been cleared away, and air originating in the region of the Hawaiian Islands will have had time to make the 2,000-odd-mile journey to the

Pacific coast. Once in this southwesterly air stream, you will not go far wrong if you assume that mild, cloudy, humid weather with indifferent visibility and low ceilings will be the order of the day until either the wind changes or the barometer starts to fall.

If the high has its center somewhere between Hawaii and the Aleutians, the chances are that the air reaching the Northwestern states after an interval of two or three days will have originated in high rather than low latitudes. The weather associated with this—maritime polar—air stream will be very different. Along the coasts in spring and summer, good visibility, broken skies (cumulus or cumulonimbus cloud) with occasional showers (heavier on the mountains than on the flat), moderate ceilings, and temperatures slightly below average will be characteristic. In winter there will be a greater percentage of overcast skies and rainy days. As this maritime polar air drifts overland with the prevailing west-to-east circulation, most of its moisture gets left behind on the windward slopes of the mountains, so that by the time it descends to the Great Plains it is dry and warm—in fact the kind of weather associated with the chinook. From the aviator's viewpoint this "dehydrated" maritime polar air is just about ideal; it is nonturbulent, that is, free from bumps; ceilings are generally unlimited, that is, the icing hazard is small; and visibility is good except for smoke and haze in industrial areas. This kind of air stream has been known to travel eastward across the continent from coast to coast.

Suppose our high now turns eastward, and takes up a position over the Yukon and northern British Columbia. What follows? The Canadian prairies and central lowlands of the United States soon find themselves in the thrall of a northerly air stream notable in winter for its dryness and clear skies, and for its shiveringly low, subzero temperatures. The snout of the advancing cold wave, or "norther" as it is often called in Oklahoma and Texas, is usually marked by cold-front phenomena. These cold waves are also the begetters of the blizzard whose howling blasts, laced with powdered, blinding snow that has been whipped off the ground, bring sudden death to man and beast. In late spring a norther usually can be held responsible for the untimely frosts that work so much havoc in the orchards of the Mountain states and Ontario: the clear skies encourage rapid night radiation. In summer this kind of air is still comparatively dry, but in coming south over the lake-strewn prairie provinces of Canada, with their long hours of warm sunshine, it contrives to pick up enough moisture as well as heat in its lowest layers to be verging on instability by the time it reaches the United States. Cumulus clouds, often threatening in appearance, build up over the heated land surface by day, but seldom come to anything over the Great Plains. Provided the wind is light, the days are hot and the nights are cool. Farther east and southeast, the convective activity of this air is stronger: thanks to the greater surface heating it receives, and the presence of the Great Lakes, showery, thundery weather often characterizes its southern perimeter.

When the high moves farther over to the Hudson Bay–Baffin Strait region, then the Atlantic seaboard from the Maritimes and Quebec down to the Middle Atlantic states becomes subject to an easterly or northeasterly air stream, known as Atlantic maritime polar air. This does not happen very often, since the normal movement of all Northern Hemisphere pressure systems is from a westerly to an easterly point of the compass. When it does happen, however, it gives rise to a very distinctive kind of weather. Starting life in the northlands, the cold, dry air travels southward along the margin of the western North Atlantic, but because the sea temperatures are low, and because it spends comparatively little time over the water, it undergoes less heating than its Pacific counterpart. And so it arrives over our eastern seaboard as a raw, disagreeable wind, addicted to drizzling rain and snow, low ceilings, and poor visibility. On the other hand, the overcast skies do prevent the escape into outer space of such heat as there is: for this reason, subzero temperatures are not common. Since the pressure situation favorable to the penetration of this air mass southwestward to the Appalachians is also well suited to frontogenesis, that is, the development of a warm front along the margin of the maritime tropical air that frequents the Bermuda-Florida region, this type of weather, fortunately, is short-lived as well as fairly uncommon. In summer a northeasterly stream of air is much more popular, as it is likely to spell relief from a heat wave.

Then there are those occasions, more common in summer than in winter, when an enlarged Azores-Bermuda high combines with a depression over the Gulf of Mexico to give a southerly or southeasterly flow of maritime tropical air from the Caribbean to the very heart of the continent. In winter this means that temperatures will stay above normal, humidities will be high, and there will be considerable cloudiness especially during the night and early morning: during the middle of the day the clouds tend to disperse, and fine weather is then the rule. In the absence of hill barriers and fronts, all forms of precipitation, other than a fine drizzle, are unlikely. Visibility is indifferent when there is plenty of cloud about, ceilings are low, and fog is common, especially if the land has just emerged from a cold spell. In summer the weather of the entire eastern half of the United States is regulated by this moist, heat-wave-producing air mass. But whereas in winter it gets cooled at the surface, that is, becomes more and more stable, during its northward trajectory, in summer it gets warmer, for then the central lowlands are considerably hotter by day than the waters of the Caribbean, where the air mass most likely originated. This means that the nocturnal stratus-type clouds disperse during the morning, only to re-form in the shape of swelling cumulus: by late afternoon these have frequently developed into full-fledged thunderheads. It is from these that a fair proportion of the summer rains of the interior, for instance, those of the Corn and Wheat Belts, is derived. Except near sunrise, when valley fogs and mists are often a feature, the visibility is good and the ceilings are ample.

Finally, there are those quiet days when such wind as there is comes from nowhere in particular, because the anticyclone is centered right over the continent and the pressure gradient is too slack to produce a steady *flow* of air. In summer such conditions are synonymous with fine settled weather and high daytime temperatures. (The lapse rate of temperature in anticyclones is usually small, a circumstance that does not favor the development of clouds or sea breezes—two of the chief cooling agencies.) At other times of the year, especially late autumn and winter, the absence of air movement and the small lapse rate make for murky skies and poor visibility. Whether fog forms or not depends on the origin of the anticyclone. When it develops as an offshoot from the Bermuda high, it is warm and well supplied with water vapor. Cooled by its northward migration, and under the influence of radiation, it frequently causes ground fog at night. As the winter sun is low in the heavens, it often has difficulty in warming up the ground enough to disperse the fog; so that once it has formed, it may last for days. When the anticyclone develops as an offshoot from the circumpolar high, the air is cold and comparatively dry: moreover it gets warmed up very little indeed during its southerly drift. Consequently very exceptional cooling of the surface layers is required before the air reaches saturation point and the visibility begins to fall. However, the cooling is usually enough to produce an inversion of temperature aloft; because rising air and smoke cannot escape through this, their only alternative is to spread laterally, producing, near big cities and industrial areas, the familiar anticyclonic gloom. In such circumstances the contrast between the Pittsburgh industrial region, or the New York metropolitan district, and the open country fifty to sixty miles away is very marked: the latter quite likely will be enjoying bright sunshine, while the former is languishing in twilight.

Such, in the broadest terms, is the lineage of the main air masses affecting the weather of the North American continent. That they do not always behave with due regard to their pedigree is evident to every student of weather. The root of the trouble is that anticyclones, like their more capricious competitors the depressions, seldom return to the exact scene of their exploits; even when they do, they do not always remain long enough to reproduce their previous form. For the most part, it seems that Dame Nature is too interested in developing new situations to bother about copying old ones.

Weather vanes and warnings

Of more frequent prognostic importance than wind direction is wind shift, particularly in well-exposed localities. Seafarers and country folk in all parts of the world have sensed this for centuries and enshrined the fact in a score and more sayings of the following type:

A veering wind, fair weather;
A backing wind, foul weather.

When the wind backs, and the weather glass falls,
Then be on your guard against gales and squalls.

Winds that change against the sun
Are always sure to backward run.

When the wind goes against the sun,
Trust it not, for back 'twill run.

If in unsettled weather the wind veers from southwest to west or northwest at sunset, expect finer weather for a day or two.

If the wind veers from north to northeast in winter, intense cold follows.

If the wind is northeast three days without rain,
Eight days will pass before south wind again.

When the wind shifts in a drought, expect rain.

The dynamic foundation for these rules of thumb, though entirely unknown to their authors, is, for the most part, firm enough. It doesn't follow though that they should be applied without discrimination to all parts of this continent, for they originated in Europe, which has its own special brands of weather, some of them unique. But because the basic structure of pressure systems is the same in all parts of the world, some of these sayings can be applied to this continent, and others, equally serviceable, can be, and have been, devised to fit local circumstances of elevation, exposure, and relief. Thus, at Cape Mendocino, in northern California, experience shows that if a northwest wind shifts to northeast, remaining there two or three days without rain, and then shifts to the south and back again to the northeast with very little rain, fair weather may be expected. In parts of Texas you will be told that brisk winds from the south for several days are generally followed by a "norther," while in North Carolina, the fishermen will assure you that in winter a southwest wind that has blown for three days will veer to the northwest between one and two in the morning and blow with increasing force. The timing may be out, but the sequence is one that every meteorologist understands. And, locally, in every state of the Union wind shifts, sometimes of as little as a couple of points, carry for the keen-eyed observer a meaning far greater than that possessed by any regional forecast couched, as it needs must be, in general terms.

All of which gives point to the practice of our forefathers in topping their church towers and steeples with weathercocks or wind vanes. Alas, that their high office is no longer appreciated by the passer-by! Originally intended to remind the people how St. Peter denied his Master as much as to tell them how the wind was blowing, today they seldom serve any purpose: many have long since fought their last battle with the wind; few are fashioned in the likeness of the twice-crowing cock; and of those that are and those that work, more than enough were orientated with the help of the compass! (In the New York region at the present time the compass points about 11 degrees west of true north; in Montana, about 19 degrees east of true north.) Of those that are left, perhaps two out of five will be on buildings with such an indifferent exposure that under no circumstances will they give a true indication of the free air wind, that is, the direction of the wind as determined by the pressure distribution, unaffected by the eddies set up by trees, buildings, and surface undulations. To be reasonably sure of the right answer, a weather vane should be at least 50 to 60 feet above the level of its immediate surroundings. If the vane satisfies these requirements, but happens to be situated in a deeply engulfed valley, like those, say, of the lower Saguenay in the Province of Quebec or the Monongahela near Pittsburgh, it will probably deceive you into believing that the wind spends most of its time blowing from two directions—180 degrees apart. Such is the strength of the "funnel effect" which all of us notice when we try to do battle with an umbrella in a narrow windy street.

In passing we should perhaps also caution the eager observer against unqualified reliance on smoke trails. For one thing, the direction of smoke from a low chimney is more likely to reflect local "relief" than a well-exposed wind vane, and for another, there is the fact that smoke apparently moving to the right from a chimney situated to northward may be coming from northwest, west, or southwest. Provided there is a breeze, the indicative value of smoke is greatest in the early morning before the sun has had a chance to set up turbulent, gusty, up-and-down air currents which, especially in hot weather, are capable of producing quite strong local winds bearing little relation to the direction of the regional wind which is much more influential in weather affairs than the local wind.

". . . *the pilgrim steps of spring*"

Americans who have lived through an English winter (and not all have) will understand the preoccupation of English poets with spring. And, indeed, the English spring is a thing of rare beauty and gentility. It comes unheralded and without ostentation: its tread is as soft as the southerly breezes that bring it and as measured as any pilgrim's. And like the good pilgrim, it is in no hurry: it may even stay throughout all the summer.

In North America, Dame Nature is mostly in so much of a hurry to shed her winter's weeds and don the garb of summer that it would be more apt, if less poetic, to speak of the giant strides of spring.

There are many ways of measuring the northward advance of spring, from a climatic point of view. Of course for those who insist on treating spring as an astronomical event, there can be no "advance": spring is something that comes with the calendar on March 20 (or 21), the date of the vernal equinox. But the vernal equinox is a poor peg on which to hang the spring: it starts nothing of a thermal sort, any more than any other fixed date in the calendar. Just how meaningless it is becomes apparent when we compare the temperatures which are to be expected, around the date of the equinox, in different parts of the continent.

MEAN EQUINOCTIAL TEMPERATURES FOR SELECTED PLACES IN NORTH AMERICA

Southern Florida		69.0°F.
New Jersey		43.0°F.
Maine		30.0°F.
Newfoundland		31.0°F.
Canadian arctic archipelago		−20.0°F. (or worse!)
Northwest Territories	*ca.*	0.0°F.
Southern Manitoba		18.0°F.
Upper Michigan *		29.0°F.
Iowa		41.0°F.
Northern Ohio		41.0°F.
Mississippi		60.0°F.
Southern Louisiana		64.0°F.
Western Texas		60.0°F.
Kansas		48.0°F.
Montana		36.0°F.
Vancouver Island		42.0°F.
Western Oregon		47.0°F.
Utah		43.0°F.
Northern California		51.0°F.
Southern California		58.0°F.
Colorado		40.0°F.
Southern Arizona		59.0°F.

* Usually the coldest locality (apart from a few mountain peaks) in the Union at that time.

Of the several criteria by which we may measure the march of spring, two, namely, the arrival of the spring thaw and the beginning of the seasonal plant cycle, are probably the most valid. The significant isotherms are 32 and 43°F. When the mean temperature rises above the first figure, snow begins to melt by night as well as by day, the runoff into stream and pond increases, the hard earth softens, "And there follows a mist and a weeping rain." When it reaches 43°F. or thereabouts (for the critical temperature varies with the species), plants, long dormant and unmoved by the caresses of the winter sun, swell with bud and shoot, and gardeners, long immured and unstrung, bend their backs to the spade.

The accompanying maps show, in much generalized form, the northward march of both isotherms. Their common properties are striking. They both show a large section of the Southeast and Far West to lie outside the orbit of the temperatures in question and, so, to have no winter worthy of the name. Tennesseans caught in the toils of a January ice storm would no doubt want to dispute this claim, and so we hasten to remind them that, as in the case of all isotherms, we are dealing with a mean condition that conceals the wide day-to-day fluctuations, and the scarcely less wide year-to-year fluctuations. A second common feature is the contrast between the overland and coastal rate of advance. In the high plains spring, measured

Fig. 7(a). Beginning of spring: as measured by the arrival of the thaw (Courtesy of Professor S. S. Visher).

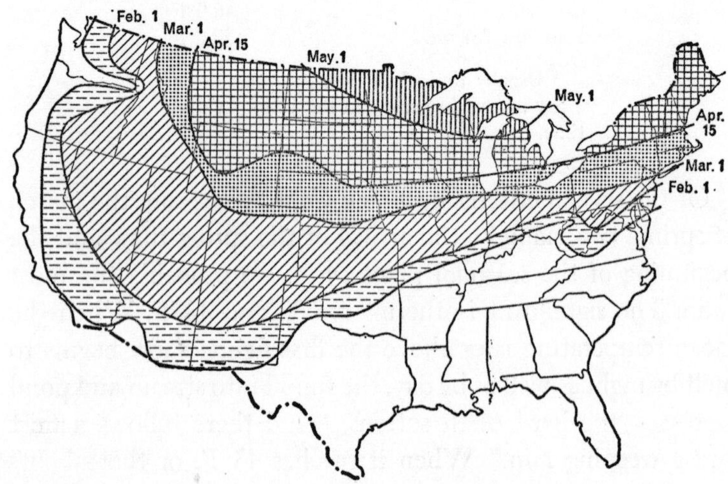

either way, advances northward at the rate of about 15 miles a day: along the northeast coast, the rate is less than 5 miles a day. The two maps also concur in showing the American winter as making its most determined rear-guard action, away from the mountains, in the northern Great Lakes–northern Minnesota region. Over eastern Canada winter yields to spring even more reluctantly: along the lower St. Lawrence Valley the thaw does not arrive before late April or early May, that is, *after* it has arrived in the Yukon some 1,500 miles nearer the pole.

The differences between the two maps are hardly less notable. By the criterion of thaw, spring reaches the Corn Belt around the first fortnight of March: by the criterion of plant growth, it arrives in mid-April. Again, whereas four-fifths of the Union is usually on the sunny side of the frost line by the equinox, only one-half has attained a mean temperature of 43°F. by that date.

Fig. 7(b). As measured by the start of the seasonal plant cycle (Courtesy of the Weather Bureau, U.S. Department of Commerce)

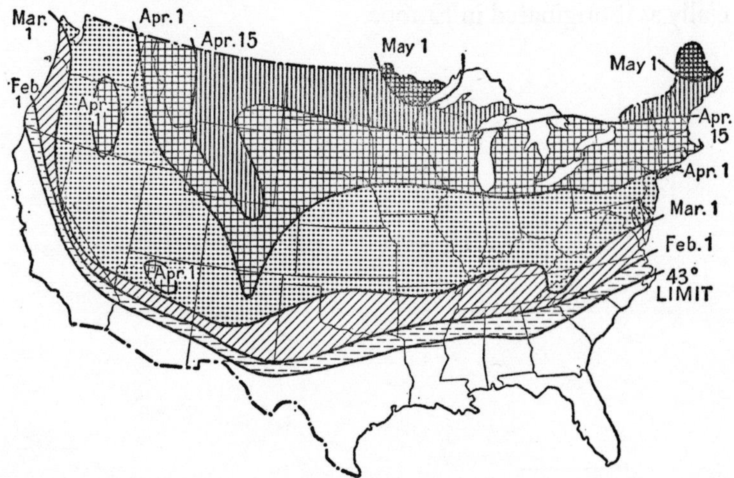

In like a lion: out like a lamb?

Those of us who were brought up on the old saying that if March comes in like a lion it will go out like a lamb, probably believe it. But we have yet to hear of the part of the world where the rule can stand the fierce light of statistical examination. We once tried it for a couple of places in the British Isles, but with no great success. We found that, over a period of sixteen years or so, the average speed of the wind at Kew at the beginning of the month was just under 10 miles an hour; at the end of the month it proved to be just over 10 miles an hour. In other words, both beginning and end behaved more like the lamb than the lion. On no occasion did March come in like a lion: a fresh breeze, say 19 to 24 miles an hour, was the nearest approach to leonine qualities. At Lerwick in the Shetland Isles, by way of contrast, March came in with a gale six years out of the sixteen years we examined, and went out the same way almost as often.

We see no meteorological reason why the rule should prove to be more reliable in North America than in Europe, especially as it originated in Europe.

April

"The uncertain glory of an April day"

THOUGH COMPARISONS between the English and American spring are not called for, and if attempted would almost certainly be odious, it seems that there is pretty general agreement on one score, namely, the capricious disposition of the month of April on both sides of the Atlantic. To this the poets, English and American, old and modern, bear ample testimony. To Shakespeare, April is "proud-pied" as well as possessed of an "uncertain glory." To Henry Kirke White, it is, by turns,

A little sun, a little rain,
And then night sweeps along the plain,
*And all things fade away.**

To Robert Frost, it appears in a more peevish guise (understandably enough to one who spent so large a part of his youth in northern New England where spring is unconscionably late in coming):

You know how it is with an April day:
When the sun is out and the wind is still,

* "Ode to Disappointment."

You're one month on in the middle of May.
But if you so much as dare to speak,
A cloud comes over the sunlit arch,
A wind comes off a frozen peak,
*And you're two months back in the middle of March.**

And the agreement is well founded, as a consideration of the following facts will show.

Firstly, by April the deep and durable depressions characteristic of the Northern Hemisphere winter have gone: those that survive are inclined to be less intense and more ephemeral, often being mere border incidents between two opposing air masses. Though they are quite capable of producing bad weather, the chances are that these spring depressions will not produce long spells of such weather, and that they will not follow one another with the monotony of winter storms. Secondly, about this time of the year the difference between the temperatures ruling in the polar and mid-latitude areas of the Northern Hemisphere is at its greatest. The northern third of the North American continent is still snow- and ice-bound, but the southern third is already hot, enjoying daytime temperatures in the 70s. In consequence, the mean pressure over the South tends to decline from its winter maximum, while the pressure over the northland tends to be maintained at or near its winter maximum. Because Nature abhors an imbalance of this kind as much as she does a vacuum (a species of which it is, in fact), equalizing flows of air—surface air southward, upper air northward—are sporadically set up. With each new meridional flow comes a change of weather. Thirdly, because most of the inhabited land of North America is by then warmer than both the northland and the surrounding ocean, which responds more slowly to the influence of the returning sun

* Robert Frost, "Two Tramps in Mud Time," *Complete Poems, 1949*, Henry Holt and Company, Inc., New York.

than the bare earth, the behavior of these mobile air masses is inclined to be more erratic than in winter. In winter, cold air coming down from the arctic may arrive in mid-latitudes almost as dry and cloudless as when it started out: in spring it will pick up moisture over every open water body and streaming valley, and the farther south it comes, the warmer it becomes and the greater its "pickup" capacity. It is easy to see that such air, while incapable perhaps of downright wickedness, would have no difficulty in earning a reputation for caprice, today assuming a baleful mien because it spent yesterday inhaling moisture over the Great Lakes, and tomorrow smiling on a grateful plain because it emptied itself today on the flanks of a mountain. Similarly in winter, moist air coming in from the warm waters of the Gulf of Mexico would be cooled, and so any inclination it might have to be cloudy or foggy would be strengthened on its passage poleward. In spring, air of the same general quality would be warmed on reaching the mainland, especially in daytime. With the warming would come a lowering of the relative humidity: if small, this might do no more than lift the fog, but if great, it could lift the cloud base, lighten the sky, and scatter the overcast, and so make a notable contribution to the grab bag of assorted weathers that is spring.

Needless to say, Nature sometimes introduces her spring fashions well before April is in: at other times she keeps them back until the month is nearly out. Occasionally she forgets to show them at all.

Season of showers

We can now begin to see why April is associated in the popular mind with showery weather. Because the vigorous cyclonic activity of winter is on the wane by then, frontal rains, invariably continuous, are less in evidence. And because by then onshore winds are more likely to be warmed and so dried, than cooled and so brought closer to saturation, even frontal rains have a habit of being less steady and continuous than in fall and winter. But a third factor is also involved, namely, atmospheric instability. April is a time of year when the upper atmosphere, especially when it is dominated by polar air masses, is still cold after the long winter, even though, as we have seen, the surface layers acquire warmth and moisture from the underlying earth, now for the most part free of snow and responding readily to the play of the burgeoning sun. The result is a sharp temperature contrast between the lower and upper air levels, a state of affairs greatly favoring convective overturning.* The warm moist air rises, bubble fashion, and cools as it rises: however, since its rate of cooling (known as the adiabatic lapse rate) is in the circumstances likely to be less than the vertical temperature gradient of the environment through which it is rising, it will frequently remain warmer, and lighter, than its environment, and so continue to rise until it has reached its dew point, that is, its condensation level.

Probably the heaviest springtime showers are those experienced on the Pacific coast in association with maritime polar air. This air frequently spends no longer on its southward journey than continental polar air, but because it travels south over the waters of the North Pacific, it is able to gather up much more moisture and heat than its continental twin, all the while remaining cold aloft. Whereas in winter such an air mass might easily give, over the land, low sheet clouds and steady drizzle, even rain perhaps, in spring the steepening of the lapse rate as the air passes over the warm land surface, together with the stronger sunlight, promotes the development of cumulonimbus clouds and showers.

In spite of its repute, April is not noticeably a very wet

* See June, pp. 123 to 127, for a fuller account of the convective process.

month. Indeed, in no sector of the continent is it the wettest of the twelve; over most of New England, the Maritimes, and the Province of Quebec it is actually the driest month of the year. The explanation of this apparent anomaly would seem to lie largely in the fact that winter and spring showers are nothing like as heavy as summer showers. For this reason: the amount of water vapor present in a given volume of saturated air increases very rapidly with the temperature; the amount of water set free when saturated air is cooled by a given amount, say 10°F., is very much greater when the initial temperature is high, as in August, than when it is fairly low, as in March and April. If saturated air at 70°F. is cooled 10°F., about 5 grams of water will be condensed out of every cubic meter of air; cooling from 40°F. to 30°F. would, however, produce only about 2 grams of condensed water.

A *shower by any other name*

Being a meteorologist is not without its handicaps. In the first place, he is a marked man: he can go nowhere without being questioned about the weather for tomorrow, the prospects for the week end, the effect of the latest atomic explosion, and so on—*ad nauseam*. In the second place, he can never escape from his calling—even in his own home. If his son is caught in a storm without his rubbers, the meteorologist is to blame. If his wife comes home wilted from a shopping expedition, it's because his temperature forecast went sour. If the rain he promised as he went off duty does not materialize, he is depressed and spends his time wondering why; if it does, everybody else is depressed and he spends his time explaining that he is only a meteorologist, not a magician. In the third place, the curse of Babel is upon him. The language he uses is shot through with confusion. Many of his most commonly used words carry different meanings to different people; many more are used, interchangeably, to describe a single phenomenon; and some which have had a long and venerable history no longer mean what they did. Part of the trouble, of course, is that the things with which the meteorologist is concerned, such as heat and cold, fine weather and foul, are the stock in trade of ordinary conversation the world over and have been so ever since man first became interested in

The state and inclination of the day.

To make matters worse, after hundreds of years of free and easy usage, the professors have taken over some of the most familiar words and charged them with a special connotation. No doubt this is preferable to coining brand-new words, though the professors are good at that too, but it can be baffling to the layman.

Typical of the confusion that has crept into our terminology is that surrounding the word "shower." When Chaucer wrote of "Aprille with his shoures soote," his readers knew quite well what he had in mind, namely, falls of rains separated by bright intervals: they were not necessarily of short duration (Shakespeare, it will be recalled, speaks of small showers lasting long), nor were they associated with any special types of cloud—let alone atmospheric processes, about which, of course, next to nothing was known. Today it is different. When the meteorologist tells us that the weather is going to be showery, he has in mind specific types of cloud and atmospheric processes; if pressed, he will sometimes lay down an upper time limit which, by exceeding, a shower automatically ceases to be a shower. Just how technical it has all become may be judged from the following excerpted instruction promulgated by the U.S. Weather Bureau for the benefit of its corps of observers: *

* Circular N, Instructions for Airway Meteorological Service, 1941, p. 41.

> Showers are characterized by the suddenness with which the precipitation (rain, snow, snow pellets, etc.) starts or stops and its rapid changes of intensity: but also by the aspect of the sky—rapid changes between dark, threatening clouds and clearings of the sky (of short duration, often with an intensely blue sky). Sometimes no definite clearing occurs between the showers, or the precipitation does not even stop entirely between them; the showery character of the precipitation is then revealed by the more or less rapid alterations of the lighter and darker clouds.

The equally authoritative *Weather Glossary* published by the U.S. Weather Bureau quotes this with approval and adds that the word "shower" is only to be applied to "precipitation of a convective origin, and hence distinct from ordinary frontal or orographic precipitation."

This may be all very well for the expert, though I do not observe that he invariably observes the nice distinctions demanded of him when issuing a forecast, but it is tough on the amateur, for from the underside of an overcast sky which may be present, we are told, in showery weather, even the experts would have a hard time distinguishing convective clouds from frontal and orographic clouds. I suppose that, when in doubt, the layman can always fall back on the term "occasional precipitation," though it would be a little difficult to make poetry that way. Somehow, it sounds better to sing of the course of true love being "full of showers" than full of occasional precipitation.

Rainbows come in all sizes and colors

No shower would seem really complete without the rainbow; yet many is the time we have had the former without the latter. The reason for this apparent anomaly is physical. Centuries ago Descartes showed that the bow is the natural result of the reflection and refraction of the sun's rays by falling drops of rain. Some of the light entering the raindrops is reflected back from the inner surfaces of their far sides, and since this light is also broken into its constituent spectrum colors and the rays that leave the drops do so at angles determined by their colors, an observer with his back to the sun sees a number of concentric colored rings.

The size of a rainbow, that is, its length from end to end, varies greatly, depending on the portion of the complete circle, of which it is a part, that is visible, and on its distance from the observer: however, its angular radius * is always substantially the same, ranging, in the case of the primary bow, from about 41 degrees for the violet end of the spectrum to about 43 degrees for the red. The secondary and fainter bow that is sometimes to be seen on the outer side of the primary bow, and which results from the double reflection of the rays within the raindrops, has an angular radius of about 51 degrees. The simple Descartian theory offers no explanation of the so-called supernumerary bows that occur below the primary and above the secondary bows. They are bands due to interference, the width and spacing of which depend on the diameter of the raindrops.

As these angular radii are invariable, the formation of a rainbow is restricted to times when the sun's altitude is less than 42 degrees, assuming that the observer is stationed at sea level. The lower the sun's altitude, the more there is of the bow. By the same token, the higher up the observer is, the more he sees: by going high enough in an aircraft, he may even see the bow as a complete circle. At the surface not more than half of the bow is ever visible, because its center is always exactly opposite the sun, that is, always as far below the horizon as the sun is above it. This explains why the bow is so much more conspicuous in early morning or late afternoon than it is when the sun

* That is, the angle which the radius of the bow subtends at the eye.

is higher in the heavens, and why, of course, it is never seen in the tropics around noon, or even in middle latitudes, at that hour, during the summer.

The colors are due to the unequal refraction, internal reflection, and diffraction of sunlight, or moonlight, by the water droplets. In the brightness and purity of their colors rainbows differ greatly, one from another, according to the size of the raindrops that produce them and to the uniformity, or lack of it, in their size. When the drops are small, merging of adjacent colors occurs, and instead of starting with red and finishing with violet, the bow is bounded by orange and pink. When the drops are less than about 1/500 inch in diameter, as in ordinary fog, there is so much merging of the color scheme that nothing is left except the color you started with, namely, white. It is then that you get the "fogbow." It is only when the drops are really large, as they usually are in convectional showers, that the full multicolored glory of the rainbow—"exceeding beautiful in the brightness thereof" as the author of the book of *Ecclesiasticus* puts it—is revealed.

It doesn't always rain before the rainbow

The rainbow inspired the weather-wise long before it did the lyric writer of modern times, and although the proverbial lore which has come down to us about it is of mixed quality, it is based on observation, which is rather more than can be said for the words of some popular songs. The wisest of the many sayings are probably the following:

Rainbow at night, sailors' delight;
Rainbow in the morning, sailors take warning.

Rainbow to windward, foul fall the day;
Rainbow to leeward, damp runs away.

In regions where rain belts generally travel from some westerly point to some easterly one, as in the central and northern parts of America, windward means westward, and leeward eastward. Hence a rainbow seldom occurs to windward except in the morning, when the sun is in the east or southeast; when it does occur, it means that the rain forming the bow is approaching. But it may mean more than just that. Morning showers are most likely to occur when warm, moist surface air is topped by cooler, drier air in which nocturnal radiation has brought down the temperature of the ceiling of the cloud, formed in the moist air, to the point where the increased weight of the chilled upper air causes it to descend, violently overturning the warm air beneath. Such showers may open a period of unsettled, squally weather, than which nothing is more foul in the estimation of the seafarer. On the other hand, a rainbow "at night," that is, around sunset, is almost certainly a rainbow to leeward and indicates, firstly, that clear skies lie to windward and, secondly, that the humidity is fairly low, seeing that it presumably took the maximum convection of the day to produce the shower and the bow along with it. For that reason, general rains are improbable.

Thunder in spring

The overturning of the atmosphere that brings April showers is responsible for most of the thunder we get at that season of the year. As a heat thunderstorm is then practically out of the question except in the Deep South, the necessary conditions of instability—moist air and a steep temperature lapse rate—are provided by the passage of cold air over relatively warm water. Just as many of the sharpest showers in spring are associated with westerly winds which have a polar origin, so cool-season thunder is most likely to occur in air that has come down from high latitudes via the Pacific or the Atlantic. One of its favorite haunts is mountain country. The upward motion imparted to unstable air on encountering a transverse relief barrier is often just enough to touch off the incipient convection. Away from the mountains the same mechanism can be set in motion when maritime polar air overruns warmer air—as sometimes happens at a cold front—or, alternatively, walls up against it, thereby inducing a similarly vigorous and sudden overturning of the atmosphere.

Whatever the precise mechanism, we may take it as axiomatic that thunder in early spring implies an invasion, first aloft and afterward at the surface, of cold air, which gives point to the saying:

Thunder in spring,
Cold will bring.

Coming, as it often does, hard on the heels of a mild spell, the cold air helps to postpone the threatened unseasonable growth of vegetation, and while it does not ensure that fruit trees will not blossom until the frost hazard has vanished, it certainly does contribute to that end. The longer the cold spell lasts, thunder or no thunder, the greater its contribution to the ensuing season's fruitfulness. Presumably the originator of the couplet

When April blows his horn *
It's good for hay and corn

had this in mind, but the man who first opined that

A cold April
The barn will fill

got closer to the real reason.

* That is, thunders.

Feels like frost?

In early spring, when the barometer is high and there is a gentle drift of air down from the arctic, the advent of a still and starry night is likely to send the night temperature down to freezing point, or below, almost anywhere in the northern half of the Union, turning the hedges, in David Morton's words,

. . . a whitening line of spray . . . ,
*Staining the grass with shivered, golden things.**

Every object exposed to the sky on such a night loses heat by radiation. The flow of heat rays is unseen but continuous, and the degree of cold attained by the surface of the object depends mainly on the ability of the air surrounding it to counteract that loss by its own warmth. This may sound a little complicated, but if you picture a single leaf at the top of a tree, say, 50 feet high, disbursing its very modest income of warmth in the chill of a spring night, you will appreciate that the leaf can become very little colder † than the air which surrounds it. If the air at our treetop stands at a temperature which during the night falls no lower than 35°F., the leaf surface is unlikely to drop below, or even to, freezing point, but the chilling effect of a drop of even a few degrees in the temperature of the leaf surface will be enough to start up a minute trickle of cooled air which will gravitate earthward to join all the other minute trickles from other leaves and exposed surfaces of all kinds and so form a film of cold air over the ground surface. As this film thickens, the radiation loss from exposed surfaces which are submerged beneath it increases, for the neutralizing effect of contact with warmer air is lost. Soon, since cold air is heavier

* Sonnet, "Acquaintance."

† Its ability to become even a degree or so colder than the ambient air depends upon the amount of inherent moisture which can be evaporated from its surface.

than air a few degrees less cold, the chilled air becomes deep enough for gravity to impel it to move. And so the drift to lower levels begins. Descending from the slopes of the steeper hills, its progress is slowed as less steep ground is reached. Further collection of chilled air may have to take place on these lower levels before a sufficient volume and weight of the heavier, cold air can get going again. Always the urge of this icy drift is to fill up existing hollows first, to overflow them, and to pass on to the lowest possible level where it can collect in pools. The ultimate depth of the frost-laden air is determined, firstly, by the amount of chilling which goes on during the night, in other words, by the severity of the frost; secondly, by the size of the "feed" area—by the area of higher ground from which the cold air drains; and thirdly, by the possibility of ultimate drainage to wide-open spaces or to sea level.

Fruit trees and frost

If you have a garden on a knoll 50 feet high, set in the middle of an open plain with no higher land nearby, it is extremely unlikely that any spring frost save one of phenomenal severity will spoil your fruit blossoms. Cold winds may prevent pollenizing by insects and gales may check tree growth, but frost will not trouble you unduly. This is because the small amount of cold air draining from your particular hillock will not be enough to raise the level of the frosty air on the plain below, a level which in the most severe spring frosts is unlikely to rise more than 10 feet above soil level. If, on the other hand, you have a garden in a saucerlike depression, then it is inviting trouble to plant fruit trees in it: even in Florida and California "frost holes" have been the cause of many a citrus-grove failure, though frost there is a winter rather than a spring phenomenon.

The important thing is the *relative* height of your site. A high position associated with terrain which will shed cold air is excellent as a frost preventive, but one which allows cold air from still higher levels to collect upon it, or which has contours that guide currents of accumulated cold air draining from such higher land so that they pass right over it, is very far from safe. If you live in a valley, avoid the lowest levels at all costs. In a wide shallow valley like that of the middle reaches of the Connecticut, the really dangerous ground frosts nearly all occur within 20 feet of the river level. In a deeply engulfed valley like that of the Monongahela near Pittsburgh, the upper limit of the danger zone is higher, about 200 feet above the valley floor. Near the sea and by open estuaries, so large an area is often available for the flow of chilled air to fan out that frosts are serious only where the drainage is blocked by houses and tree belts. Then seas and wide river mouths also reduce frost risk to the lands adjoining them by virtue of the comparative warmth of their waters; when this is communicated to the overlying layers of air, it sometimes happens that sheltered valleys will be drowned in frosty air, while neighboring estuaries and coastal flats remain several degrees above freezing point.

Not every frost is a killer

But the relation between freezing point and frost—let alone frost damage—is, so the authorities tell us, not so simple as we might think.

According to the *Weather Glossary* of the U.S. Weather Bureau, the temperature, as registered by a minimum thermometer exposed to the sky and located just above a grass surface, needs to fall almost 2°F. below freezing point (to 30.4°F.) before it is legitimate to speak of a ground frost—the kind most gardeners and farmers are interested in. In choosing this value, the Weather Bureau was presumably influenced by the knowledge that, while fresh water begins to freeze, on the average, when the temperature drops to 32°F., hoarfrost and similar accretions do not normally make their appearance at the ground level until the temperature has dropped a degree or so lower. Even so, the propriety of choosing this particular value could be questioned since, under certain circumstances, damage to the cells of living plants can be caused before the temperature drops to 30.4°F. This is particularly likely to be the case when the moisture content of the air is high. Thus, whereas a ground temperature of 32°F. would have next to no effect on a watermelon plant if the dew point of the air were 26 degrees, it might be quite harmful if the dew point were 32°F.

Other factors that enter into the frost-damage equation include the wind speed (a moving stream of subfreezing air, say 30°F., can usually do more damage than a stagnant pool of air at, let us say, 26°F.), the duration of the subfreezing period (a temperature of 28°F. experienced only for 10 minutes is much less likely to cause damage than a temperature of 32°F. lasting half the night), and thirdly, the stage of growth reached by the plant concerned (thus, plants about to form fruit buds are more susceptible to frost damage than plants still in the flowering stage). Ideally the minimum temperature of the wet-bulb thermometer set at ground level would provide a more helpful yardstick by which to measure intensity of frost than the ordinary grass minimum. Unfortunately, however, accurate wet-bulb readings are not easily obtained when the temperature falls below 32°F.

In the circumstances, there is much to be said for regarding a grass minimum temperature of 32°F. or below as constituting a frost. Where frost is concerned, there is no great safety in numbers.

How to forecast frost

Whether there will or will not be frost on a given night depends on a number of factors, such as the soil-surface temperature at sunset, the dew-point temperature at the same hour, and the rate at which heat is conducted to the surface to replace that lost through radiation, this rate in turn depending upon such things as the density, moisture content, and specific thermal conductivity of the various soil types involved. We might well imagine, therefore, that the task of forecasting local frost is not one to be lightly undertaken by the amateur. As a matter of fact, it is perfectly possible to get the right answer on most occasions. If in the early evening the sky is clear, there is little or no wind, the dry-bulb thermometer stands round about 40 to 45°F. and the wet-bulb three or four degrees lower (that is, if the air is dry), then a ground frost is fairly certain. If, on the other hand, the air is very moist, an evening temperature of 45°F. need cause no alarm; and when the relative humidity is high and there is a decent breeze, even a temperature of 40°F. may not be followed by frost. Should a fog or blanket of low cloud appear later in the evening, you can practically rule out the risk altogether.

Naturally, conditions vary from place to place, but the following rule of thumb is likely to give good results in open country. On spring evenings when conditions favor rapid radiation, the minimum night temperature can be calculated by subtracting 0 to 8°F. from the midafternoon (say 3 o'clock) dew point, the exact number to be subtracted being determined by reference to the wind speed and the relative humidity, as shown in the accompanying table.

To take an example: if the dew point of the air at three o'clock is 36°F., the relative humidity 80 per cent, and a wind of 10 miles per hour is expected to blow during the night, then the minimum night temperature is given by $36 - 4 = 32°F$.

Mean wind speed expected during night	Relative humidity at 3 o'clock	Formula for obtaining minimum temperature (D = 3 o'clock dew point)
Less than 7 m.p.h.	Less than 85%	$D - 8$
	More than 85%	$D - 6$
7 to 14 m.p.h.	Less than 85%	$D - 4$
	More than 85%	$D - 1$
More than 14 m.p.h.	Less than 85%	$D - 2$
	More than 85%	$D - 0$

If you do not possess a wet-bulb thermometer, there's a more rough and ready way of estimating the minimum temperature that involves the use of a dry-bulb thermometer only. The method assumes that, in anticyclonic spring weather with cloudy or sunny days and calm, clear nights, there is a uniform rate of fall in temperature from the afternoon maximum through the night to the early morning minimum, and that the times for such maximum and minimum temperatures will be approximately the same for all such days. This means to say that if you know today's maximum temperature and you take a second reading midway between the time of the maximum and the estimated time of tomorrow morning's minimum, then the difference between the second two readings will be the same as the difference between the first two. Thus, if the maximum temperature on any given day, say at 3:30 P.M. local standard time, is 70°F., and the minimum temperature is expected to occur round about 5:00 A.M. the following morning, and the temperature at 10:15 P.M., that is, midway between the times of the known maximum and the estimated minimum, is 50°F., then the difference between the "midway" temperature and the maximum temperature (20°F. in this case) will, if subtracted from the midway temperature, give the minimum temperature likely to be recorded, namely, 30°F.

If neither of these rules works out too well in your particular district, why not try and find other similar rules which do?

Frost frequency

Maps giving the frequency of killing frosts * over various parts of North America show that the coasts of Southern California and Florida are the least affected areas, with more than 320 frostless days in the year, and that, mountains apart, the barren lands of northern Canada are the most affected: Aklavik, near the mouth of the Mackenzie, has, for example, an average frost-free period of only sixty-five days; Whitehorse, in the Yukon, has less than fifty.†

REGIONAL VARIATIONS IN LENGTH OF FROST-FREE SEASON IN THE UNITED STATES

	Average frost-free season (days)	Average killing frost date	
		Last in spring ‡	First in fall
Los Angeles, Calif.	359	Jan. 3	Dec. 28
Palm Beach, Fla.	322	Feb. 4	Dec. 23
New Orleans, La.	292	Feb. 20	Dec. 9
Portland, Ore.	263	Mar. 6	Nov. 24
Atlanta, Ga.	237	Mar. 23	Nov. 9
New York, N.Y.	211	Apr. 9	Nov. 6
Chicago, Ill.	196	Apr. 13	Oct. 26
Denver, Colo.	171	Apr. 26	Oct. 14
Bangor, Me.	150	May 9	Oct. 6
Fort Laramie, Wyo.	125	May 20	Sept. 22
Butte, Mont.	110	May 29	Sept. 16
Aroostook, Me.	107	June 7	Sept. 22

* Defined, in this instance, as a frost that is destructive to vegetation and staple products.

† At some of these arctic stations there is no guarantee that the temperature will not fall below freezing any day in the year: Fort Ross, approximately 72°N, 94°W, has reported 20 degrees of frost in July, the warmest month of the year.

‡ See Fig. 8.

Throughout the cotton states, the frost-free period is about 200 days long. Throughout the Corn Belt, it is not less than 140 days. In northern Maine and Minnesota, the northern Mountain states, and the Prairie Provinces, the average period between spring and fall frosts is from 100 to 125 days. While some hardy cereals and vegetables can contrive to complete their cycle of growth in under ninety days, the risk of damage by early or late frost becomes considerable in these marginal areas, with the result that at present very little commercial agriculture is carried on north of the ninety-day line.

"The noise of many waters"

A generation of city dwellers can hardly be expected to share the enthusiasm of a Thoreau for the spring thaw. For what is it but a time of self-exposure, when the abandoned trash of winter, erstwhile hid from our eyes and consciences by a

Fig. 8. Average dates of last killing frost in spring. (*Courtesy of the Weather Bureau, U.S. Department of Commerce*)

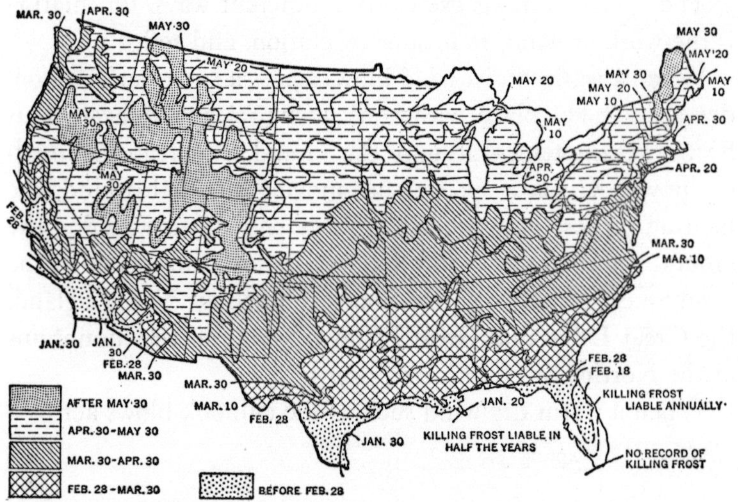

mantle of snow, stares accusingly at us from every naked gutter? Of ugliness and tumult, when nothing is truly clean and nothing perfectly at rest? Of alarm for the householder and jeopardy for the pedestrian, when water invades the cellar and floods are in the streets?

Yet there is another side to the picture—one that Thoreau has portrayed for us in his *Walden* in language that captures the power of the thaw as well as its poetry: "At length the sun's rays have attained the right angle, and warm winds blow up mist and rain and melt the snowbanks, and the sun, dispersing the mist, smiles on a checkered landscape of russet and white smoking with incense, through which the traveller picks his way from islet to islet, cheered by the music of a thousand tinkling rills and rivulets whose veins are filled with the blood of winter which they are bearing off. . . . The frost comes out of the ground like a dormant quadruped from its burrow, and seeks the sea with music, or migrates to other climes in clouds. Thaw with his gentle persuasion is more powerful than Thor with his hammer. The one melts, the other but breaks in pieces. . . ." *

The "persuasion" is exercised in different ways, for melting is the work of wind, rain, sun, vegetation, and soil.

When a warm moist wind blows across a snow surface, condensation takes place with consequent release of heat. This heat raises the temperature of the air and so increases its melting power. Given a spell of fast-moving air of this kind, the melting process may proceed quickly enough to waterlog the ground and produce serious flooding: indeed, this is one of the commonest causes of spring floods throughout New England, the Great Lakes and Great Plains region, and the mountains of the Northwest.

When a warm dry wind such as the chinook blows across a

* Chap. 17 ("Spring").

snow surface, a winter's accumulation may disappear practically overnight; however, the flooding risk is not so great as in the case of moist air, since a considerable percentage of the snow is vaporized directly into the dry atmosphere.

Contrary to the popular belief, rain, if unaided, seldom succeeds in persuading snow to melt very fast: a 5-inch fall of rain with a temperature of 41°F. is unlikely to release more than one-third of an inch of snow water. But when heavy rains of this order occur in conjunction with warm windy weather, the melting rate of snow rises sharply; it is then that the danger of heavy spring floods is acute. Most of the bad Ohio Valley floods and the phenomenal Red River (1950) and Kansas (1952) floods can, in large measure, be traced to the door of these two agencies working in concert.

Nor is the sun always the efficient destroyer of snow it is reputed to be. On a clean snow surface, the sun has to work very hard to remove any snow, for most of its radiation is reflected straight back into space. With a dirty snow surface it is different, for each little speck of dirt acts as a short-wave (light) receiver of radiation and a long-wave (heat) transmitter to the surrounding snow and air. And a blackened layer of snow may be able to continue its melting work even after it has been covered up by new snow. Placed horizontally on open ground, blackened thermometers, which tend to behave in the presence of sunlight in much the same way as specks of dirt, have been known to record higher temperatures, depth for depth of snow (up to a depth of one foot or so), than unblackened thermometers, showing that some sunlight is absorbed by the snow. Once the sun has a "transformer" to work with, the speed with which it is able to melt the snow is governed largely by such things as aspect and interception. Generally speaking, snow disappears more slowly on slopes sheltered from the sun and wind than on slopes exposed to sun and wind, partly because there is more snow there to start with, and partly because the rate of evaporation is roughly proportional to the angle of incidence of the sun's rays and the amount of ventilation, that is, the speed of the wind. It is also likely to melt more quickly in open than in forested country, both because trees, even leafless deciduous trees, cut down air movement, and therefore evaporation, and because they intercept varying amounts of snow and sunlight. Dense coniferous forests may retain in their canopies anything up to 90 per cent of a heavy fall of snow and thus increase the superficial area from which evaporation of the snow may proceed. Open stands of conifers intercept smaller amounts, and deciduous stands even less, but their power to reradiate the incoming sunlight and so warm the surface air and melt the snow is all the greater on that account.

Over terrain where the variations in slope, aspect, exposure, and vegetation are wide, the resulting areal differences in the melting rate may be large enough to regulate the discharge of snow water and so virtually eliminate the flood hazard.

The effectiveness of the soil as a melting agent depends on its temperature. If the ground became well-frozen before the first snows of winter fell, not much heat is likely to be communicated to the overlying snow cover—not enough, at any rate, to influence the melting rate appreciably. On the other hand, if the ground was still unfrozen when the snow began to fly, its stored-up warmth, insulated from the atmosphere (and as we have seen, there is no better insulator than well-aerated snow), can go to work melting the underside of the snow: as long as the snow cover remains, the residual heat of the soil may well be enough to keep the lowest stratum of snow in a state of liquefaction. In this way, the ground-water supply is increased, and the risk of spring flooding through quick runoff is decreased.

May

"Fair fresshe May"

CHAUCER may have been the first Englishman to rhapsodize over the month of May, the month that

. . . priketh every gentil herte,
And maketh him out of his sleep to sterte

but certainly he was not the last. There has been scarcely a poet since his time who has not been similarly moved, whether by the earth in May, the mornings o' May, the flowery meads of May, or the behavior of maids—and their swains—in May.

For those who know and love England in May there is much to be said for this poetic preoccupation, for it is of all the English months the singingest, even though it can, when in the mood, produce many of the symptoms of a relapsed winter including killing frosts, flurries of snow, and howling gales.

It is noticeable, however, that poets on this side of the Atlantic have been more sparing in their praise of May. Judging from the dearth of references to the month in American poesy, you would almost think it was difficult to find rhymes for the word. And perhaps it is—apposite words, that is. Unlike June, which rhymes beautifully with such lyrical words as "moon," "lagoon," and "swoon," May has to keep company with such drabs as "pray," "dismay," and "hay" (but who ever heard of a Yankee farmer cutting hay in May?). Perhaps the real reason for their reservations about the month is more meteorological than terminological. After all, over most of the United States May is a month to be regarded circumspectly, with mingled hopes and fears, with caution as well as with charity—with very considerable reservation in fact. It can be as dulcet as a flute, but also as harsh as a police whistle: its sun can woo a woman out of her clothes, but its winds can send her scurrying to the furriers. It can caress with one hand: it can buffet with the other. Before it is half over, it can have played all the tunes in the English poets' book, and still reach into its repertoire for a tornado and a shower or two of baseball-sized hail. Even Florida is not immune to its visitations of wind and the sound of its waterspouts, and California is less "fresshe" than "fair" by the time the month is out.

Tornadoes

If there's one atmospheric experience most people would rather not have, it's tangling with a tornado. For a tornado is loud and raucous; its path is as devious as a drunken man's and just about as unpredictable. It is no respecter of property and will as soon demolish a row of well-built shops as crumple a wooden shack. It is likewise no respecter of dignity: it can pluck the feathers off a hen and the clothes off a man as easily as it can strip the leaves off a tree, and it can send any one of them soaring skyward in defiance of the laws of gravity. Maybe no cow ever jumped over the moon, but before now a herd of Kansas steers has been seen involuntarily taking off in its direction. When last observed, the animals were said to look like "gigantic birds."

Seen for the first time—and preferably from a distance—the funnel-shaped cloud so characteristic of a tornado has a beguiling fragility that almost makes one doubt its powers of destruction, for the writhing "rope" that trails earthward from the parent cloud is seldom more than 600 feet in diameter, and is commonly less than 200.

The predisposing cause of a tornado is the interaction of two highly contrasted air masses, usually maritime tropical and continental, or maritime, polar. To "trigger" off the tornado, the warm air must underlie the cold air and, ideally, should be at least 8,000 to 10,000 feet thick. The cold air should be dry with a steep lapse rate, that is, its temperature should fall off rapidly with height, and overrun the warm air at an angle to produce what the meteorologist calls "shear"; this encourages the formation of eddies in the plane of contact, in the same way as eddies occur in a body of water where two currents of different velocity converge.

The eddy, or vortex, may simply be regarded as a dynamic by-product of the enormous turbulence produced under such atmospheric conditions. Incipient vortices are likewise present in most thunderclouds (as glider pilots know well enough), but it is only when the gyratory motion becomes really intense that the vortex descends from the cloud base to the surface.

One result of the intense gyration is to produce a partial vacuum, that is, very low pressure at the center of the vortex. It is on this account that buildings lying in the path of a tornado are frequently seen to explode: the air inside them being at normal pressure exerts a thrust that pushes windows, doors, and walls outward.

On this continent the usual locale for tornadoes is along the cold-front margin of a well-developed warm sector, and their usual line of advance is parallel to the cold front, but there are, alas, all too many exceptions to these rules—to the constant discomfiture of the forecaster. What is more certain (though never dead certain) is that they will approach from a southwesterly quarter and move off to the northeast; that their speed of advance will be between 20 and 50 miles per hour; that their internal wind velocity will be anything up to 350 miles per hour, perhaps more; that their trail of ruin will not be above 100 miles long (25 miles is nearer the average); and, bad criminals that they are, that they will not return to the exact scene of their crimes. They have been known to, though: Baldwyn, Mississippi, was ravaged twice in 25 minutes on March 16, 1942, with a total loss of life of sixty-five persons.

Notwithstanding popular opinion to the contrary, tornadoes are confined neither to one part of the year nor to one part of the country. They have been reported in every month and in every state.

FREQUENCY OF TORNADOES AND TORNADO DAYS IN THE UNITED STATES, BY MONTHS (1920–1949) *

Month	Tornadoes	Tornado days
January	3	3
February	3	3
March	12	9
April	17	14
May	21	18
June	18	17
July	8	12
August	5	8
September	5	6
October	3	3
November	3	3
December	2	2

* Fawbush, Miller, and Starrett, "An Empirical Method of Forecasting Tornado Development," *Bulletin of the American Meteorological Society*, January, 1951.

In the Southern states, they are most frequent in late winter and spring: March is the peak month in Alabama, Georgia, Mississippi, Tennessee, and Kentucky; April in Florida, North and South Carolina, Louisiana, Arkansas, Texas, and Missouri. In the Middle West they are commonest in May and June when the tornado season, as we can see from the accompanying table, is at its height.

One of the most destructive tornadoes on record occurred in the off season, in the month of September. On the evening of September 1, 1952, a "twister" formed, unheralded and highly localized, near the Carswell Air Force Base in Texas. In a matter of minutes it did 48 million dollars' worth of damage, mainly to the heavy bombers (B-36s) that lined the field; 106 of them were reported as being put out of action—more than enough for one field, or one country, for that matter! At the nearby Fort Worth Municipal Airport the winds at no time exceeded 58 miles per hour; at four other fields within 100 miles of Carswell the wind did not exceed 20 miles per hour. In the tornado the maximum velocity may have been as

Fig. 9. Total number of tornadoes per 50-mile square reported in the period 1920–1949. (After Fawbush, Miller, and Starrett, "An Empirical Method of Forecasting Tornado Development," Bulletin, American Meteorological Society, 1951.) (Courtesy of the Society.)

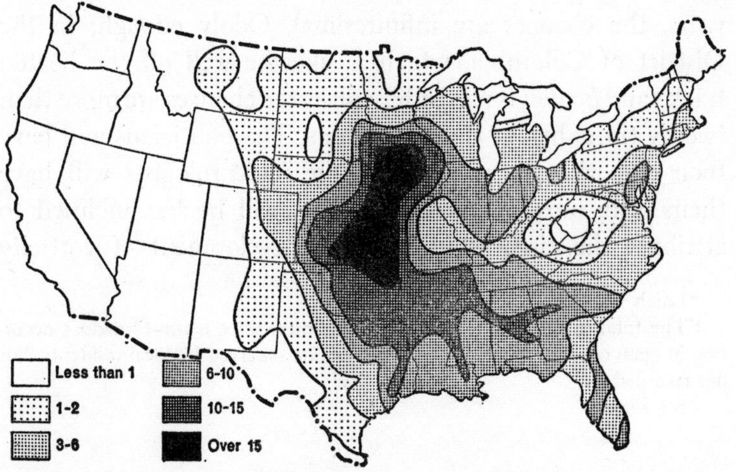

much as 350 miles per hour, for by the physical principle of the conservation of angular momentum a cyclonic, rotary wind of 50 miles per hour at a distance of 5 miles from the center of the vortex (about the distance of the Fort Worth field from the Carswell base) would theoretically become a wind of 500 miles per hour near the center of the vortex. Even if ground friction dissipated half of the kinetic energy, this would still leave a wind of about 350 miles per hour!

In the face of such elemental force, the words of the ancient prophet acquire a shocking realism: "Thou shalt fan them, and the wind shall carry them away, and the whirlwind shall scatter them." *

The state with the largest tally of recorded † tornadoes to its debit is Kansas, with 587 during the thirty-four-year period ending 1949, followed closely by Iowa, with 512. As the map ‡ clearly indicates, these states also rank high for hazard. The chances of a given square mile of land being struck sooner or later by a tornado are 1 in 1,203 in Iowa and 1 in 1,613 in Kansas. In Arkansas, which ranks third, they are 1 in 1,933, and in Oklahoma, which is fourth on the list, they are 1 in 2,262. In Nevada, which has only reported one tornado in thirty-four years, the chances are infinitesimal. Oddly enough, in the District of Columbia, which is likewise well off the beaten track (and *beaten* is used advisedly), the chances are more than twenty times higher than in Kansas. The politicians will have their own theories about this: the meteorologists will have theirs also; most of them, however, will be less inclined to attribute the circumstance to the development of vorticity

* Isaiah 41:16.

† The total number is probably much greater, since many tornadoes occurring in open country are unobserved: others are observed by local residents, but not recorded.

‡ See Fig. 9.

in an unstable environment created by hot air than they will to the laws of chance! *

Waterspouts

The waterspout is the somewhat milder-mannered marine counterpart of the tornado. However, the two are far from identical—either in causation or character. Thus, a waterspout can form in a cloudless sky, though, admittedly, a cloudy sky is more customary. It can appear first at water level or simultaneously at the surface and in the heavens. It may have either a clockwise or an anticlockwise rotation: a tornado invariably has cyclonic, that is, anticlockwise, rotation in the Northern Hemisphere. It rarely lasts more than an hour, and is likely to complete its life cycle inside 30 minutes. It may consist of fine mist and spray, or of dense cloud. It may yield no precipitation; on the other hand, it may produce rain and hail aplenty, and even solid chunks of ice. At its base there may be a cone of water surrounded by a frosting of foam, or there may be nothing but a shallow circular depression. Its wind velocities may be very high or very low. A naval vessel that passed through a waterspout in West Indian waters reported scarcely more wind than you would expect to meet in a fog.

In its most developed form it is a writhing spiral of water vapor and water particles. Because of the lowered pressure induced by the vorticity, the air drawn into the spiral is cooled and condenses to form the dark inner core of water particles that is a common feature of a really vigorous spout. The bigger the core, the stronger apparently is the suction power of the spout, and the greater the admixture of salt-water

* In a thirty-four-year period of observations, the 69 square miles of Washington, D.C., have had four tornadoes. Statisticians are of the opinion that this is nothing more than a random distribution, and that there is a good chance of the next thirty-four years being tornado-less.

particles with the condensed sweet-water particles derived from the ambient air. In a few well-authenticated instances, waterspouts have yielded salt-water rain showers. Two or three hours following the dispersal of the gigantic waterspout that occurred off Martha's Vineyard on August 19, 1896, the residents of the island were deluged by a salt-water downpour, clearly indicating that sea water not only had been carried up the approximately 3,000-foot spiral in substantial quantity, but also that it had been carried by convection throughout the parent cloud.

The enormous suction power of a well-developed waterspout can probably be held to explain, as well, the occasional stories about rains of fishes and frogs. These stories are found in the lore and literature of many lands, and although many of them have been embellished in the retelling, they are unquestionably well founded. One of the most striking comes from New Zealand. On July 13, 1949, the township of Hastings reported that "during a brief rainstorm, thousands of fish averaging four inches in length fell on a ten-acre field" in its vicinity. Similar stories of recent vintage come from Belfast, Northern Ireland, where "dozens of tiny red fish were found on the roof of a farmhouse and on the ground about it"; from Aberdare, Wales, where, according to an eyewitness, "the fish came down in a body like" covering a strip of ground about 80 yards long and 12 yards wide, and measuring up to 5 inches in length; from New York, where they fell in the streets; and from India, where they came down on a barrack square. In almost every case the visitation seems to have been accompanied by torrential rain of a convectional type, to have occurred within easy reach of the sea (or some other extensive water body), to have been short-lived and confined to a small area—all of which lends support to the waterspout theory of their origin.

While no two descriptions of waterspouts are identical,

there is pretty general agreement about the cone of solid water that commonly appears at the base of the spout. This seldom rises more than 20 feet above the level of the water surface. Probably the greatest height it could ever attain would be 35 feet: a column higher than this would weigh more than the pressure of the atmosphere on the surrounding sea could support.*

Because of their marine origin, comparative rarity, transient nature, and liability to occur at night as well as during the day, not so much is known about the seasonal and geographical frequency of waterspouts as is known about tornadoes. For the most part, they are warm-weather phenomena, and occur between May and October in regions of relatively high water temperature. Their favorite breeding place seems to be the doldrums—that equatorial belt of fitful winds and calms, of almost constant convection, high sea temperatures, and high humidities. As far as the North American continent is concerned, they are most likely to occur around the shores of the Gulf of Mexico and along the western margin of the Gulf Stream. In early summer they are not infrequently reported off the coast of Florida: as the season advances they tend to be reported farther north, and by August they may sometimes be seen off the coasts of southern New England. However, they have been sighted over the Grand Banks off Newfoundland as early as April and May; so it would be inaccurate to think of

* The pressure of the atmosphere on the surface of the earth may be measured in different ways. Customarily it is measured as the weight which is exerted upon a mercury surface exposed to the free air. At sea level in normal weather the weight of the atmosphere on a bowl of mercury so exposed is sufficient to support a 30-inch column of the same liquid contained in a tube, the upper end of which is sealed and the lower end submerged beneath the surface of the mercury-filled bowl. If, in place of mercury, water is used (engineers often do use it), a tube about 13½ times longer is required, mercury being about that much heavier than water: this means that the atmosphere can, under normal sea-level conditions, support a column of water approximately 35 *feet* high.

an orderly procession of waterspouts north and south with the seasons.

One of the most spectacular spouts to be reported in American waters in recent years occurred on the afternoon of June 13, 1952, in the vicinity of St. Petersburg, Florida. Forming near the shore it "made a terrific roar as it passed over the shallow water [of Big Bayou]. A wave five feet high was rushing ahead of it . . . as it hit land the earth appeared to explode. Trees, sand and all manner of material roared skyward. It disappeared in a mist a few minutes later." * There were fortunately no casualties except for some fish: one, all of 7 inches in length, was declared to have fallen out of the sky 10 miles from the spout.

If these heaven-borne fish get any bigger, we shall soon expect to hear that it has been raining catfish and dogfish, if not cats and dogs!

". . . *The flail of the lashing hail*"

Hail is at once the cruellest weapon in Nature's armory, and the most incalculable. It can destroy one farmer's prospects of a harvest in a matter of seconds: it can leave his neighbor's unimpaired. It can slay a flock of sheep (it has killed children before now) in one field, while the sun continues to shine in the next. To the harassed meteorologist its behavior is even more Machiavellian than that of an ice storm. Difficult as it undoubtedly is for him to forecast the onset of an ice storm, he knows pretty well what its course and duration will be once it has started: just about all he can do with a hailstorm is to measure the size of the stones—and they have a habit of melting as soon as he gets his hands on them. He is not even too sure any more about the way in which hail forms—and until he

* See *Weatherwise*, Vol. 5 (1952), p. 91.

knows this, of course, he isn't likely to stumble upon any very satisfactory prognostic rules.

Meteorologists used to have a very pretty theory about the formation of hail based on its commonly observed onionlike structure. It went something like this. Because a thundercloud * is a sort of atmospheric Jacob's ladder for the transport of myriads of ascending and descending particles of water, internal collisions are unavoidable. When particles collide, they grow larger by annexation and thus their weight increases and their speed alters—increasing if they are falling, decreasing if they are rising—and the risk of further collisions grows with every new one. If in the course of their upward progress, these enlarged water drops should enter the subfreezing zone of the cloud (almost all thunderclouds seem to have such a zone), they would quickly be coated with a thin layer of ice: they might even be frozen solid if allowed to stay in that zone long enough. Sooner or later, however, the air lift would fail, and the now frozen water drops, that is, hailstones, would begin their earthward course. On reaching the above-freezing zone they would acquire, by collision with water droplets and by condensation, a liquid film which, if the air lift should be renewed and they were returned to the subfreezing zone, would freeze and so add a new outer "skin" of ice. As hailstones have been found with no less than twenty-four layers of ice, it was contended by the advocates of this theory that this shuttlecock process could be repeated for at least twelve round trips, by which time the hailstone was presumably so large that it could not be supported by even the strongest updraft. Not the least merit of this theory is that it explains, as no other one does quite so well, the alternation of concentric clear and cloudy layers characteristic of so many full-grown hailstones—the cloudy layers being acquired in the snow and ice-crystal zone

* See July, pp. 152–156.

immediately above the freezing level, and the clear layers being acquired beneath that zone by collision with water droplets which froze either on contact or as soon as the stones were shot back into the freezing zone by the next vigorous updraft they encountered.

But it seems that many meteorologists have discarded this theory in favor of one which allows the frozen nucleus of a hailstone only one descent, during which it successively encounters ice-cooled water droplets and snowflakes. According to this theory, the size to which the stone grows depends on how many ice-cold droplets and snowflakes it encounters: which is another way of saying that the deeper the subfreezing layer of the cloud, the greater the risk of heavy hail, irrespective of the strength of the vertical air currents.

Whichever theory is right—and the atmosphere is big enough to accommodate both of them, I rather fancy—two things are certain. First, that there are a great many thunderstorms with deep freezing zones that never produce any hail and, second, that many of the really big hailstones—the kind people write to the papers about—are themselves aggregations of smaller hailstones which could by no stretch of the imagination be said to have an onionlike structure.

Hailstones the size of grapefruit

While at least 99 per cent of all hailstones have a diameter of considerably less than one inch—the average size in this country is between ¼ and ¾ inch—seldom a season passes without a report of much larger stones having fallen. If they do not exceed 2 inches in diameter, they call for nothing more than a photograph in the local paper. By the time they get to be of "tennis-ball" or "baseball" size, they call for a foot ruler. Anything bigger calls for an affidavit. When stones 17 inches in circumference, that is, almost 6 inches in diameter, began to bombard the township of Potter, Nebraska, Mr. Norcross quite rightly decided that the only way to establish the fact was to invoke the assistance of the local notary public: the following statement was duly "subscribed and sworn to" in his presence.

> To whom it may concern:
>
> I, J. J. Norcross, proprietor of the Potter Drug Co., do affirm the following facts:
>
> That on July 6, 1928, following the hailstorm in Potter, Nebr., I gathered several hailstones and measured and weighed them on standard store scales, and that one stone measured 17 ins. in circumference and that it weighed one and a half pounds . . . [it] was round and hard, with a smooth surface, and upon breaking it open I found it was composed of concentric layers built around one centre. . . .

The hazard of hail

From what we have said, it might be supposed that the risk of hail would be greatest when and where the thunderstorm hazard is greatest. Generally speaking, this is not so.

Thus, whereas a place like Tampa, Florida, is liable to have as many as ninety thunderstorm days a year,* it is quite unlikely to get more than one hailstorm a year. In a forty-year period (1904–1943) it actually had only twenty-one days with hail, and most of these fell in the months of April and May; the thunderstorms, on the other hand, occurred mostly during the months of July and August. Furthermore, it gets about twice as many thunderstorms as Dodge City, Kansas, which is near the heart of the hail belt and is likely to have between four and five days with hail in the course of a twelvemonth.

* See July, p. 156.

Taking the country as a whole, May is the peak month for hailstorms, as against July for thunderstorms, and the hail hazard is only about one-twentieth as great as the thunderstorm hazard. Even Cheyenne, Wyoming, which among its many claims to fame is the fact that it is the most hail-ridden city in America, gets only one-fifth as many hailstorms * as thunderstorms, and gets them mostly in May and June, whereas it gets most of its thunderstorms in the months of July and August. Monthly differences in the hail risk are reflected in the accompanying table which was compiled by listing the month of maximum occurrence of hail for each of some 200 weather-reporting stations.

Jan.	Feb.	Mar.	Apr.	May	June	July	Aug.	Sept.	Oct.	Nov.	Dec.
4	2	24	56	72	36	11	1	1	5	1	0

Fig. 10. Average annual number of days with hail. (*Courtesy of the Weather Bureau, U.S. Department of Commerce*)

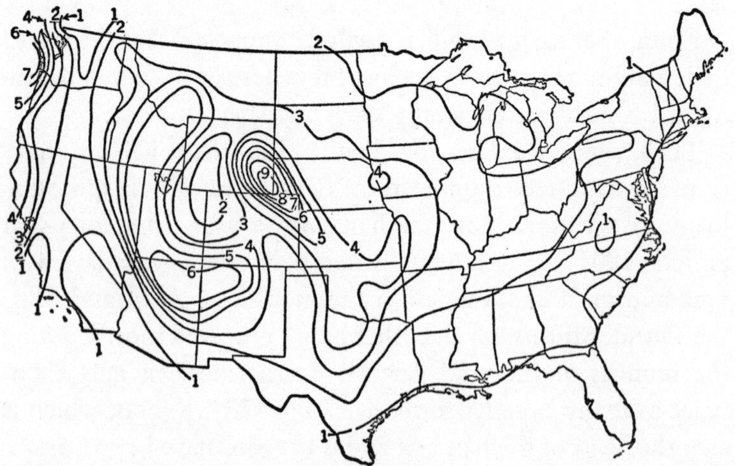

* Between nine and ten a year on the average.

With very few exceptions, the zone of greatest hail frequency * tends to "follow the sun" on its apparent northward journey. In March the zone extends in an arc from central Texas through southeastern Oklahoma to Arkansas and southern Missouri. In April it broadens and lengthens to extend from central Texas to Colorado, from Colorado to southern Illinois, from southern Illinois to northern Alabama, and from northern Alabama through Arkansas back to Texas. In May the zone stretches from the Canadian border in Montana south to the Rio Grande in Texas, and from Idaho to Indiana. In June it laps over into southern Alberta and Saskatchewan, but elsewhere withdraws somewhat toward its center in Wyoming. By July, as the table suggests, the zone has contracted still further: the only areas where the mean frequency of hailstorms exceeds one a month are located around Cheyenne, Wyoming, and Butte, Montana. The same two areas have about the same hail risk in August, but elsewhere the risk of a hailstorm has declined by then to less than one in fifty.

Most of the stations—and there are only a very few as the table shows—which report a maximum hail frequency in winter are located west of the Rockies, notably along the Pacific coast. Hailstorms in this region are generally associated with cold-front activity which is likewise at its seasonal maximum: the cool, moisture-charged polar maritime air which becomes progressively more unstable during the course of its long sea trajectory is easily teased into demonstrating its convective potentialities, especially when it is under pressure from orographic, that is, lifting, as well as frontal forces.

At the same time, it would appear that most of the continental hailstorms owe their origin more to frontally induced

* Defined for this purpose as the zone in which there is likely to be at least one-half a day with hail per month.

than thermally induced instability: at any rate, the spring and early summer movements of the zone of maximum hail occurrence coincide pretty closely with the movements of the zone of maximum cold-front activity in the same season. This does not mean that there is no such thing as a "local hailstorm," but it does seem to imply that such storms are very much less common than the "local thunderstorm."

Since frontal activity declines markedly as spring advances northward across the continent, it is not difficult to see, according to this view, why the risk of hailstorms declines as the risk of thunderstorms increases. But it isn't a complete explanation, for the almost hailless months of August and September are by no means "frontless," nor is May, the peak month for hail, the peak month for fronts. Possibly the anomaly is accounted for by taking into consideration the following two facts: first, that the freezing level is located at such great elevations above continental America in high summer (frequently as much as 25,000 feet above the surface) that comparatively few convectional currents, even those assisted by a frontal "booster," are able to reach it, let alone penetrate it far enough to have their load of raindrops frozen; and second, that the raindrops so frozen stand an excellent chance of being melted while falling to earth through the 4- to 5-mile-thick layer of warm air. In spring, on the other hand, the freezing zone in a frontal or convectional cloud may be not more than 10,000 feet above the surface: as a consequence, moisture-lifting mechanisms do not need to be nearly so vigorous then as in summer to effect the vertical transport of raindrops into the subfreezing, that is, the hail-making, layers of the atmosphere.

What perhaps causes many people to associate hail with the midsummer rather than the spring is the damage factor. In the winter half of the year a hailstorm can do comparatively little harm to crops: furthermore, the average size of hailstones is smaller then than in the summer. In July a 5-minute bombardment of a flowering cotton crop or a ripening fruit or vegetable crop makes headlines—and spells disaster to the luckless grower.

Hail breakers, rain makers, and other meteorological do-gooders

It goes without saying that nobody really has any use for hail, except perhaps those insurance companies which make a good business of insuring farmers against hail damage; over large sections of the Great Plains the rate runs about $11 per $100 for small grains, and even more for fruit and vegetable crops. Not that there's much these companies can do about it, all the time the hail hazard is what it is.

However, there are a good many people who seem determined to do something about it. Indeed, more than a few of them have been trying to do something about it for a good many years. As long ago as 1900, an international congress was convened for the purpose of finding ways and means of preventing crop damage by hail. One of the ways that was tried was shooting explosive charges into thunderclouds from cannon and rockets. It was argued that this would disturb the circulation within the cloud and prevent the formation of hail. However, it seems that this technique proved rather expensive, the accident rate among the assembled scientists being quite high. Later it was thought that the setting up of an extensive grid of large lightning rods might do the trick, on the supposition that this would reduce the electrical charge of a thundercloud, and so reduce its propensity for separating the positively charged water droplets and ice fragments from the heavier negatively charged water drops and hailstones: without this separation the electrical field in the cloud would be destroyed, and the raindrops more likely to fall out of the base of the cloud than to be drawn upward to the freezing zone by the attraction of oppositely charged particles near its top. But this device does not seem to have had any greater success than the other: at least meteorologists have never been able to decide whether the results were significant or not.

More recently, attempts at hail suppression have been made by seeding clouds with silver iodide crystals. The meteorologists concerned claimed that by so doing they could increase the number of condensation nuclei in a given thundercloud to the point where the resulting hailstones would be too small to do any damage, if indeed they did not completely melt before reaching the ground. Some claimed they could do better than that, and increase the number of condensation nuclei to the point where the resulting water particles and ice crystals were unable to grow large enough to survive their slow "parachute" drop to the earth: in other words, by "overseeding" the cloud, they could prevent precipitation altogether. So far, the claims made appear to be rather more substantial than the results.

However, far be it from us to impugn the integrity of these men. When they say they have made it rain, hail, or snow, they unquestionably believe they have done so. In some instances no doubt they have done so; but in most of these instances, so the skeptical meteorologists of the U.S. Weather Bureau maintain, it would have rained, hailed, or snowed anyway—about five minutes later.

The reasons for their skepticism are not far to seek. Before a cloud can be made, artificially, to precipitate moisture, a number of conditions have to be satisfied. In the first place, the cloud must be at least 4,000 feet deep and dense enough to contain a large number of water drops: thin stratiform clouds will not do. In the second place, the temperature and wind conditions must be such as to maintain the cloud in a state of turbulence. In the third place, and closely related, the vertical velocities within the cloud must be appreciable: in the case of a cloud that does not penetrate into the freezing zone, they need to be at least 15 feet per second. Then, again, in the case of precipitation caused by the collision of supercooled water drops and ice crystals, the cloud must extend well into the freezing zone. Such a combination of atmospheric conditions is thought to be quite rare except in a cloud that is already on the verge of precipitating. However, it seems entirely possible that the seeding of such clouds can increase the yield of moisture from them, not only over the seeding zone but, under exceptionally favorable circumstances, many hundreds of miles downwind.

Dr. Irving Langmuir, rain maker par excellence, and Nobel Prize man in chemistry to boot, is even convinced that his seeding operations in New Mexico have had an effect on the rainfall of the eastern seaboard. Each Thursday between December 15, 1949, and February 23, 1950, he turned on his silver iodide smoke generators in the Albuquerque region of New Mexico. Each following Tuesday there was widespread rain over the eastern third of the country. In Buffalo it rained a total of 4.38 inches on the twelve Tuesdays concerned, as against only 0.32 inch on the twelve following Saturdays. In Philadelphia, during the same period, it rained 2.27 inches on the Tuesdays, and only 0.19 inch on the Saturdays. When he moved his seeding day from Thursday to Friday, Wednesday took the place of Tuesday as the day of general rains in the East: when he shifted it to Wednesday, it rained the following Monday—again five days later—in the East. Of course, you can always claim that there was no causal connection between the two sets of events: that they were the result of chance. If you think that the odds against such a succession of chances are rather long (and they run into the millions), you can always say that they were the result of some unknown factor associated with man's weekly activity, or some extraterrestrial influence. Alternatively, you can just put it down to the periodic release of silver iodide smoke 2,500 miles away from the affected locality, as Dr. Langmuir does. If you do, you'll probably be kept awake o' nights wondering what scientists less amiably disposed than Dr. Langmuir might be able to do with less amiable substances.

The art of doing nothing much about the weather

I trust that I am as open-minded as the next man when it comes to tinkering about with things, within limits, that is: but when it comes to tinkering with the atmosphere, I have a feeling that we are getting "off limits." I admit that I have no great fancy for an unseasonable May frost, or a May hailstorm, and that there have been days when I have been sorely tempted to ring for one of Dr. Langmuir's silver iodide generators in the hope that its smoke might rise like incense to heaven and cause the rain to descend upon the chapped ground. However, I have restrained the impulse, for the more I ponder the idea of monkeying with the weather, the less I like it. For two reasons.

In the first place, there is no guarantee that the changes induced by the tinkerers would do more good than harm. The conjuring up of a May shower might elate a cottongrower in California, but it could easily ruin the ripening strawberry crop of his neighbor. The neutralizing, at source, of a January cold wave might please the hotelkeeper in Palm Beach, but it could destroy the business of his confrere in Lake Placid. Surely the world has enough troubles on its hands without spawning any more. And, anyway, who would arbitrate between the competing farmers and chambers of commerce? And could they do it fast enough to save the strawberry crop, and the skating rink? Heaven forbid that the government should assume

. . . the fate of skies' estate:
Or that Congress should start a filibuster
On when to clear and when to bluster.
They'd still be at it in '59
*Half for rain and half for shine.**

We have already had more than one eloquent demonstration of the troubles that arise when men suspect their fellows of interfering with "the course of Nature." In the wake of the destructive wind- and rainstorms of November 25–26, 1950, a group of businessmen, farmers, and resort operators in upstate New York filed claims for more than 2 million dollars with the City of New York, charging that Dr. Wallace E. Howell, a distinguished meteorologist then in the city's employ as a "rain maker," trespassed knowingly, willfully, and intentionally on their lands by "causing a violent and torrential precipitation of rain" on the aforementioned dates. It matters little that these rain-making experiments were subsequently reported to have *decreased* rather than increased the precipitation, or that the City of New York is in no condition financially to listen to such a *cri de coeur;* the good people of the Catskills are still minded to get their man—and the money. Meanwhile there has been a noticeable cooling off of civic interest in cloud-seeding operations.

In the second place, there is no telling whether these twentieth-century alchemists can control their inventions, let alone forecast correctly the effect of unleashing them upon the earth. Even in so simple a matter as cloud seeding, it seems that the same operation is capable of stimulating nucleation of moisture particles one day and of inhibiting such nucleation

* With apologies to *The New York Times.*

the next. If you "seed" only a modest amount of silver iodide or dry ice into a rain cloud, you can expect it to rain: if you seed it more generously, you can expect the cloud to dissipate. The only trouble is that nobody so far knows how big a "modest" amount has to become before it is "generous."

When it comes to more elaborate tinkering schemes, the uncertainties multiply. There are so many unknowns in the atmospheric equation. Who can tell, for example, what would be the precise result of warming up Hudson Bay, as some have seriously suggested trying to do, with atomically energized heating units? The sponsors of the suggestion maintain that the Bay, instead of freezing almost solid each December and January, would remain open, so that the winds originating over the Keewatin and Mackenzie lowlands of northern Canada—the source region for many of our cold waves and blizzards—would have had their sting taken out by the time they reached Chicago and Montreal. An attractive argument, to be sure, but what of its soundness? Assuming that the Bay could be heated up (and it is nine times the size of Alabama to begin with), what would follow? One possibility seems to have been given little attention, and it is this. As the cold air traveled southward across the open waters of the Bay, it would not only be warmed up, it would also absorb a great deal of moisture vapor, for the capacity of cold, dry air for water vapor increases rapidly with the temperature. (Thus air at 32°F. can hold about twice as much moisture as air at 10°F., and about four times as much as air at 0°F.) On reaching the height of land to the south of the Bay, part of this newly acquired load of moisture would be discharged in the form of snow, for not even the superoptimists believe that such a device could warm up the whole Bay to the point where the winter precipitation would all occur as rain. If the snowfall were increased by, say, 20 to 30 inches, it is conceivable that the annual deposit of snow would be greater than the annual loss by melting and evaporation. Were this to happen, then a new ice age would be slowly, but surely, initiated—the very last thing the sponsors of the suggestion have in mind.

All in all, there is something to be said for doing nothing much about the weather.

Dogwood winter

One of the things that never ceases to amaze the student of North American weather is its errancy. Try to make rules for it, and you will find that they are more often honored in the breach than in the observance. Try to describe the weather of a given month in a sentence or so, and you will quickly discover that, like Emerson's Nature, it is "a mutable cloud, which is always and never the same." Base a forecast on the mean values of temperature, rainfall, cloudiness, and visibility, and you will find that normalcy receives no greater benediction from the Good Lord than it does from bad businessmen. At the same time, beneath the apparently wild and disorderly succession of meteorological events, it is possible to observe a regard for seasons, a pattern—almost a rhythm—of behavior and a sense of timing that is nothing short of uncanny.

It was some such conviction as this—particularly in regard to the timing of departures from the seasonal march of temperature—that sent Alexander Buchan, the nineteenth-century meteorologist, delving into the weather records of his native Scotland. What he found was very striking. Among other things, Buchan noticed that between the coldest days of winter and the hottest days of summer the smooth upward run of the temperature curve was interrupted here and there by "singularities," that is, by quite conspicuous departures from the expected value for the periods in question. After the expected rise toward the end of January, there was frequently a marked fall about the second week in February (7 to 14). In the next two or three months the temperature progressed on the whole in keeping with the march of the sun, but April (11 to 14), May (9 to 14), and June (29 to July 4) showed frequent setbacks before the temperature peak of the year was reached in mid-July. After the expected drop toward the end of that month, early August (6 to 11) often showed a marked rise. September and October displayed no noticeable departures from the seasonal trend, but November (6 to 13) frequently produced one markedly cold spell, and December (3 to 14) a markedly warm one.

One of the most frequently observed spells—and one of the most widely experienced—is Buchan's third cold spell. According to E. L. Hawke, one-time secretary of the Royal Meteorological Society and author of a book on the subject—*Buchan's Days*—out of all the wealth of weather lore that has been handed down through the ages, there is, perhaps, none more "justifiably credited than the tradition of a wintry snap around the middle of May." * In only three out of the fifty years' records which Buchan examined was this spell "not distinctly marked": in all the others it occurred somewhere between May 8 and 15, usually between May 9 and 14, and lasted three to five days. The spell was frequently accompanied by hard frost and occasionally by snow and sleet.

On the continent of Europe the most favored days for the visitation of cold weather are May 11 to 13. Because these are notable saints' days—the days of St. Mamertius, St. Servatius, and St. Pancras—this cold spell has always been known among Europeans as the days of the "Ice Saints" or "Ice Men."

In the United States a temporary temperature relapse in May commonly goes by the name of "dogwood winter," if not

* *Buchan's Days,* 1937, p. 107.

among us citified folk, certainly among those living in the back country of the eastern seaboard states and the Appalachians. "Don't you know what dogwood winter is?" demanded the man from Hickory, North Carolina. "There is always a spell of it in May when the dogwood tree is in bloom. For several days there is cold, disagreeable cloudy weather, and often a touch of frost." * And oddly enough, it is as likely as not to come with the "Ice Men."

* *American Folklore,* 1907, p. 235.

June

"The billowy clouds of June"

Of all the months of the year, none has been so widely sung, or greatly loved, as June—and with reason. Over most of the forty-eight states it is a warm month, but in few is it oppressive. Almost everywhere it is a wholesome month. Except for a late straggler, the bad fogs of winter are gone: the pollens of high summer are still to come. Few die from heatstroke, none from cold. It is, furthermore, a beautiful month. Nature is still adorned in the livery of spring: there is as yet no sign of soilure or of decay. There is color on every side, but the colors soothe, without tiring: they do not shock the eye or excite the mind as those of October. And the heavens declare the storms of winter to be past. Cyclonic activity is weaker than it has been for many months: frontal clouds are shorter-lived, and in their place are more often seen cumulus-flecked skies,

. . . long rows of sails on foam,
White-fringed by the sun,
Deployed like ancient caravels upon an azure sea.

The birth of a cumulus

To get any sort of a cloud, we must first have water vapor, that is, invisible particles of water suspended in the atmosphere. (It is true we sometimes talk about "clouds" of dust or sand, but these, being heavier than air, seldom even get their feet off the ground, and quickly collapse when the wind which drives them drops.) But the presence of water vapor in the air does not mean that the sky will be cloudy. It is quite possible for a cubic yard of atmosphere to have 1 ounce of water in it and to be cloudless: it is equally possible for it to have as little as ⅒ ounce of water and to look like a hunk of fog. Why should this be? It is largely a matter of temperature. Warm air can absorb far more water vapor than cold air: air at 80°F., the temperature of a good hot summer day, can hold just over five times as much water vapor in the invisible state as air at freezing point, a fact which helps to explain why you see your breath in winter but not in summer. In this respect, air is rather like coffee, for example. The warmer the coffee, the more sugar you can dissolve in it: if the coffee is cold, no matter how hard you stir, you are pretty sure to find that there is some sugar left in the bottom of the cup.

Now there is no fundamental difference between human breath and natural cloud. The only reason a cloud ever forms is because warm moist air gets "puffed" to colder places in the atmosphere where the excess moisture condenses out—in just the same way as breath condenses when it is puffed from warm lungs into cold air. Suppose we collect a ten-pound "puff" or parcel of summer air at a temperature of 80°F. containing, for the sake of argument, 3¾ ounces of water vapor, and take it up for a ride in a helicopter. In case this strikes you as a very odd amount, we should say that 3¾ ounces is just about all the water vapor that can be put into 10 pounds of air at 80°F.

without its turning, there and then, into a cloud. As we rise vertically, the parcel cools: 5,000 feet up it will have cooled down to about 65°F. At 10,000 feet it will have cooled down to about 50°F. At 15,000 feet it will probably be down to freezing point. If we were to open up our parcel at this upper level, we should find a good 3 ounces of visible cloud particles floating around (the particles might even have condensed into water), because at freezing point a 10-pound parcel of air can hold only about ¾ ounces of water vapor; anything over and above that amount has to be precipitated as water droplets or ice crystals. It is this moisture-gathering, lifting, cooling, and condensing process which Nature employs in the manufacture of cumulus clouds, and, for that matter, most other types of cloud as well.

We are all familiar with the fact that at great depths in the ocean the pressure increases to submarine-crushing intensity. The air we breathe can be likened to an atmospheric ocean, which has its surface more than a hundred miles above the earth, and in which the pressure decreases steadily with height above the "floor," that is, the earth's surface. Thus when we took our 10-pound parcel for a vertical ride, its pressure fell with the pressure of the outside air. And as the pressure fell, the parcel cooled, a fact which can be easily appreciated by anybody who has felt the chill of air escaping from a suddenly deflated automobile tire. The rate of cooling, under such circumstances, is quite independent of the outside air temperature, being, below the cloud level, a steady 5.4°F. per 1,000 feet of rise. This is technically referred to as the dry adiabatic lapse rate.

While this explains how a cloud forms as a result of the original amount of water vapor becoming too great for the new temperature of the air, it does not explain how the moisture first got into the parcel of rising air, or why it first started to rise. In all likelihood the moisture got there through the agency of evaporation. Evaporation is a process with which we are all familiar: it takes place every time there is a fall of rain, and every time we fill a bird bath or water the backyard. Fanned by the wind, the surface film of water turns to vapor and goes off into the air. The stronger the wind and the drier and warmer the air, the more rapid the loss of moisture to the air. Just how rapid this evaporating process can be may be inferred from the fact that the mean annual evaporation from open water bodies in southern Arizona is between 90 and 100 inches, or more than ten times the mean annual rainfall. And it is not only bodies of open water which provide evaporating surfaces. Trees and plants are continually sweating out moisture: American scientists have found, for instance, that a single corn plant loses up to 10 pounds of water a day during its peak growing period. Altogether this adds up to quite a pile of moisture—millions of tons of it, in fact—daily being converted into water vapor.

To lift this enormous weight of microscopic particles into the atmosphere, Nature utilizes several devices. The chief of these is convection—the vertical movement of air we have all observed taking place over a bonfire or at the top of a smokestack on a windless day. Now air will rise of its own accord only if it happens to be lighter than the air around it, which is much the same thing as saying, if it happens to be warmer. It is easy enough to check the truth of this statement by comparing the difference in behavior of toy balloons in summer and winter. A balloon filled with warm air from our lungs rises nicely on a cold day, but scarcely at all on a very hot day; that is, it rises because the air inside the balloon is lighter than the air outside. In Nature this state of affairs is readily produced in a number of ways, for instance, by the summer sun falling on the road and roof surfaces of a town, surrounded by woodland and pasture.

The latter absorb much more of the incoming heat than the former, with the result that during the daytime the air temperature in a town rises above—and, until the evening at least, remains above—the air temperature of the surrounding country. Thus a 10-pound parcel of town air, being lighter on a fine summer day than the air around, floats upward, like our toy balloon on a cold day, its place being taken by the cooler country air. This, in turn, is heated above the temperature of its environment, and therefore rises. At first our rising parcel is warm, and can easily hold all its water vapor; but as it cools it sooner or later reaches a point where it has a surplus of water vapor. This is called the condensation level, and here cumulus cloud begins to form. Provided its temperature is still higher than that of the outside air, the air will go on ascending until it reaches a level where its temperature is the same as that of the outside air. There it will rest, and no more cloud will condense above that height. The reason the parcel can rise no farther is the same as that which causes a cork released at the bottom of a bucket of water to come to rest at the surface, namely, the fact that it is no longer lighter than its environment.

You can make a first approximation of the height at which cumulus cloud will form, if you once know the temperature of the surface air and its dew point. Subtract the dew point from the air temperature and multiply by 230. This means, to take a concrete illustration, that on a day when the surface temperature is 80°F. and the dew point 67°F., the base of any convectional cloud that forms will probably be round about 3,000 feet. If you are also interested in the degree of cloudiness likely to develop during the convective period, divide the relative humidity of the air by six (the measurement of it being made when you see your first trace of cumulus cloud), and subtract six from your answer. The resulting figure will give the number of tenths of the sky likely to be obscured when convection is at a maximum.

The stuff clouds are made of

But this is not the full story. Alone, the convective process will not produce a cloud the size of a man's hand, let alone any "woollen fleeces" or

. . . rocks of jet
Crowned like a diamond wreath.

The manufacture of visible water drops requires something else. This something is a nucleus—or rather millions of nuclei—to which particles of invisible water vapor can be attracted. In the atmosphere these nuclei are supplied by such substances as pollen, plant spores, smoke, salt (from sea spray), volcanic ash, and meteoric dust. Most of these nuclei are too small to be seen by eye, though a single bead of sunlight entering a darkened room will usually reveal a few thousand of the larger specimens. The way these nuclei go about their work can be demonstrated in a laboratory by introducing a wisp of tobacco smoke into a glass flask containing saturated dust-free air; water is almost instantly precipitated. Without those smoke particles there would be no sign of cloud until the air contained four to five times as much invisible water vapor as the amount corresponding to the saturation value for that particular temperature—a state of affairs known as supersaturation, and one which is occasionally responsible for the appearance of aircraft trails.

It must be borne in mind, however, that these condensation nuclei are concerned with the formation of cloud particles—not raindrops. Many of us tend to look on clouds as rain, or at any rate as potential rain, suspended in mid-air. Generally speaking, this is incorrect. Ordinary air contains upward of 3,000 to 4,000 nuclei per cubic inch; the water droplets that condense on them must therefore be very small, even if we assume that only one in every two or three is particularly partial to water vapor. As a matter of fact, the average cloud particle is only about 1/500 inch in diameter. Such a particle is obviously very light and falls only slowly through the air—not more than eight feet or so a minute. Falling at this rate, it would not stand much chance of growing large enough, by annexation, to form a sizable drop of water, that is, a drop with an average diameter of 1/10 to 1/12 inch. Something more than a nucleus is needed to turn a cloud particle into a water drop heavy enough to reach the earth—though precisely what that "something" is even the pundits are not in every case agreed.

How do clouds stay up?

This question is no longer the puzzle it was to the men of Job's day. Like them we may still be unable to "number the clouds by wisdom," and still be far from knowing all there is to know about the "spreadings" of clouds, but "the balancings of the clouds" are reasonably well understood. We now know that clouds are composed, not—as Ruskin argued—of "hollow spherical globules . . . in which the enclosed vacuity just balanced the enclosing water," but of myriads of solid and liquid particles which are prevented from falling, in the case of cumulus-type clouds at any rate, by the lift of the ascending air currents feeding and forming the cloud. The stronger these currents are, the more chance there is of the cloud staying up. Should the convection cease, as it generally does toward evening when the main supply of energy is shut off, the cumulus cloud may well start to fall, but as descending air warms up under the influence of compression the water particles evaporate and so vanish into thin air long before they reach the earth's surface. Ordinary fine-weather cumulus cloud rarely survives nightfall on this account.* Where convection has been so strong that the minute water particles have been able to coalesce into large drops, some may fall to earth as rain. Meanwhile the cloud responsible will, in all probability, have dissolved away completely. Anybody who finds it difficult to believe that convection more than counterbalances the effect of gravity has only to watch a sailplane soaring skyward.

Clouds are maintained aloft by the upward lift of wind deflected from mountainsides and by frontal, as well as convective, agencies. Perhaps it would be nearer the mark to say "replenished," rather than maintained, because the particle composition of the cloud is changing all the time. Even in a thoroughly vigorous convectional cloud, particles are continually falling out of the cloud base, the smaller ones very slowly, the larger ones more swiftly, owing to their greater weight in proportion to their surface. But as long as conditions favor condensation, cloud particles will keep forming and replacing those that drop out of the running. In the case of warm damp air meeting a mountain, cloud particles continue to form all the time the pressure gradient is such that it compels air of the same quality to climb the same mountain. And a like principle operates in respect to frontal situations.

Daytime breezes

With June warmth comes June wind—a casual wind, to be sure, and fickle in comparison with the strong prevailing winds of winter and early spring, but not to be less well regarded on

* Although the evaporation of clouds subsiding in this way is as common in one lunar phase as another, their disappearance is most noticeable round about full moon—a fact which no doubt helps to explain the old French saying that "the full moon eats clouds."

that account. For consider its quality. It is a benign wind: it can lift the drooping spirit of a man as no December gale or July squall can do. It is, too, a soft wind: it does not normally amount to much in a miles-per-hour kind of way, but it can make music in a bough that is a benediction to all who hear it, and it can dry the sodden earth better than any tornado. And it is a scented wind, for it is cradled in hayfields, woodlands, and gardens: it may not be a "wind from the south," but it comes

With a honeyed mouth:
A scent of drenching leaves,
Brier and beech and lime,
*White elder flower and thyme.**

On a hot summer morning, the air may be still and oppressive, and all the portents are for a searingly hot day. The birds are silent, the children are listless, even the leaves on the trees hang limp. And then from nowhere comes a gentle breeze. At first it may barely stir the poplars, but as the day advances it gathers strength until the whole world of Nature is caught up in its folds and consoled.

How does such a breeze arise, and on days, moreover, when there is no surface pressure gradient to speak of? The answer lies in the convective process to which the surface of the earth is subject by daytime. As we have seen,† this process involves the vertical exchange and partial mixing, with consequent transfer of momentum, of large masses of air. Because of this, a horizontal movement of the stationary surface air is started up and at the same time the horizontal movement of the almost frictionless upper layers is slowed down.‡ This con-

* Winifred Mary Letts, "A Soft Day."

† See pp. 125–127.

‡ Among the direct evidences that can be cited in support of this slowing down is the behavior of the wind atop the Eiffel Tower, where the diurnal maximum is usually experienced at night, that is, when the loss of horizontal speed due to vertical exchange of air is a minimum.

vection-cum-mixing process and associated breeze usually reach their maximum in the early afternoon, that is, at or about the time of the day's maximum temperature.

Because they are so closely linked with temperature variations, diurnal wind variations are much more conspicuous in summer than in winter, and more so in quiet settled weather than in unsettled weather, when they may disappear entirely. They are also greater in hilly country than in open lowland. In the former the unequal heating of the various slopes sets in motion convective currents more readily than in the latter. For example, south-facing valley slopes are inclined at a greater angle to the incoming rays of the morning sun than north-facing slopes, or even the flat floor of the valley. The air in contact with the warmed surface is therefore induced to rise, and the cooler, heavier air above is induced to flow in to take its place, before the same mechanism has had time to get under way in the surrounding plains. Once begun, the convection, and, so, the displacement of air which accompanies it, is reinforced by the flow of colder air sliding down the shaded slopes. Over a flat plain there is no such source of "feed" for the convection after it has been initiated; the colder air can come only from aloft; that is, its velocity is more vertical than horizontal, and is consequently not felt so strongly by the observer.

In hill country these daytime winds are sometimes spoken of as valley breezes, or, in more technical parlance, as anabatic winds.

"Sailing" weather

Long before man gave a thought to engineless flight, birds had availed themselves of the "lift" which moving air possesses —a lift which enabled them to overcome the force of gravity.

The seemingly unpropelled motion of a gull to windward of a steep cliff or in the shadow of a great bank of cloud, which all of us at one time or another have watched transfixed, depends on those unseen but ever-undulating air waves which surge to and fro across the sky. The annual migrations of the golden plover and arctic tern from one hemisphere to another and back again are scarcely less dependent on the low-level perturbations of the atmosphere set up by ocean waves and swell. Small though they are, in the aggregate they provide incalculable amounts of momentum for coasting—"free air" in fact!

It is not very different with the modern sailplane. To glide through the air a sailplane needs only the wind and an obstacle like a ridge or sand dune which forces the wind to rise. Launched into such an upcurrent, a sailplane can stay aloft as long as the wind blows, and with its help may rise as much as four times the height of the obstacle, and so long as the wind-driven current is rising as fast as, or faster than, the sailplane falls, the plane will remain airborne.

However, to attain great height, a sailplane normally needs something more than the turbulence produced by the passage of an air current over an undulating terrain: it needs the benefit of powerful convectional, that is, vertical rather than horizontal, air currents. These currents, known to sailplane pilots as "thermals," are the product of the unequal heating by the sun of the earth's variegated cover. Because woodland, pasture, plowed fields, water, and built-up land absorb and reemit the sun's energy at different rates, the upward flow of heat from the earth on a sunny day is very uneven. The air over a heated city, for instance, starts to rise far sooner than the air over the nearby open country, and the air in contact with the open country will rise long before the air of the same constitution does over a neighboring lake or river.

As a parcel of air is heated, it expands: in expanding it becomes lighter than the air around it which proceeds to undercut it and so flips the "trigger" that sets the parcel on its way heavenward. These thermals range in diameter from a few feet to a few miles. Generally, the smaller ones prevail in the morning, the larger ones in the afternoon. The job of the sailplane pilot is to detect them and to find his way from one to the next without losing so much height that he has to land his machine.

The weaker thermals can be detected by a variometer, an instrument which registers changes of air pressure: if the variometer shows that pressure is falling, the plane is rising; if it shows that the pressure is rising, the plane is losing height. The stronger thermals can be detected in other ways as well. As a rule they can be felt: even a motor-powered plane can feel them in spite of its great horizontal velocity. Frequently they can be seen, or perhaps we should say that the convectional clouds to which they characteristically give rise in humid regions can be seen. A string—or "street," in sailplane parlance—of such clouds will gladden the heart of any pilot because each cloud provides him with an ascending "escalator" that will make good the loss of height sustained in flying through the downward-moving currents of air which must, in the nature of things, alternate with the upward-moving currents. By following such a street, it is perfectly possible for an experienced pilot to travel 200 miles or more cross-country. With luck he may even make 400 miles. In Russia, where there is said to be nationwide enthusiasm for this sport (and large government subventions!), a pilot has made a cross-country flight of 500 miles. The pilot in this instance was a girl.

Sometimes the escalators can be too strong even for the fancy of the most ardent devotee. When a pilot is clumsy, or unlucky, enough to get his plane entrained in the ascending-current zone of an active cumulonimbus (a convectional cloud that has acquired much bigger dimensions and much greater energy than the ordinary fair-weather cumulus), then the ascent may well be elevator-like, rather than escalator-like, for the currents in such a cloud can exceed a vertical velocity of 50 miles per hour and may carry a plane up to 30,000 feet in no time at all. One pilot, commenting on such an experience, said, "It was as if I were in a canoe on a pinwheel on a rocket." Other pilots, less fortunate, have had to take to their parachutes—only to find themselves soaring heavenward still farther!

Under exceptional circumstances, sailplane altitude records have been established without the aid of thermals. Thus in 1940 a height of 37,000 feet was reached over the Alps by a pilot who took advantage of a "standing wave" located in the lee of a mountain range. The dynamics of a standing, or gravity, wave are much the same whether the fluid is air or water. Waves of this kind are found in every stream and river of the land, wherever the gravity-impelled flow of water is obstructed by a boulder or tree stump. Each such obstruction sets up a chain of lee waves which hold their position and form, though the water in them is continually moving downstream. Analogous waves are formed in the atmosphere when the streamline flow of air is broken by a mountain peak or range of hills lying athwart its path. Other things being equal, the stronger the flow of air and the bigger the obstruction, the higher the resulting wave and the greater the likelihood of subsidiary (secondary and tertiary) waves being set up down-wind. Frequently the presence of these waves is betrayed by a stationary lens-shaped, or lenticular, cloud. Depending on the lapse rate of the air and its speed, this cloud (or series of clouds) may be located at an elevation anywhere up to three times, and at a distance down-wind anywhere up to six times, the height of the obstruction. It is thanks to such standing waves that pilots have occasionally been able to attain elevations of 5 to 6 miles, even penetrating the base of the stratosphere.

Man-made thermals

Sometimes convection currents, quite vigorous ones too, are brought into being by "unnatural" causes.

One of the loveliest and largest cumulus clouds I ever saw formed over the western edge of the great Australian desert in the late afternoon. By all the rules it was a most unlikely time and place for such a cloud, for the surface air was dry, the sky was otherwise cloudless, and the sun was well past its heat-raising peak. Whence, then, the solitary "towering cloud of jet"? Its source was a bush fire: in the dry season, the scrub vegetation that manages to keep a foothold in this semiarid region is very inflammable and is frequently burned off by the sheep farmers. The heat generated by the fire—much greater, of course, than the heat generated over a comparable area by the sun's rays—produced a superadiabatic lapse rate of such dimensions that the rising air column immediately above the fire found itself consistently warmer than its environment until it reached condensation level, which in that dry air could not have been less than a mile above ground level. The causal connection between the fire and the cloud was clear from the telltale column of smoke linking the two.

Similar thermals are often reported above, or to leeward of, industrial chimney stacks and smoldering slag heaps. In daytime it may be impossible to distinguish those produced artificially from those produced by solar radiation, but whereas the latter usually decay at sundown, the former show no such sensitivity to diurnal fluctuation. On the strength of these thermals many a sailplane pilot who has all but run out of "air" has found himself suddenly soaring heavenward at a vertical velocity of 10 miles an hour, or more: and there are well-authenticated stories of pilots gaining between 6,000 and 7,000 feet of lift in this way.

In air that is both very moist and very unstable, such as that commonly encountered in the South in summer, man-made thermals can assume quite spectacular proportions. On one occasion, the engineer in charge of a construction gang working in the Florida Everglades announced that he would produce some respite from the noonday heat of the sun by firing a patch of the tall grass in which his men were working. In next to no time the hot ascending air had reached the condensation level and was being transformed into an umbrella of cumulus clouds. Soon the clouds were mushrooming—hydrogen-bomb * fashion—into thunderheads: within half an hour or so the air was filled with "a sound of abundance of rain." If there is a moral to this story, I suspect that it has more to do with engineers making good amateur meteorologists than with Dame Nature being on the side of laboring man. After all, most bush fires make things hotter—not cooler!

Too bright to last?

If, in June (and the same applies to the other warm-weather months), the air is moist, the temperature falls off sharply with height, and the pressure gradient is slack, you can generally reckon on plenty of cumulus cloud forming within four or five hours of sunrise. Air that has traveled down from high latitudes over an extensive water surface—for instance, maritime polar air approaching the coastal lowlands of British Columbia

* The hydrogen bomb is, itself, a manufacturer of thermals—the most vehement and most spacious known to man.

and Washington from the North Pacific, or continental polar air reaching the Ohio Valley via Hudson Bay and the Great Lakes—is particularly likely to cloud up by midday, and so cut off most of the afternoon's heat supply, much to the discomfiture of sunbathers and holidaymakers generally. Visibility in such air is, on the whole, very good, partly owing to the steep lapse rate which encourages convection (which, in turn, makes for the vertical removal of atmospheric impurities), and partly because the air has traveled over a clean part of the world. This, coupled with the absence of cloud in the early morning, is largely responsible for that "too-bright-to-last" appearance which long experience has taught us to associate with such air. However, in winter the amount of incoming solar radiation is not, as a rule, sufficient to upset the delicate equilibrium of maritime polar air, let alone continental polar air, so that the days remain brighter, and may even be characterized by continuous sunshine.

Tropical air behaves in a rather different way. Except near its source region, it is not usually given to convection, though its high humidity results in summer mornings frequently being cloudy for a start. Much of the incoming sun heat is absorbed by this cloud, which is thereby evaporated. Once the cloud has dispersed, the surface warms up. The characteristic stability of tropical air means that a great deal of heat must be taken up by the surface layers of the atmosphere before convection is able to set in. Thus the tendency in tropical air is for the middle hours of the day to be warm and sunny.

When it rains, it pours

Summer rain, unlike winter rain, is mostly convectional in nature, that is to say, it is produced by local heating of moist unstable air masses. On this account it is more likely to come in the form of passing showers, often of a thundery nature, than steady day-long downpours. But what it may lack in continuity it makes up for in intensity and amount.

The concentration of heavy rains in the summer months is brought out strikingly in the accompanying table. It shows the month-by-month distribution over the forty-eight states of the highest recorded 24-hour precipitation.

Jan.	Feb.	Mar.	Apr.	May	June	July	Aug.	Sept.	Oct.	Nov.	Dec.
4	1	3	0	2	8	9	6	8	4	2	1

(The table is based on stations with an observing record of ten years or more.)

We see from this that whereas in no state of the Union has the wettest-on-record 24-hour spell ever come in April, and in only two states * has it occurred in May, it has occurred in thirty-one states in the ensuing four months. This marked clustering of exceptionally heavy rains during the warmest months of the year agrees well with the seasonal incidence of thunderstorms † and with what we know of the water-vapor content of the air masses that frequent our continental areas (where, incidentally, most of the very high 24-hour maxima have been recorded) during the summer.

And not only do most of the states have their wettest days during the summer, they also have far wetter days in summer than in winter. Thus, in Texas the maximum 24-hour rainfall recorded during the winter (December through March) is 12.75 inches: the maximum for a summer day (June through September) is 23.11 inches. The corresponding figures for Montana are 2.60 inches and 11.50 inches. But let us not hurry to the wrong conclusion. Taking the state as a whole, the average rainfall in Texas for the four months, June through

* Kansas and Wyoming.

† See under July, pp. 156–158.

September, is only approximately 11 inches, and in Montana, less than 7 inches.

The wet spots—and the dry

Because the rain that falls in the warm months of the year is largely convectional in character, the pattern of its distribution across the country is different from that of the precipitation falling in winter, which is mostly either cyclonic or orographic in character.

The major differences are brought out in the accompanying maps, the first showing the average rainfall for the months April through September, and the second showing the average annual precipitation. It will immediately be seen that the annual map bears a much closer resemblance to the relief map of the country than the warm-season map, notwithstanding

Fig. 11. Average warm-season (April–September) precipitation in inches. (Courtesy of the Weather Bureau, U.S. Department of Commerce)

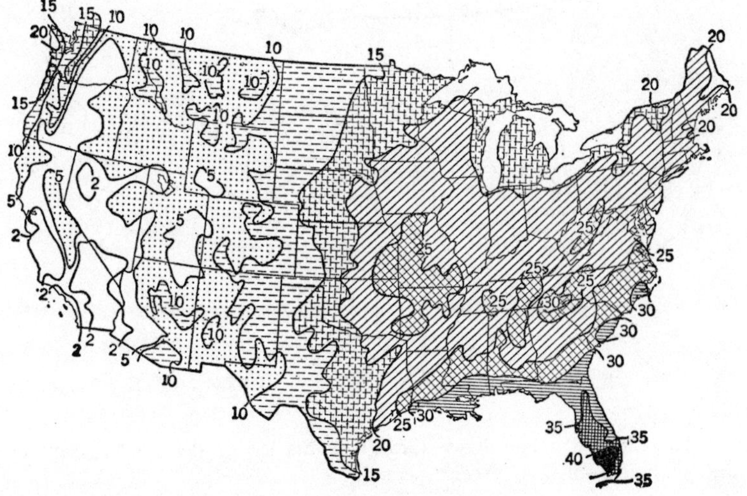

the fact that the full effect of the orographic rains of winter is masked by combining summer and winter distributions in the one map. Whereas the outlines of almost all the great mountain systems of the country are clearly etched by the annual isohyets,* only those of the extreme Northwest and the southern Appalachians are disclosed on the warm-season map. Over the rest of the country the isohyets follow a sinuous and often baffling course. About the only useful generalization that emerges from a study of them is that warm-season rains, with the exception of those falling in the Northwest, tend to decrease with distance from the southeast coast. Thus the average for Florida is between 30 and 40 inches; the average for Tennessee, between 20 and 25 inches; for Kansas, between 15 and 20 inches; for Wyoming, between 5 and 10 inches; and for Nevada and Southern California, less than 5 inches. And this is more or less what you would expect, bearing in mind that

Fig. 12. Average annual precipitation in inches (simplified). (Courtesy of the Weather Bureau, U.S. Department of Commerce)

* An isohyet is a line drawn through points having the same amount of precipitation during any specified period.

most of our summer rains (again with the exception of the Pacific Northwest which lies athwart the track of the prevailing westerlies even in summer) are associated with continental invasions of moist unstable air from the Gulf of Mexico and nearby doldrum belt. Florida, being nearest to the source of these air masses and subject to very strong insolation, is most likely to experience rains of a convectional type. Nevada and Southern California, being those parts of the Union farthest away from the source region of both the convectional rains of the Southeast and the predominantly cyclonic-cum-orographic rains of the Northwest, are least likely to experience summer rains of any type.

At the same time, it is only fair to point out that while the driest spot in the United States in summer is located in the arid Southwest—Death Valley, where the rainfall averages no more than ½ inch for the six-month period April through September—the wettest spot is *not* located in Florida, the state with the largest mean summer rainfall. In Florida the laurels for raininess go to Fort Meade in Polk County which, if it ever feels so disposed, can boast of an average rainfall (April through September) of 44.22 inches: and there are several other stations in the state that have almost as much to boast about. The Union record must go, it seems, to New Hampshire—to Mount Washington—where the average precipitation, some of it in the form of snow, over the same period is likely to be nearer 50 inches than 40.* However, Mount Washington is probably the only mountain in any part of the country that can muster higher figures than Fort Meade: certainly none of the long-established rainfall stations in the western Cordilleras can begin to compete—which simply goes to show how dominant everywhere the convectional term is in the summer-rainfall equation.

* For the years 1872–1890 it was 48.57 inches.

"Summer's royal progress"

Judging by their dress and holiday habits, most people seem to think that summer is something that is regulated by the astronomers, in much the same way as Easter is: that it begins on or about June 21, the summer solstice, and ends on or about September 23, the autumn equinox. But actually summer is a climatic, not an astronomical phenomenon, and in no populous part of the continent does its onset, as determined by temperature criteria, coincide with the date on which the sun stands overhead at the northern tropic.

Exactly when it does start depends on the precise temperature criterion selected. Of the many that could be chosen, the most unambiguous is the average date of the commencement of the warmest quarter of the year—after all, what is summer, if not the season of greatest heat? These dates are shown on the accompanying map, which has been adapted from one drawn by Prof. Stephen Visher of Indiana University.

Fig. 13(a). Beginning of summer as measured by the date of the start of the warmest 3 months of the year.

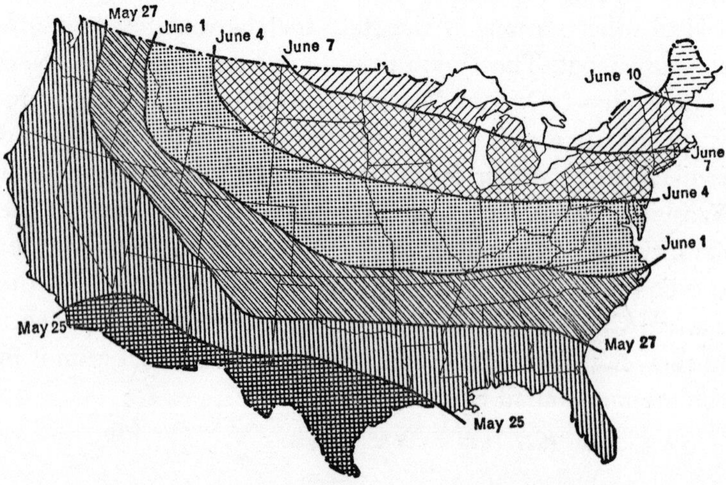

It reveals that summer, on this basis, comes first to southern Texas and the southernmost counties of Arizona, New Mexico, and California: in these localities it has begun by May 25. By the beginning of June it has arrived in almost half the Union, from North Carolina westward to Missouri and thence northward to Idaho. By the first week of June it has taken possession of practically the entire Union and the western half of Canada. A week later, June 15, it has gained a toehold (a rather precarious one by American standards) in the Maritimes and southern Quebec. Only in the northern subarctic part of Quebec, Labrador, and Newfoundland is its arrival delayed as late as the solstice.

A more useful yardstick by which to measure the arrival of the summer season would be the attainment of a given temperature—one that spells "summer" in the mind of the average person. But to find such a temperature is a tougher assignment than you might imagine, for what is summer to an "average" Eskimo living around the shores of Ungava Bay in northern

Fig. 13(b). As measured by the northward advance of the 68°F. isotherm. (Figs. 7(a) and 7(b) courtesy of Professor S. S. Visher)

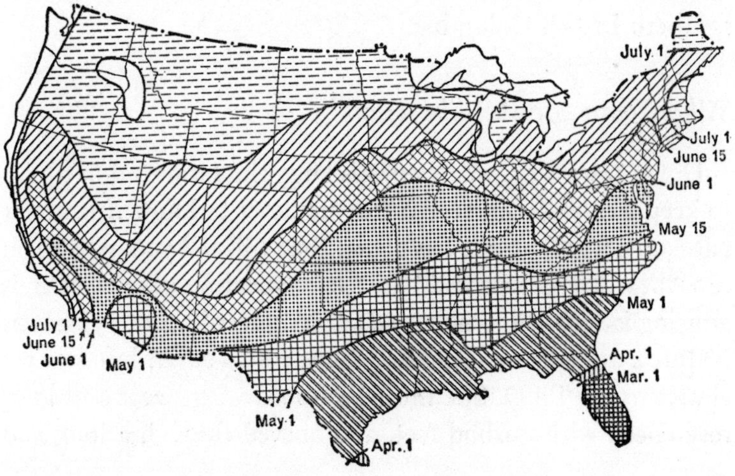

Quebec would hardly pass for a very indifferent spring to the residents of San Francisco, just as the characteristic summer of San Francisco would evoke no great applause from the inhabitants of San Diego or Miami. Perhaps the nearest thing we can get to an agreed figure is the lowest air temperature at which a lightly clothed person at rest feels comfortable; and certainly the ability to live *au naturel*, or nearly so, is for many people the supreme test and proof of "summeriness." The doctors tell us that, while it varies from subject to subject, for most ordinarily healthy, red-blooded, and pink-skinned Americans the critical temperature is around 68°F. As the accompanying map shows, such a temperature is reached normally by May 1 in the Deep South, by about June 1 along the mid-Atlantic seaboard and in the Mississippi Valley, but not much before July 1 in the northern high plains. It is never reached along the Pacific coast (north of about the latitude of Santa Barbara), the northern New England coast, and the adjacent Maritime Provinces and lower St. Lawrence Valley. The only parts of Canada so favored are the middle St. Lawrence–Great Lakes lowlands (and then only for two to three weeks in July), the southern sector of the prairies, and the sheltered valleys of southern British Columbia.

When corn grows "like crazy"

Down Iowa way, where corn is king, the farmers don't have to keep a calendar or read a thermometer to know if summer has come. You know it has come, they will tell you, when you can "hear the corn grow." Just *how* you tell, aurally, if it is growing is something no city dweller is ever likely to discover. Nature's ways are not disclosed to the casual passer-by—nor yet always to the Ph.D. She must be wooed with sweat and love, reverenced with unshod feet, and obeyed through a long and painful apprenticeship. A lifetime may not be long enough to learn her secret.

However, for those of us who "have ears which hear not" the corn as it grows, there's always a chance that we have eyes which can *see* it grow. For when the summer has really come to the fat lands of the Middle West, a cornstalk will grow as much as 6 inches in a single night. So when next you find yourself in Iowa on such a night (and you couldn't possibly pass it by unnoticed—what with the temperature and the relative humidity both in the high 80s!), why not see just how much it does grow? You wouldn't be able to go to sleep on such a night, anyway.

For the statistically inclined, we should perhaps add that, while strains of corn differ somewhat in their temperature requirements for germination and seedling development, few are able to germinate satisfactorily below 50°F., and below 55°F. the seedlings of most strains are inclined to be very susceptible to disease. When the mean night temperature rises above 58°F., and the mean day temperature rises above 70°F. (which normally it does in Iowa toward the end of June), daily growth becomes perceptible, always assuming, of course, that the ground is well stocked with moisture from the winter thaw and ensuing spring rains.

July

Midsummer

ASTRONOMICALLY, midsummer may be a constant: geographically it is a variable—rather more of a variable, in fact, than midwinter. The figures in the accompanying table represent in each case the average of several stations and while, on that account, they hide the extreme lags, they leave us in no doubt as to the magnitude of the mean lags.

In very few areas is there a lag of less than three weeks, and over at least one-third of the Union it is more than six weeks. The biggest lags, as we might expect, are found in the coastal states where midsummer tends to coincide with the peak sea temperatures. In southern Florida and around the shores of the Gulf of Mexico, in the Pacific Northwest, and the Maritime Provinces of Canada, the maximum seldom occurs before the end of July, and August is frequently a hotter month than July.

The smallest lags are reported from the Mountain states, for example, New Mexico, where the retarding influence of the sea is at a minimum and the solar-radiation factor is at a maximum, and, paradoxically, from northern California where you would expect the marine factor to be paramount and so make for a belated midsummer. But California is a law unto itself, in the thermal sphere as in many another. It has everything from a midsummer *before* the summer solstice to a midsummer *after* the autumn equinox. A few favored localities have two distinct midsummers, one in June and a second in September—a phenomenon which is not reported, as far as we know, from any other part of the world. Without question the most spectacular feature of the Californian summer as a whole is its

WARMEST WEEK OF THE YEAR

(as measured by average weekly mean temperatures)

Eastern U.S.A.	
Maine	July 16–22
Vermont	July 16–22
Massachusetts	July 16–22
Rhode Island	July 16–22, 23–29
Connecticut	July 16–22
New Jersey	July 23–29
Delaware	July 23–29
E. Pennsylvania	July 23–29
C. Virginia	July 23–29
W. S. Carolina	July 30–Aug. 5
N. Alabama	July 30–Aug. 5
C. Georgia	July 30–Aug. 5
N. Florida	July 30–Aug. 5
S. Florida	Aug. 6–Aug. 12
E. New York	July 23–29

Central U.S.A.	
N. Mississippi	Aug. 6–12
E. Tennessee	July 23–29
S. Ohio	July 23–29
W. Texas	July 16–22
SE. Texas	Aug. 6–12
North Dakota	July 16–22
W. Nebraska	July 16–22
E. Kansas	July 23–29
W. Oklahoma	July 30–Aug. 5

Central U.S.A. (*continued*)	
N. Minnesota	July 16–22, 23–29
C. Wisconsin	July 16–22
Iowa	July 23–29
SW. Missouri	Aug. 6–12
C. Illinois	July 23–29
S. Arkansas	Aug. 6–12
S. Louisiana	July 9–15
	Aug. 6–12
Upper Michigan	July 23–29
N. Indiana	July 23–29
N. Ohio	July 16–22, 23–29

Western U.S.A.	
W. Washington	Aug. 6–12
E. Oregon	July 23–29
SE. Idaho	July 23–29
W. Montana	July 23–29
NE. Wyoming	July 16–22
NW. California	July 9–15
C. California	July 16–22
S. California	July 23–29
Nevada	July 23–29
SE. Utah	July 16–22
SE. Colorado	July 23–29
S. Arizona	July 16–22
NE. New Mexico	July 9–15

lateness. Many localities show a lag between solstice and temperature maximum of at least a month: even well inland a delay of thirty to thirty-five days, and in the mountains thirty-five to forty days, is not unusual. Along parts of the coast the delay is as much as three months: at Point Reyes, about 20 miles northwest of the Golden Gate, it is ninety-four days, and at San Francisco, ninety-three days. Yet, almost next door, in the San Mateo district of the San Francisco Peninsula, in addition to the late September maximum there is another, and slightly higher one, in June, preceding by a few days the summer solstice.

As anybody living in the San Francisco Bay area will tell you, the immediate cause of these temperature anomalies is the coastal fog which attains its maximum frequency and density in July and August. Professor John Leighley of the University of California, whose temperature time-lag studies we had an occasion to refer to earlier, puts it as follows:

> The peculiar march of temperature at San Francisco during the whole period between April and November argues strongly that the long delay of maximum at northern California stations is not merely an exaggeration of the delay recorded, say, in San Diego's curve,* but a different phenomenon, the result of truncation of the temperature curve through the screening off of solar radiation by the summer fog at the time when the curve would normally attain its peak. After the season of frequent fog, a recovery of the influence of solar radiation produces the abnormally delayed maximum. The occurrence of early maxima at a few stations . . . argues in the same direction, as does common experience of the conspicuous contrast in temperature between clear and foggy spells of weather in summer.

* This, while exhibiting rather more than the usual amount of retardation of the maximum, some fifty to fifty-five days, has no trace of a second maximum, let alone of a truncated maximum.

Fig. 14.

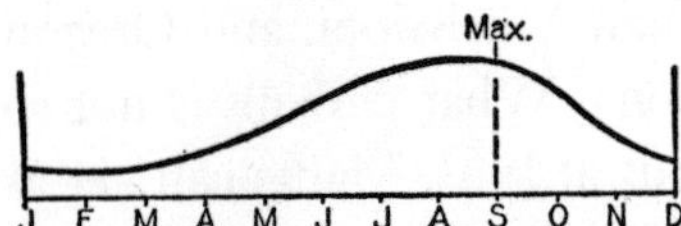

I. Idealized march of temperature at coastal locality not subject to prolonged summer fog.

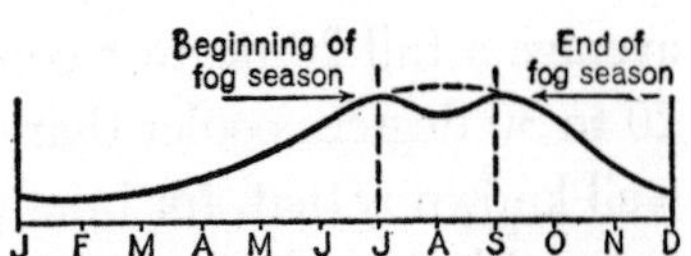

II. Idealized march of temperature at coastal locality subject to prolonged summer fog (July–Aug.).

How hot can it get?

The answer to this question is not so simple as you might imagine. For three reasons, if not more. Firstly, the hottest places on the earth are not the most likely to have thermometers lying around—they are too hot, by day at least, to be comfortable for lizards, let alone for humans. Secondly, a great deal depends on where and how you measure the temperature: thus the temperature of a bare rock surface fully exposed to the midday sun is a very different quantity from the temperature of the air above it. Sven Hedin, the great Swedish explorer, tells that when he was in the Pamir Mountains region of Central Asia there was a 101°F. difference between the temperature of the free air and that of a black-bulb thermometer resting on the ground immediately beneath it.* Thirdly, there is always the question of how good your thermometer is. The dime-store kind most of us keep at our back door will generally give us the answer to the nearest five degrees, but may, over the years, develop eccentricities that will make its readings entirely worthless for record-keeping purposes. Properly calibrated and tested instruments cost far more, but, if properly exposed, will give satisfactory results for a lifetime.

It goes without saying that parts of this country have very

* Even in this country we seem to recall having heard of eggs being fried on the pavement on a not immoderately hot summer afternoon.

much hotter summers than others. Thus Maine in July will average a full 20 degrees cooler than Mississippi, and Oregon 20 to 30 degrees cooler than Arizona. What perhaps is not so well known is that, for brief periods at least, Maine can get as hot as Florida—hotter, in fact. Thus the thirty-six-year record for Millinocket, Penobscot County, is 106°F., whereas the record (forty-year) for Miami is only 96°F. Much the same is true of the interior of the country. The highest temperature ever recorded in Birmingham, Alabama, is 7°F. lower than the highest recorded in Bismarck, North Dakota (107 as against 114°F.). Even in the West there is very little to choose between the 120°F. record for Texas, the 116°F. for New Mexico, the 119°F. for Oregon, and the 118°F. for Washington.

As a matter of fact, temperatures of 100 degrees and over can be, and have been, reported from each of the forty-eight states. They have also been reported from Alaska as far north as the Arctic Circle.

On the basis of existing records, the hottest spot of all in the continent is Death Valley, California. On July 10, 1913, the air temperature in that valley reached 134°F., which was within 3 degrees of the highest such temperature ever recorded on the face of the earth, in Tripoli. The temperature of the desert floor at the time was approximately 180°F., or a mere 32°F. below the ordinary boiling point of water!

The dog days

The period from about July 3 to August 11 was generally supposed by the peoples of ancient Greece and Rome to yield the hottest weather of the year, and not without cause if their summers were anything like those of the Mediterranean in our day. The usually accepted explanation of the high temperatures occurring around this time was that Sirius, the Dog Star, and the brightest star in the sky, added its heat to the heat of the sun as they rose and set together which, of course, they do, approximately, at that season. Because it was a very bright star, Sirius was taken to be a very hot star and to be only as far away from the earth as its size and brilliance suggested. In actual fact, Sirius is many times brighter than the sun, has a temperature nearly twice as high, and is all of 53 trillion miles, or 570,000 times the distance of the sun, from the earth. This is just as well, for had Sirius been adding its heat to that of the sun and from an equal distance, the people of the Mediterranean would really have had something to complain about.

While we moderns may quarrel with the astronomy and meteorology of the ancients, we can scarcely improve on their philosophy; for what better hot-weather advice was ever given to suffering mortals than that proffered by the poet Hesiod —"When Sirius parches head and knees, and the body is dried up by reason of the heat, then sit in the shade and drink"?

St. Swithin's forty days

When St. Swithin died, he was buried, at his own request, outside Winchester Cathedral in England where he had been bishop. A century later he was canonized, and it was deemed becoming that his remains should henceforth lie in more hallowed ground, inside the cathedral. The good saint's protest was a rain which delayed the reinterment by lasting for forty days: hence the legend that if it rains on St. Swithin's Day, July 15, it will rain for forty days.

But this legend is, happily, no better founded than most others. An examination of the rainfall records covering the period from 1841 to 1904 shows that a wet St. Swithin's Day in southeast England is followed on the average by only seventeen wet days in the next forty. And there is, of course, no reason whatever to suppose that it would prove more reliable as a weather rule in the New World than in the Old. The full irrationality of the legend is seen when we recall that France and Belgium each have their own St. Swithin's Day. In France it is June 8 (called St. Médard's Day); in Belgium it is July 27 (called St. Godelièvе's Day). Now, from the weather standpoint there is not a lot to choose between southeastern England and the neighboring parts of France and Belgium; in other words, if it were to rain for forty days in, say, northern France from June 8, it would most likely be raining off and on in southern England throughout the same period. By July 15, therefore, it would already have been raining thirty-eight days, and by the end of the St. Swithin's period, seventy-eight days. As the St. Godelièvе rains would not have ended until September 5, we accordingly arrive at the figure of ninety days, instead of a mere forty, as the expected duration of the St. Swithin rains, which I fancy even the English might find a little hard to take.

"Black clouds, with heaven's artillery fraught"

Most people reckon they can tell a thundercloud when they see one, although perhaps not many would use Milton's language to describe it, let alone Shakespeare's:

Yond' same black cloud,
Yond' huge one looks like a foul bombard that would shed his liquor . . .
Yond' same cloud cannot choose but fall by pailfuls.

The majority of us would probably have no fault to find with the more prosaic words of the meteorologist who defines it as "Heavy masses of cloud, with great vertical development, whose cumuliform summits rise in the form of mountains or towers, the upper parts having a fibrous texture and often spreading out in the shape of an anvil."

Like ordinary cumulus, cumulonimbus—to give the thundercloud its official title—is a convectional cloud; but whereas cumulus is a fair-weather cloud, cumulonimbus presages "showers of rain or snow and sometimes of hail." The essential conditions for its development are: first, that there should be a sufficiently large surface area over and around which there is an almost unlimited supply of moist air verging on instability; second, that there should be little or no wind, for wind keeps the atmosphere stirred, and so discourages local overheating which is the primary condition; and third, that there should be some initial impulse to start the convection. In the case of the heat thunderstorm, that is, the usual summertime variety, the sun supplies the impulse by heating the surface of the ground: this in turn heats the underside of the air mass above the surface by contact and radiation. This causes the layer of air next to the surface to expand which, apparently, it cannot do in bulk, but only by breaking up into cells through the center of which the heated air rises. As it rises it cools: cooling leads to condensation: condensation liberates heat, often enough heat to allow the convection to continue to a height of 4 or 5 miles. As the late Sir Napier Shaw once put it, the thundercloud "is a gigantic, if comparatively slow, explosion of moist air, the latent heat of the moist air acting as fuel."

It is safe to say that until very recently nobody really knew what goes on inside a thundercloud. Few people had ever been inside one, and fewer still had come out again. Those who had were unanimous on one point, namely, that the turbulence is terrific. One sailplane pilot reported that his machine was lifted 5,000 feet in a couple of minutes, at the end of which he had to take to his parachute, only to be carried still higher up.

However, as the result of a most thorough investigation carried out in 1946–1947 by the U.S. Armed Forces in collaboration with a number of civilian agencies, it is now possible to speak about the structure and dynamics of a thundercloud with a degree of certitude not hitherto attainable. This investigation involved no fewer than 1,363 aircraft flights through thunderstorms at various altitudes, all of them made without damage to plane or pilot, incidentally; it also involved the setting up of a micro-weather observing network, complete with radiosonde and radio-direction-finding equipment, and four radar wind-finding stations.

The most important single fact to emerge from this investigation is the cellular structure of the thunderstorm. The fully developed storm is now known to consist, not of a single convective cell, but of several (up to six in some cases), each having a distinctive air circulation, and equally distinctive weather phenomena. Some cater to updrafts only, others have both updraft and downdraft areas, while still others handle downdrafts exclusively. For the most part, these differences can be related to the age of the cell.

In the early stage of its development, termed by Prof. Horace Byers, director of the project, the "cumulus stage," the cell consists entirely of updraft. At their most vigorous the ascending currents were found to attain almost 100 feet per second, or considerably more than 60 miles per hour. When the accumulation of water drops in the upper part of such a cell exceeds the weight that can be supported by the updraft, the drops begin to fall through the less vigorous currents near the periphery of the cell, which is then said to pass into its "mature stage" of development. Apparently the downdraft results primarily from the frictional drag imposed upon the surrounding air by the falling raindrops. In falling through the cloud, the raindrops warm up at a rate somewhat less than the rate at which the ascending water drops cool off. This means that the downdraft which they induce is colder, level for level, than the updraft. By the time it reaches the earth and begins to spread out laterally, it has the quality of a cold-air mass, and its leading edge behaves just like a miniature cold front, complete with wind squall, downpour of rain, noticeable drop in humidity, and equally noticeable upward "kick" in the barograph trace. If the downdraft is very vigorous and prolonged, the resulting flow of cold air will, of course, spread far beyond the limits of the precipitating cell. As soon as it begins to undercut the zone of updraft, the convective process is automatically curtailed, and the third stage in the life cycle of the cell, called the "dissipating stage," is reached, for it is then only a matter of time before the entire cell, deprived of fresh supplies of moist rising air, loses its water-drop content. When this happens, large-scale vertical motion, downward and upward, comes to an end.

It may be properly objected, of course, that, on this theory, no thunderstorm could possibly last more than an hour or so, since every downdraft carries with it its own destruction. What happens, apparently, is that the outflowing current of cold air succeeds in triggering a new cell nearby the one it destroys. Dr. Byers and his colleagues found that new cells were especially likely to form where two cold outflows from mature cells collided, thereby "occluding," or undercutting, the lighter warm air between them and setting in motion a new updraft. They also found that in a number of instances new cells developed before there had been time for the cold-air outflow to make its "frontal" influence felt; and frequently a cluster of cells would appear almost simultaneously, though why this should be so is less readily explained.

The distribution of turbulence in a thundercloud was also fully investigated, and was shown to confirm what meteorologists had long suspected, namely, that it is least in the lowest levels, below 10,000 feet, and greatest at the middle altitudes of the cloud, say, between 15,000 and 20,000 feet. The hail and lightning hazards were also greatest in these intermediate levels.

Thunderstorm frequency

This varies from less than five days a year along the Pacific coast to more than ninety days along the Gulf coast of Florida. Throughout the central lowlands–high plains–eastern Rocky Mountain region, thunderstorms are experienced on thirty to fifty days a year. An exception to this generalization is provided by the Pike's Peak region where they are recorded on more than sixty days a year. Over practically the whole of Canada, eastern New England, and the Pacific slopes of the Rockies, the frequency is below twenty. As a rule of thumb, we can say that the thunderstorm risk decreases with distance from the southeastern seaboard. This suggests that thunderstorms are most likely to occur in areas frequented by maritime tropical air, which originates either over the Gulf of Mexico or the Gulf Stream, and characteristically fans out northwestward over the Mississippi lowlands. Apart from the Pike's Peak region, thunderstorms do not seem to be conspicuously more frequent on high ground than they are on low, though it is possible that more thunderstorms would be reported in mountainous country if there were more weather stations there to report them.

The salient features of the seasonal distribution of thunderstorms across the Union are revealed in the accompanying table and map.

MONTH OF MAXIMUM THUNDERSTORM ACTIVITY

(based on an analysis of the records of more than 200 U.S. Weather Stations)

Jan.	Feb.	Mar.	Apr.	May	June	July	Aug.	Sept.	Oct.	Nov.	Dec.
2	3	2	1	10	51	129	14	5	0	0	1

It will be seen that, over the country as a whole, July is easily the most thundery month. In fact, it usually gets more storms than all the other eleven months put together. Over the eastern third of the Union, it leads all the other months and, for the most part, by a handsome margin. The same is true of large sectors of the high plains and the cordilleran region. In the central lowlands June is the month of maximum frequency, and likewise in most of the Pacific Northwest. May leads in Texas and central California. The only place in the entire country where the winter half year shows a greater thunderstorm frequency than the summer half is along the Pacific coast: March and April lead all the other months in Southern California; December, January, and February farther north.

In other words, the season of most heat is, with surprisingly few exceptions, the season of most thunderstorms. In the northernmost tier of mid-continental states, more than two out of every three thunderstorms occur between June and Septem-

Fig. 15. Months of maximum average number of thunderstorm days. (Courtesy of Weather Bureau, U.S. Department of Commerce)

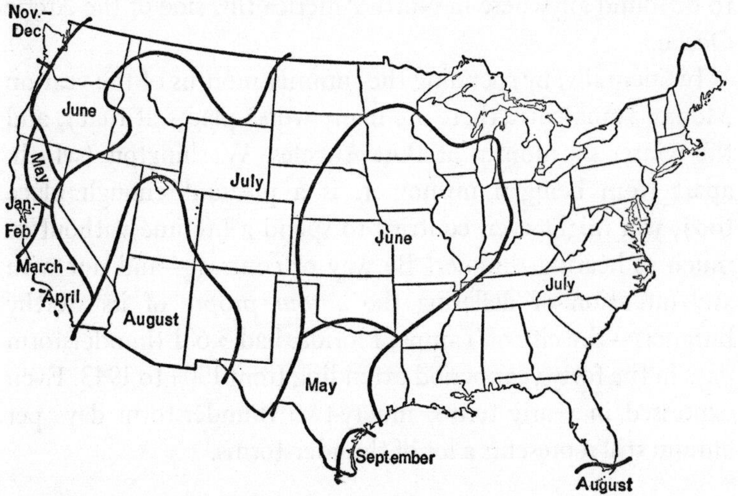

ber; farther south, more than one in every two. The exceptions to the rule owe their existence to a variety of circumstances; in the case of Southern California, to the aridity of the summer air (after April maritime tropical and polar air masses, without which even the strongest convection current must labor in vain to build up a tower of cumulus cloud, give the region a wide berth); and in the case of the northwestern seaboard maximum, to the much greater frontal activity of winter coupled with the associated forced uplift of the unstable polar maritime air masses commonly involved in such activity as they pass inland over the coast ranges.

Those who have no particular liking for thunderstorms and would, if given the chance, choose to live in a locality as nearly thunderstorm-free as possible, may be interested in the following statistics: In seventeen years, the weather station on Mount Tamalpais, central California, has recorded twenty-nine days with thunderstorms, giving an average of 1.7 thunderstorm days per annum. In twenty-seven years San Jose, central California, has recorded thirty-eight such days, giving an average of only 1.4 days per annum, and just about the lowest frequency to be found anywhere in North America this side of the Arctic Ocean.

Incidentally, by spending the summer months of the year on Mount Tamalpais (there are many worse places at that), and the winter six months at Port Angeles, Washington (which, apart from being a misnomer, is a pleasant enough place too), you might even contrive to spend a lifetime without so much as hearing thunder! By way of contrast—and not with any intention of deflating the *amour propre* of its worthy burghers—the city of Tampa, Florida, had 3,681 thunderstorm days in the forty-year period extending from 1904 to 1943. Even expressed in yearly terms, ninety-two thunderstorm days per annum still represents a lot of thunderstorms.

The diurnal clustering of thunderstorms is almost as conspicuous as the seasonal. Over at least half the Union more than 50 per cent of the summer variety of thunderstorms occur between the hours of noon and six o'clock in the evening (local time). Over the Southeast and in the cordilleran region, less than 20 per cent of the summer storms occur between 6 P.M. and midnight, and, with the exception of the Gulf coast, the coast of California, and Wisconsin, such storms are four times as uncommon between midnight and noon as they are between noon and midnight. The exceptions can probably be explained on the ground that marine influences take precedence over continental influences in those regions: as water-surface temperatures change little from day to night, the vertical lapse rate within a convectional cloud over or near water tends to be greatest around dawn, by which time the cooling of the upper cloud surfaces has reached its diurnal maximum; that is, the thermodynamic instability, or thundery

Fig. 16. Average annual number of days with thunderstorms. (Courtesy of Weather Bureau, U.S. Department of Commerce)

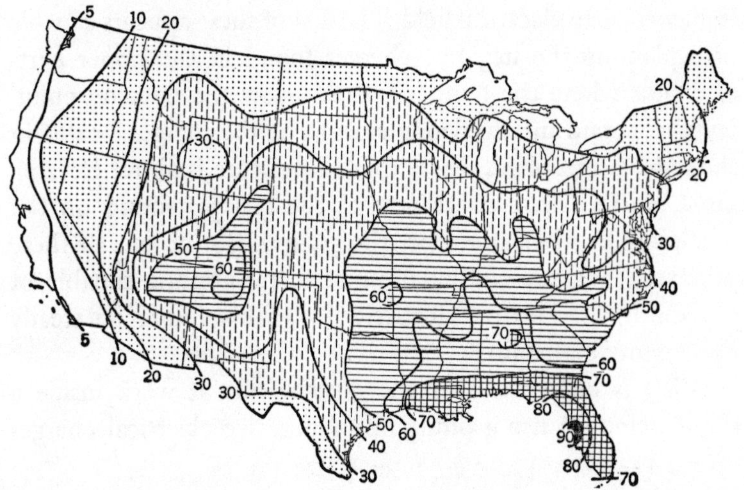

propensity, of a convectional cloud mass over water is greatest around dawn.

"Lightning that mocks the night, Brief even as bright"

Thunderclouds generate electricity much as power stations do. In fact, a thundercloud is a kind of wind-driven dynamo; but how it works nobody quite knows. Dr. B. F. J. Schonland, head of the Bernard Price Institute for Geophysical Research, University of Witwatersrand, Johannesburg, who ought to know if anybody should, having spent the best part of a lifetime studying the subject, recently admitted that there is still "no final answer" to the question of how clouds and rain become electrified. "The difficulty . . . is not to discover a suitable mechanism but to determine which of a number of possible ways in which [raindrops or ice crystals] can be charged is the one which plays the leading part. . . ." * There are, it seems, at least three ways in which the charging can happen: by contact between ice particles, by the breaking of raindrops, and by the absorption of positive and negative ions under the influence of an electrical field. The first of these appears capable of explaining the negative charges found in the upper parts of clouds where the temperature is below the freezing point, and the second and third may account for the charges located in the lower atmosphere where the temperature is above freezing point, and all may contribute to the charges found on the precipitation when it reaches the ground. But no one of these processes, nor any combination of them, appears capable of explaining the positive electricity invariably found on steady light or moderate rain.

What is known is that the mechanisms at work inside a thundercloud cause a piling up of negative electrical charges

* *The Flight of Thunderbolts*, 1950, pp. 122–123.

in one part and of positive charges in another. This piling up is continued by the mechanical forces working against the mutual attraction of these opposite accumulating charges until the electrical attraction becomes so great that a dart of electrons is shot from one charge to the other. This dart temporarily destroys the insulating properties of the air along a discharge channel down which the separated charges can now rush freely to reunite. This rush of current generates light, heat, and sound and also sends out radio waves, longer than light and heat waves, which are heard on our radio receivers as static. Some idea of the interference range of these waves is given by the fact that lightning flashes originating in the doldrum belt have been known to disturb the reception by listeners in Norway of English radio programs, all of 3,500 miles away.

The generating capacity of a thundercloud is monumental. A single flash of lightning has been estimated to develop a million times the voltage used in ordinary house wiring. Although flashes vary widely in the power they transmit and also in the voltage that is behind them, it is probably not unusual for a cloud emitting a flash every 10 seconds to develop about 1 million kilowatts, or not much less than the present generating capacity of all the dams across the Tennessee Valley.

Where it strikes twice

Lightning is not a single spark, but many. Three things have happened by the time you see the flash, or the fork. First, and taking about 1/1,000,000 second, a leader stroke has blazed a trail for the ensuing bolt. Second, and lasting 5 to 200/1,000,000 second, a surge of high-voltage electricity has raced back up the blazed trail from the contact point on the earth, and anything—be it a tree, or an animal, or a building—that stood on the contact spot has been forced to carry the deadly charge.

Third, a sustained current between cloud and ground, lasting 1/1,000 to 1/10 second, has burned, melted, ignited, or vaporized the object struck.

Danger from lightning in a thunderstorm is never great, but it always exists. In the United States alone it kills between 400 and 500 persons each year, injures 1,500 more, and terrifies millions. The danger is greater in some places than in others. Ferroconcrete buildings are practically lightningproof, for the current follows the steel until it is safely grounded. The Empire State Building in New York City, the tallest structure in the world, has been struck hundreds of times—15 times in 15 minutes during one violent thunderstorm—but it is doubtful whether the people inside it have ever known anything about it.

Although ordinary brick houses are not especially safe, it is much safer to be inside one of them than outside when there is a storm. But it is good policy to stay away from the fireplace, because lightning is much more likely to strike the chimney (being the tallest part of the building) than any other part, always assuming that there is no lightning rod to lead the current harmlessly to the ground. Away from the fireplace, it does not much matter where you are, for, contrary to popular opinion, it is no more dangerous near the window, open or closed, than it is near a solid wall. A lightning discharge is as likely to be blown through a wall as it is through a window. Nor is there any reason to suppose that a good draft of air gives added security.

If you are caught out-of-doors, avoid high ground, especially when you happen to be the highest object and your feet are "earthed." Swinging a metal-shafted club overhead has been the last mortal act of many a wet-weather golfer. Likewise, avoid tall, isolated trees. If you must shelter under trees, choose the smooth-barked variety. Nearly six times as many oaks are struck as beech trees. Caves, holes, depressions of any sort are comparatively safe. Even squatting in a ditch, however wet it may be, is preferable to seeking the protection against rain of a tall tree or an isolated shed. If you can't take cover in a house, one of the safest places to be is in an all-steel closed automobile, for the steel body will conduct the current away from the occupants. The same is true of all-metal airplanes.

You can tell how close lightning is by counting the seconds between the flash and the thunderclap. If the thunder follows 10 seconds after a lightning stroke, the lightning struck a point about 2 miles off, for sound travels a mile in approximately five seconds. And if you are the nervous sort, comfort yourself with the following facts: if you heard the thunder, the lightning didn't strike. If you saw the lightning, it missed you. If it did strike you, the chances are that you wouldn't be doing much worrying about it.

So much for the debit side. There is also a credit side, however: even the darkest cumulonimbus has a silver lining, it seems. In the course of its quick passage earthward, the lightning flash frees the nitrogen in the enveloping air, just as high-voltage electricity does in the commercial nitrogen-fixation process. This gift to plant life comes down with the raindrops. Dr. Schonland has calculated that 100 million tons of fixed nitrogen is spread over the earth each year by lightning.

St. Elmo's fire

Another manifestation of a highly charged atmosphere is the so-called St. Elmo's fire. Not being very brilliant, the "fire" is mostly observed at night when the luminous spots and semblances of flame which betray its presence can take on a thoroughly portentous appearance.

*Last night I saw St. Elmo's stars,**
With their glimmering lanterns, all at play
On the tops of the masts, the tips of the spars,
And I knew we should have foul weather today.

On high mountains such discharges are particularly well developed in snowstorms. Frequently the hissing sound of the discharge may be heard, when the "fire" is invisible. As the amount of electricity involved is very small, there is no danger of fire, in spite of the name.

The phenomenon is probably less valuable prognostically over land than over the sea. Over land it merely indicates that the electrical condition of the atmosphere is tense, which is not the same thing as saying that it is about to erupt in a thunderstorm. Over the sea it is unlikely to occur other than near a front or in the doldrum belt, both of which are quite capable of giving a navigator plenty of trouble.

"*A reglar round roarin' savage peal*"

Understandably the poets do not have as much to say about the thunderstorm as they do about other meteorological phenomena, and what they do say is scarcely in its favor. But to men of Davy Crockett's ilk there was no finer music or a greater spectacle than a "hull team of storm-brewed thunder": besides this the roar of Niagara, the growling of the sea, and "the barking o' them big iron bull dogs" was "no more than a penny trumpet to the hand organ of a hurrycane." To Davy Crockett, "the greatest treat in all creation" was a peal of thunder. "It sets everything but a coward and a darned culprit shouting in the very heart and soul till both on 'em swell so etarnal big with nat'ral glorification that one feels as if he could swoller the entire creation at a gap, hug the hull universe at once, then

* Longfellow's poetical equivalent for fire.

go to sleep so full of thunder glory, that he'll wake up with his head an entire electrical machine, and his arms a teetotal thunderbolt. . . ." *

If Crockett is right, then most of us must be either cowards or culprits, for we have still to meet the man who can relax, let alone go to sleep, while the skies are playing a tattoo over his head. Yet, when all is said and done, thunder is probably the most unhurtful element of the atmosphere. It does not kill as frost does the rising sap; it does not steal, as heavy rains do the soil; it does not covet any man's house, as hurricanes and tornadoes do; nor does it bear false witness. Clouds may deceive and rainbows lie, but no one may misconstrue the language of thunder: it makes its meaning clear wherever it is heard.

The usual explanation of the cause of thunder—which is probably too simple, but which in the absence of scientific proof to the contrary is still found in textbooks—is that the sudden and intense heating occurring along the path of a lightning discharge produces an abrupt expansion of the air particles. The subsequent collision of these particles as they return to fill up the partial vacuum thus created produces the noise. (Much the same sort of thing takes place when a gun is fired.) Meantime the expansion has set up a compression wave in the surrounding atmosphere; this travels outward like any other wave. The commonly observed "roll" of thunder is a time-lapse phenomenon. The fact that lightning follows a zigzag path on its way to earth means that the sound waves, although all starting out simultaneously, have different distances to travel and so do not arrive simultaneously. Frequently the roll is prolonged by the occurrence of multiple discharges, in quick succession, within the storm cloud, and by the presence of mountains, hills, and valleys that provide sound-reflecting surfaces.

* Richard M. Dorson, ed., *Davy Crockett: American Comic Legend,* 1939, p. 14.

Thunderstorm today?

If you want to know whether you can trust the promise of a hot summer morning, watch the clouds. If by ten or eleven o'clock (local time) there is very little wind and the fair-weather cumulus clouds characteristic of such a day are rapidly growing in size and depth, think twice before planning an afternoon in the country; for there's truth in the old tag:

In the morning mountains,
In the evening fountains.

As we have already seen,* the rate of convective cloud development is largely determined by the lapse rate, or vertical temperature gradient. The more unstable the air is in the morning, the quicker will clouds form and the sooner will overturning of the air within them reach the point where the burden of condensed water vapor no longer can be sustained aloft.

To decide what is going to happen *before* any clouds are about is more difficult and, among other things, calls for a wet-and-dry-bulb thermometer, a book of tables, and a barometer. If you find that the dew point at eight o'clock in the morning is between 55 and 60°F., then you can take it that the air has plenty of moisture. Given three or four hours of uninterrupted sunshine, it is quite likely that much of this moisture will be carried aloft by convection, cooled to condensation point, and precipitated by the late afternoon. Precipitation in the form of thundershowers is all the more likely if the barometer shows a tendency to fall throughout the day. If, on the other hand, the dew point is below, say, 40°F., a most unusual amount of surface heating would be needed to produce the "mountains" that precede the "fountains," for not even a falling barometer can coax rain out of a dry atmosphere.

* See June, pp. 136–137.

Predicting the course a storm will take once it has started sometimes has its uses. Generally speaking, thunderstorms move with the current of air that involves the main body of the storm, namely, the wind at two to three miles above the surface. This is about the level at which altocumulus clouds, often observed in the vicinity of a storm, are found; to watch the movement of these clouds is to get a pretty good idea of the speed and direction of the storm's advance. When the altocumulus appears to be moving fast, the storm is likely to come up quickly, but when it appears to be moving slowly, you will probably have ample warning of its approach. But it is not always so easy as this. For instance, pure heat thunderstorms do their best to avoid passing over cool surfaces that cut off the supply of heat, a habit that has been enshrined in the saying that "a thunderstorm will never cross a river." Though the saying should not be regarded with undue respect, it is a fact of observation that the intensity of heat storms is frequently weaker over wooded and grassland areas than over plowland and built-up areas which give off more heat to the lower atmosphere.

Squalls, line squalls, and squall lines

Squalls, frequent attendants upon a thunderstorm, are like showers: they mean different things to different people. They also mean different things in different parts of the world.

In the doldrums a squall may be nothing more than a shower of rain falling on a calm sea; on the other hand, it may be a rainless wind gusting up to gale force, and it may last for as little as 30 seconds or as long as a night; or, again, it may be any number of combinations of wind and rain, anything, in fact, from a light breeze with a drizzle to a quasi-hurricane with a cloudburst. To the mariner, in low latitudes these are all squalls. In middle latitudes there are white squalls, bull's-eye squalls, thundersqualls, dust squalls, rain squalls, and line squalls, and about the only thing they have in common is their origin: they breed in air that is unstable, that is, characterized by a strong two-way vertical movement.

Three times out of four such instability is triggered off by nothing more complicated than differential heating of the earth's surface or the advection of air from a cooler to a warmer surface; a great many summertime squalls are produced in this way. However, the more vehement squalls encountered in the tropics and on this continent seem to call for something more—a booster in fact. In the case of the doldrum squall, the boost is supplied by the converging northerly and southerly trade winds; in the case of the mid-latitude variety it is supplied by the leading edge of a rapidly moving cold front, an edge that may extend horizontally for several hundred miles. Squalls forming on or near this edge generally go by the name of "line squalls," and their locus by the name of "squall line."

But this is not to say that all cold fronts produce squall lines, or that all squall lines coincide with cold fronts. On the contrary, squall lines and line squalls frequently form between 50 and 200 miles ahead of a cold front.* The reason for this prefrontal preference of the mid-latitude squall is at first thought a little obscure, but if the behavior of flowing water is at all analogous—and in certain respects it is, for the fluid air has many of the properties of the fluid water—then it seems probable that a squall is closely related to two types of water wave, namely, the wave that runs ahead of, and parallel to, a square-bowed barge moving upstream, and the breaking wave of the seashore. The barge wave is the result of the inability of the

* Some meteorologists still reserve the term "line squall" for the turbulent showery weather commonly associated with the passage of a well-marked cold front. Others use it for any linear manifestations of severe turbulence, thereby confounding the terminological confusion still further.

converging bodies of water to disperse as fast as the accumulation is occurring: the breaking shore wave is the result of the frictional drag of the beach material coupled with the undertow which makes it impossible for the base of the wave to advance at the speed of the crest and so, in consequence, causes the crest to pitch forward and break on the beach ahead of the main body of the wave. When a cold front undercuts a warm-air mass, it impels forward and upward all the warm air that gets in the way of its path. The vertically displaced component, under favorable lapse-rate conditions, will rise high enough to condense and turn into a churning mass of wind and vapor. At the same time, the checking, by friction, of the surface speed of the advancing front causes the faster moving upper layers of the cold air to outrun the lower layers and to be injected into the rudely buffeted warm air ahead of the front. When this happens, and not every cold front is capable of the necessary violence, then the stage is set for one of Dame Nature's tantrums—what Shakespeare called "a rash, fierce blaze of riot." Though, fortunately, the tantrum is seldom long-lived, it is anything but amusing while it lasts. It can flay the ground with hail, lift the roof off a barn, uproot an orchard, riddle a plowed field with gulleys—all to a stentorian obbligato of thunder. Perhaps it was just such a phenomenon that Shelley had in mind when he wrote

I wield the flail of the lashing hail,
And whiten the green plains under;
And then again I dissolve it in rain,
And laugh as I pass in thunder.

The development of a squall line and line squall, unlike the ordinary convectional shower, is difficult to forecast, even for the professional meteorologist; in most cases it is impossible to identify it unless hourly and special observations are used, and in some cases hourly maps fail to locate it accurately, for the average time duration of line-squall weather at a given station in this country is less than 45 minutes. The amateur weatherman has little more to go on than the static in his radio set, and a mounting bank of thundercloud to windward. The immediate pre-squall phase may usually be identified by the presence of a conspicuous roll cloud, almost cylindrical in shape: this is the outrider of the main squall cloud and looks as ominous as it is. The turbulence is often so great that it can be both seen and heard. The external contours of the roll cloud are in a state of constant flux like the surface of boiling pitch, and just about as dark. Inside, heaven alone knows what is taking place, but the sound is the sound of torment. The passage of the squall proper is usually marked by thunderstorms, heavy precipitation, brief wind shifts and gusts up to 70 miles per hour, a "jumpy" barograph (that is, pressure) trace, and an abrupt temperature fall: as the squall recedes, the wind abates and veers, sometimes more than 90 degrees, and the pressure rises, unless other squall lines or a cold front is near at hand, in which case the pressure rise and wind shift will be of short duration. But there are plenty of "unusual" squalls too: in these, one or more of the usual features may be absent.

Since almost any vigorous cold front may trigger off squall-line activity, especially if lapse-rate conditions in the convergence zone are favorable to the development of thunderstorms, it follows that squalls can occur in almost any part of the United States and southern Canada, and at almost any time of the year. But, like tornadoes, with which, as the reader can see, they have marked affinities, line squalls have their preferred times and seasons. They occur mostly in the late afternoon and early evening: they are about twice as frequent in June, July, and August as they are in spring and autumn; and they are quite rare in winter. The lower Missouri and upper Mississippi

Valleys are the most frequently, and the most violently, affected areas. And at their worst, squalls have the destructive power of a tornado. The line squall that moved across southern Kansas and northern Oklahoma during the afternoon of July 14 and night of July 14–15, 1948, left behind it a 9-million-dollar trail of ruin, much of it in the form of flattened crops and property. Winds in excess of 100 miles per hour were clocked at several points along its path. In another line squall there occurred one of the worst aviation disasters in the history of this country. During the late evening of June 23, 1950, a transport plane crashed into Lake Michigan with the loss of all fifty-eight passengers and crew. A few minutes before, the plane was known to have entered an area of excessive turbulence and electrical activity. Three other planes flying in the area at the time turned back because they were unable to get through the squall: it extended up to 30,000 feet.

The exact relationship between line squalls and tornadoes is not known. What is known is that both phenomena have a liking for moist, convectively unstable air, that is, air that is in a thundery mood. In a sense both of them are "parasites" of thunderstorms, feeding on the energy which is released when a cumulonimbus cloud begins to convert its water vapor into raindrops and hail. But at times it is difficult to tell which is the "host" and which the "parasite," for line squalls and tornadoes may both occur in advance as well as in the rear of a thunderstorm.

Unfortunately, there is as yet nothing that anyone can do to "kill" either parasite or host. True, some meteorologists have begun to talk about neutralizing the lethal power of a squall at its source by sprinkling it with dry ice or silver iodide and powdered charcoal, but what they still don't know is how to identify the cloud that will spawn the squall. All thunderclouds look pretty much the same—until the wind starts to blow.

August

"It's not the heat—it's the atomized sea water"

Not a summer passes but what the 100 million Americans living east of the Mississippi complain about "the humidity." Their lawns may be as dry as the Sahara; their garden squash may be in an advanced stage of dehydration; but they will be a watershed of perspiration and limp as the clothes on their backs. At first thought, it may seem odd that summer should be the season of high humidity, but such is indeed the case. On the rainiest midwinter day in Miami, the air is unlikely to have more than 8 to 10 grams of moisture per cubic meter, whereas during a hot dry spell in August it is likely to contain 15 to 20 grams per cubic meter, and on a wet day over 30 grams per cubic meter—that is, more than three times as much as in winter.

As we saw earlier,* most of this moisture gets into the air through the agency of evaporation. If unsaturated air rests undisturbed on the surface of a sea or lake, the water steadily evaporates into it until the water-vapor content of the overlying air approaches saturation point. Much the same happens

* See June, p. 125.

when unsaturated air is in contact with wet soil or vegetation, for experiments have shown that a plant-covered area with a damp soil is almost as effective in moistening the air, in the warmer months of the year at least, as any open body of water. However, the *rate* of evaporation over a given surface is far from constant. Among other things, it varies with the speed of the wind, and the temperatures of the evaporating body and the air into which moisture is being evaporated.

If there is no wind, evaporation can proceed only by the means of "molecular diffusion." If there is a wind, the eddies forming at the plane of contact (that is, between the water and air, or soil-plant and air surfaces) keep circulating the moister surface air upward and the drier ambient air downward. In this way the upward flow of water vapor is maintained until the air near the evaporating surface reaches saturation point. This "eddy diffusion," as it is called, is an infinitely more efficient humidifying device than molecular diffusion; and the stronger the wind, the more efficient it is, since it is wind speed that largely governs the rate at which moisture from the evaporating surface can be carried aloft. But as anybody knows who has watched steam issuing from the spout of a boiling kettle, a supply of heat is also necessary to maintain the evaporation process. The amount, known as the latent heat of evaporation, varies with temperature: at 80°F., or about the mean August temperature along the east coast of Florida, the amount required to convert 1 gram of water into water vapor at the same temperature is sufficient to raise the temperature of approximately 320 grams of water 1°F. The amount required would be somewhat less at lower temperatures and greater at higher temperatures.

And then again, the effectiveness of the evaporation process varies with the dryness of the air: the drier the air to start with, the greater the evaporation. On a good "drying" day in summer (thanks to the washing machine and the laundromat most housewives are no longer much concerned about the drying qualities of the air), the surface level of a pond or lake may be lowered ½ to ¾ inch as a result of evaporation, and an almost equivalent loss of water may be sustained by plant-covered soils. The loss in a single summer month may be as much as 20 to 22 inches. (The wintertime rate of evaporation will probably be less than half of this figure, even over a desert.)

Evaporation agencies should not, however, be given all the credit for our discomfort. They have some very able partners. It seems that, if left to their own devices, a great many water-vapor particles would return to the earth or sea from whence they came as soon as the eddy diffusion ceased. But this is rarely the case. Instead, they get caught in the toils of condensation nuclei: these are the "middlemen" of the precipitation business, who process the flimsy raw material of our soggy summer atmosphere into solid water droplets for later distribution to the customers in the form of rain and hail. Over land these condensation nuclei commonly consist of hygroscopic substances, such as sulfur dioxide and sulfur trioxide, soot, and similar by-products of our industrial age. Over the sea and along the windward shores, the nuclei are more likely to consist of common salt which has been evaporated from the spray and carried aloft.

Seeking to capitalize on the known therapeutic properties of salt water, the Miami Chamber of Commerce recently went one step further and announced that the moisture usually present in the Floridian atmosphere is "not what is generally termed humidity, but is really atomized sea water. This so-called humidity is one of Florida's great health-building assets." Needless to say, the meteorologists of Miami, good scientists that they are, are now busy looking for the atomizer.

What is "humidity," anyway?

Most of us have a ready answer to this question, but it's probably not very polite. The official—U.S. Weather Bureau—answer is polite enough, but rather cautious. It runs like this: "The state of the atmosphere with respect to water vapor content: it may be measured in many different ways. See: Absolute Humidity; Dew Point; Mixing Ratio; Relative Humidity; Saturation Deficit; Specific Humidity; Vapor Pressure; Water Vapor." In other words, it would almost seem as if there is no such thing as plain, unvarnished humidity, but only a series of adjectival varieties—a supposition for which, I imagine, the meteorologists could find warm support among the laity.

To start with, absolute humidity is defined in three different ways in the *Weather Glossary* of the U.S. Weather Bureau; and of the three definitions, two contain grounds—or should we say grains?—of confusion. Thus the first reads: "The mass of water vapor present per unit volume of space, *i.e.*, the density of water vapor: usually expressed in grams per cubic meter, or grains per cubic foot." * The third tells us that, "The term is sometimes applied by heating engineers to the number of grains of moisture per pound of moist [saturated?] air. This usage corresponds to the meteorological definition of specific humidity." † And when we turn to "specific humidity" in the same *Weather Glossary*, we are still further discomfited, for nothing is said about grains—only grams. Specific humidity is, we are told, "the mass of water vapor in a unit mass of 'moist air,' usually expressed as so many grams per gram or per kilogram of moist air." And before we can be quite sure that the two are one and the same, and that grains are really not very different from grams, we are warned that specific humidity must be dis-

* Page 2 (1946 edition).
† *Ibid.*

tinguished from "mixing ratio" which, of course, implies that the two are, in fact, frequently confused, and can you wonder when you find "mixing ratio" defined as "the mass of water vapor per unit mass of perfectly dry air in a humid mixture." Even the glossary is good enough to admit that "the mixing ratio is very nearly numerically equivalent to the specific humidity."

Popular confusion is likely to be worse confounded when the talk shifts to relative humidity, for the biggest trouble about relative humidity is that its meaning changes from day to day. Thus a 50 per cent relative humidity on a day when the maximum temperature is 50°F. is a very different thing (and *feels* very different, too) from a 50 per cent relative humidity on a day when the maximum temperature reaches 70°F. On the former occasion, the air contains only some 4½ grams of water vapor per cubic meter: on the latter, it contains over 8 grams per cubic meter, or nearly twice as much. When, as not infrequently happens in an August heat wave, the maximum temperature rises to the 90s, a relative humidity of 50 per cent means that the water-vapor content is approximately double again what it was at the intermediate figure. So next time the radio announcer tries to whip you into a mood of gaiety on account of the forecaster's having said that the midafternoon relative humidity would be in the low 50s, though the air temperature would be in the high 90s, it might be as well to remind yourself that even 50 per cent of a very large amount is still quite a large amount.

Better still, head for the nearest beach where the temperatures will certainly be lower and the sea breeze will no less certainly help to mitigate the discomfort of the soggy air. Furthermore, once you are there, you can console yourself with the thought that even some of the forecasters find relative humidity very confusing. One I know goes as far as to call it the "meteorological equivalent of absolute humbug"!

"A *summer mist for fair*"

Because there is so much moisture in the atmosphere of the eastern half of the continent at this season, a little night cooling can often lead to a lot of morning fog, especially on low-lying ground. All that is required, in addition to plenty of water vapor, is still air and a clear sky. In the fall and winter, radiational cooling of this kind may give rise to very dense and enduring fog,* but in summer the chilling of the air is unlikely to extend high enough to produce more than a shallow, filmy envelope of mist. Also, summer mists, or fogs, of this type dissipate quickly under the influence of the strong sun, and seldom outlast sunrise by more than an hour or two.

The fact that such fogs occur most frequently in association with anticyclones of feeble pressure gradient has given rise to the belief, as well founded as any we know and better founded than most, that a mist in the early hours of a summer morning is the forerunner of a warm, fine day.

However, if the cooling should take place over water instead of over land, the resulting fog or mist may persist all day. For this to happen, a different kind of cooling—advective cooling—is necessary. As the name suggests, this is the product of horizontal movement, in which warm moist air is drawn across a colder water surface. Such a condition may arise in summer when tropical air streams, moving northward, pass from the interior lowlands to the Great Lakes, or, more frequently, from the warm waters of the Gulf Stream to the cold inshore waters of the Labrador Current. On the west coast,

* See November, pp. 257–265, for a fuller discussion of fog.

similar conditions may arise when near-saturated air of central Pacific origin passes over the cool waters of the California Current. Even so, it is possible for the visibility to remain quite good over open water and deteriorate only over a lee shore. In such a case it seems that all that is needed to precipitate the moisture being carried in the air is a further slight cooling, by perhaps no more than one degree—a cooling which it can experience by being lifted over high sand dunes or low cliffs. Obviously, where the lake or seashore is flat, no such cooling is likely to take place: indeed the chances are that, as the air stream moves inland, it will be warmed up, especially if it does so by day, and so become drier rather than moister. From which it follows that on a fine summer's day even a sea fog is unlikely to affect more than a narrow ribbon of coast. By contrast, during the hours of darkness when cooling of the coast by radiation may cause the temperature of the surface to fall below the dew point of the air over the neighboring water, sea fog may spread inland and become thicker than it is offshore.

Cool coasts—warm interiors

But a cool coast has its compensations. On the fact that most of our coasts are cooler in August than the lands behind them reposes the life of our beach-resort industry, the liberty of 40 million pale-faced adults to do themselves brown without baking, and the pursuit of happiness of as many more children in as many more ways. Needless to say, the precise difference between air-over-land and air-over-sea temperatures depends on where you happen to be. Along New England's east coast during a heat wave the difference may be as much as 30°F., and in ordinary weather it is likely to be as much as 15°F. No other part of North America can show comparable figures, largely, no doubt, because no other part of the continent is affected by ocean currents as cold as the Labrador Current. However, even along the coast of central California which is seldom afflicted with intemperate heat, the difference between air-over-land and air-over-sea temperatures is characteristically of the order of 5 to 6°F.

While the basic cause of this state of affairs, as everyone who was ever exposed to the physics of light, heat, and air will recall, lies with the different heat-absorbing properties of land and water, the effect of it would not be as great, either climatologically or monetarily, were it not for the fact that along vast stretches of our oceanic frontage daytime winds in summer have a habit of being onshore. These winds are of two kinds: what the meteorologist calls regional, or prevailing winds, that is, winds that obey the directions of the great atmospheric pressure magnates—the cyclones and anticyclones of mid-latitudes—and the common or garden sea breeze.

Wherever they blow onshore, and they do from the Pacific Northwest to the west coast of Florida and along the coast of Maine, the prevailing winds are esteemed for their temperature-equalizing properties. The diurnal (day-night) range of temperatures is at a minimum, and so, too, are the chances of unwonted heat and cold. But they can also be, and frequently are, purveyors of mist, low cloud, and rain, and even in fair weather they are apt to be accompanied by a high surf, partly their own manufacture and partly the product of stronger winds to seaward (and, therefore, technically *swell* rather than surf). Furthermore, they may blow for days, and nights, without intermission and without notable change of temperature. For this reason they tend to be relaxing rather than bracing. On first exposure to them, the town dweller in search of a tonic may say the air is "like wine"—and it probably is, for an overdose of it can easily send the imbiber to sleep.

The sea breeze

The sea breeze is a very different kind of wind. It is capricious and fugitive, yet demure and wholesome. For the most part it comes, unannounced, out of a clear blue sky, or at most a lightly cloud-dappled sky, and goes without fuss. He is a lucky forecaster who can tell "whence it cometh, or whither it goeth," and luckier still if he can tell you *when* it will come and go. But as a temperature depressant there is nothing to touch it. Days which threaten to send the mercury soaring into the 90s may, under the benign flattery of a sea breeze, pass without so much as registering 80°F. On occasion, its onset will cause an almost instantaneous drop of temperature of 10 to 15°F. And, for good measure, it is incapable, unaided, of raising a surf that would harm even a small child.

The mechanism of the sea breeze is comparatively simple, though perhaps not so simple as some would have us believe. Almost as soon as the sun begins to beat upon a stretch of coast on a summer morning, the layer of air immediately in contact with the land begins to heat up, and so expand, at an appreciably faster rate than the air immediately in contact with the water. Through turbulent motion, portions of this heated land air rise, cooling adiabatically as they do so; by the inertia of this motion, they create an upper reservoir of comparatively cold air over the lower heat source. The pressure difference produced aloft in this way first induces a very slight flow of air from land to sea: next, this leads to a reduction in surface pressure over the land which, in turn, causes a compensatory air flow from sea to land at the surface. We know that this is so because it is not unheard of for wind-finding balloons that have traveled several miles out to sea by the aid of an upper offshore wind to be brought back to the coast by an onshore surface wind.

However, it must not be supposed, on this account, that sea-breeze air is continually rotating within a given orbit. On the contrary, as the sea breeze strengthens, as it almost invariably does during the course of the morning, new air of terrestrial and marine origin is drawn into the circulation. Further, it seems likely that, on many occasions, the sea-breeze circulation is more nearly comparable to that set up in a tank when the vertical partition between oil and water is suddenly removed and the force of gravity pushes the heavier water under the lighter oil at the bottom of the bath, while at the top the oil slides over the water in a counter direction. This appears to apply whenever a sea breeze develops with an *offshore* gradient wind. For what happens then is that the gradient wind carries the warmed air out to sea, where it is cooled by continuous contact with the surface of the water. Through what the meteorologist calls "a turbulent stress" with the gradient wind, the cold layer is pushed seaward and "telescoped," thus raising the height of the cooled surface air and reducing the pressure differential between the sea and the land. As the morning advances, more and more of this cool air piles up until it reaches the point where the surface-pressure gradient between sea and land is reversed. When this happens the warm offshore wind finds itself overwhelmed by the cool-air mass it was the means of establishing. The cool air is then free to advance landward, undercutting the warmer gradient wind, in the manner of a cold front. On occasion the "leading edge" of such a sea breeze may even have enough "kick" in it to whip the surface of an otherwise flat sea into a flurry of activity, and to stimulate cloud formation over the land where it comes into collision with the gradient wind. If the air is sufficiently unstable to start with, the arrival of the breeze over the land may even touch off thunderstorm activity.

In North America the sea breeze seldom extends more than 25 miles inland, and unaided by an onshore gradient wind, it is unlikely to exceed a speed of 15 miles an hour. In parts of the world where the land-sea temperature contrast is very great, for instance, in central Chile and Egypt, the sea breeze may be felt up to 50 miles inland, an even greater distance out to sea, and at its diurnal peak it may reach gale force.

Many a lake shore, in this country and abroad, experiences a similar phenomenon, though it is not common for lake breezes to reach the intensity or to have the reach of sea breezes. The lake breezes experienced in the Door Peninsula region of Lake Superior, for instance, do not normally penetrate more than a mile or so inland, or exceed 10 miles an hour.

In all cases the breeze is likely to be at its strongest about midafternoon, that is, about the time of the temperature maximum over the land, and to die away before sunset. It can start anytime after sunrise, but may not do so much before noon—in the case of the "frontal" variety, even later. And it is in the habit of starting at different times in different places. Along a 50-mile stretch of coast on a given day, there may be differences of two to three hours in the time of its onset: at one point it may blow from 9 to 5, at another from 10 to 4, while at a third it may be perceptible only for an hour or so around 3 P.M.—such is the delicacy of the atmospheric balance and the potency of local topographic and micro-meteorological circumstances.

Though essentially a summer wind—for on this continent it is only in summer that lake and sea waters are characteristically cooler than their bordering lands—the sea breeze has been observed (along the Massachusetts coast) as early as February. In the tropics, it may occur in almost any month of the year, and is especially common during prolonged spells of dry weather.

The land breeze

The land breeze is the nocturnal complement of the daytime sea or lake breeze. It is the direct, dynamic result of the greater nighttime cooling of air over land than over water. Whereas sea or lake water cools down very slowly, the temperature of the land on a clear calm night falls quickly because the upward flow of heat in the ground below the surface is too slow to replace that lost by radiation and convection. Consequently, while a large water surface will seldom cool more than 1°F. during the course of a night, a land surface under favorable radiative conditions will cool as much as 20 or 25°F. Even so, it is not usual for the cooling to be carried to the point where the temperature of the air falls as far below the sea temperature as it rises above the sea temperature by day. This means that the nocturnal, or reversed, water-land temperature gradient is generally less steep than the daytime gradient, and that the resulting flow of air from land to sea, that is, the land breeze, is less strong. As the steepest temperature gradients will be found over the water between heavy, cooled air that has drifted off the land and that which has been continuously over the sea, the active land-breeze region, where the main density difference is concentrated, is entirely over the sea. The maximum development of the land breeze, in theory at least, should therefore be located over water rather than over land. Many a yachtsman and fisherman would, we suspect, be willing to endorse this theory: and even landlubbers, with half a weather eye, must often have observed that the nocturnal phenomenon of offshore cumulus cloud, characteristic of quiet weather in summertime, does not reach its maximum development over the coast (where it might be expected to do so if the land breeze was doing its most active undercutting of the warmer sea air at that point), but some miles out to sea. The landward extension of the breeze is, on this reckoning, merely the dynamic consequence of the activity over the sea.

In clear weather land breezes may begin almost any time after sundown and continue until an hour or so after sunrise. On cloudy nights their onset is retarded owing to the slower rate of land cooling (for there is nothing like an overcast sky to prevent the daytime heat from escaping into outer space), and by the same token, their termination may be delayed the next morning. Typically, the land breeze is a lighter wind than the sea breeze, rarely exceeding 10 miles an hour: where higher velocities are attributed to it, the chances are that they are the result of reinforcement of the land breeze either by a down-valley wind or by an offshore gradient wind. Also, the land breeze has a smaller horizontal and vertical reach than its daytime counterpart.

On a small scale these night and day breezes reproduce the alternating offshore and onshore wind systems associated with the great continents and reaching their greatest development in the monsoons. During winter and spring, when the land is colder than the surrounding oceans and pressure is relatively high, continental winds blow offshore, while in summer and autumn, when the land is warmer and pressure over it is relatively low, they tend to blow onshore.

"Torrents in summer"

No one who has seen a flash flood—a phenomenon of high summer in America's heartland—is ever likely to forget it, though not many of us perhaps could communicate the drama of it as pungently as Longfellow does in his famous lines:

As torrents in summer
Half-dried in their channels,
Suddenly rise, though the sky is still cloudless,

For rain has been falling
Far off at their fountains.

Not that most ordinary mortals have much cause for feeling poetic about a flash flood; the suddenness of the rise is wont not only to catch the unwary camper with his flaps up, but to bring quick death to sheep and cattle foraging along the valley bottom. There are well-authenticated stories of flash floods along the foothills of the Rockies attaining a height of 10 feet in as many minutes and subsiding almost as quickly. The damage to life and property of such a flood is matched only by the blighted hopes and fortunes of the survivors.

A measure of the damage which summertime floods (admittedly not all of them of the "flash" type) can do is disclosed in the accompanying table.

LOSS OF LIFE AND PROPERTY FROM SUMMERTIME FLOODS IN THE UNITED STATES, 1924–1937

Month	Property loss	Lives lost
June	$106,685,000	158
July	56,679,000	104
August	26,821,000	28
September	29,017,000	40

The main manufacturer of summer floods is the high-intensity storm of short duration that originates in a warm moist air mass. Such air masses develop their physical characteristics over tropical waters such as the Gulf of Mexico. Generally they are heavily charged with moisture up to about 8,000 feet, and upon occasion even up to 16,000 feet. As we saw earlier, in the chapter on July weather, this enormous moisture reservoir can be tapped in more ways than one. Over level terrain, the moisture burden is most likely to be released either through intense heating of the layer of air next to the ground or as a result of its coming in contact with a colder, more dense air mass, that is, through frontal interaction. In mountainous terrain, surface heating is unlikely to be so important a factor as forced uplift, and this can be induced as readily by the nature of the relief itself as by the presence of a frontal surface: in either case the effect is the same. As the moisture-heavy air rises, it reaches elevations of diminishing pressure where it expands and cools. The cooling, if continued long enough, leads to condensation. As the water vapor changes to liquid water drops, the latent heat of vaporization is added to the rising air current; this tends to accelerate the convection process which, in turn, accelerates the rate of condensation until nearly all the available water vapor has been precipitated. Since the motion of the air is mainly vertical, and involves comparatively high velocities, the rainfall is likely to be intense and concentrated over a small area. The concentration is likely to be all the greater when an immobile range of mountains, rather than a moving front, supplies part of the lifting mechanism. It takes but a few minutes to convert this concentration, handsomely abetted by the funneling habit of mountain streams, into "a flood of mighty waters overflowing" the land and all that is thereon.

Mountains make their own weather

Even modest mountains like the Laurentians, Adirondacks, and Ozarks have a very different climate from the valleys around them. In the first place, they are invariably wetter. In the second place, they are cooler, especially by day. By night they may sometimes be warmer, even though the loss of heat from the ground is greater at the top than at the bottom of the mountain, for the air cooled by contact with the cooled ground slides downhill, leaving the slopes and summits warmer than the valleys a thousand feet or so below. This inversion of temperature, as it is called, can be very striking. A hill only 200 feet high frequently enjoys a warm evening breeze while the lowlands below shiver under the insidious creep of cold damp air. In the third place, the wind blows harder on the mountain than in the valley. In the valley air movement is curtailed by friction and by the undulations of relief. By the time you get 1,000 to 2,000 feet above the general surface level, these "drags" are largely removed and the wind will probably be traveling twice or three times as fast. Another 2,000 feet up and the wind may be traveling twice as fast again. Even so it comes as something of a surprise to learn that winds in excess of 230 miles an hour have been recorded atop Mount Washington in New Hampshire, particularly as the summit is only a little over 6,000 feet above sea level—not nearly high enough to feel the full force of the upper air currents. It is possible that the configuration of the Presidential Range, which is known to "funnel" winds from certain quarters, had something to do with establishing this particular record. Be this as it may, it is by no means uncommon for the wind on Mount Washington to blow up to 300 per cent harder than you would expect it to do purely from a consideration of the pressure charts.

And because they are wetter, cooler, and windier, mountains have a habit of being much cloudier than the lowlands around them. Unfortunately for the tourist in search of a view, peaks which have a definite "come up and see me" look about them in early morning may easily prove anything but alluring by midday. All too frequently the prospect from them is obscured by wind-induced stratus (Scotch mist) or by heat-induced cumulus. If you are prepared to time your arrival at the summit for dawn, you are more likely to get value for your money, as summertime cloud is largely a phenomenon of daylight hours. But, of course, there is always a chance of haze blanketing out the valleys, even if it leaves the peaks alone. During the night, convection is practically nonexistent, except over water, and so the vertical exchange of air is at a minimum; fog and smoke cannot make a good getaway and, instead, settle down in the lowest layers of the atmosphere. With the coming of the sun, convection is stimulated and carries dust and moisture aloft, and thus effects an improvement in the lowland visibility. Usually this is only temporary, because as convection gets stronger, the vertical temperature gradient increases, with consequent decrease in the optical uniformity of the air. By midday, even though no clouds may have formed, the haze layer may well have risen to the mountaintop and reduced, by as much as 50 per cent, the range of horizontal visibility.

Where to look for snow in summer

Every summer sees some American tourists arrive at the Quebec border in search of snow. Their surprise at being told there is none—not even enough to make a snowman—for hundreds of miles around is only equaled by their embarrassment at having brought their skis along. The idea that the people of Canada are permanently snowbound and live in igloos dies hard, it seems.

Strange to relate, the one place where snow may sometimes be seen in the inhabited East in midsummer is in the United States, not Canada. At the head wall of the Tuckerman Ravine of Mount Washington a snowbank generally lingers on into the month of July: I have, in fact, seen it there in August, and on at least one occasion it remained until September.* Its persistence in this location—the most southerly bank of snow, level for level, anywhere in the Western Hemisphere—is a

* It was seen there in 1926 on September 15, which may mean that it survived to the following winter.

testimony to the heavy winter snows of the region (averaging more than 80 inches), the periodic "slides" that send snow from the summit plummeting down into the ravine, and the almost perennial shade in which the foot of the head wall lies.

To find a snowfield of any magnitude, the tourist must go to the western Cordilleras, and preferably to the western flanks of their more northerly reaches. In Alaska the permanent snow line lies about 5,000 feet above sea level, though the glaciers fed by these snows push their snouts much farther down—to sea level in extreme instances. Near Ketchikan and Juneau in southeastern Alaska, it is possible to ski in the mountains on a summer morning and swim in the waters of the Inside Passage in the afternoon. In southern British Columbia and in the Mount Olympus region of Washington the snow line is approximately 1,000 feet higher. Farther south, owing to increasing dryness and higher temperatures, it rises rapidly—to 10,000 feet on Mount Hood, and nearly 14,000 feet on Mount Shasta in northern California. Southward of Mount Shasta no other peak, not even Mount Whitney, the highest (14,495 feet) in the Union, is high enough to have a permanent snow line.

But it is a risky business generalizing about snow lines. Like hem lines, they are capricious things and change from season to season. Abundant snow in winter, coupled with a cloudy and humid summer, tends to depress the line; scanty snow and a dry sunny summer, to raise it. It is for this reason that the mean snow line in any given cordilleran area rises not only as you go from north to south, but also as you go from west to east, that is, from the windward to leeward side of a range.

Where summer never comes

In order to be quite sure of running into snow east of the Cordilleras, you would probably have to go as far north as

Baffin Island. And that, it appears, is what some enthusiasts are perfectly willing to do. Svenn Orvig, a former student of mine, spent the summer of 1950 sitting on the Barnes icecap in central Baffin Island (between 69° and 70°N) and was delighted to be able to report that the only time the surface of his camp was entirely free from snow was between August 1 and 5. He had the last snowfall of the 1949–1950 season on July 8 and the first snowfall of the 1950–1951 season on August 5! Had he gone a little farther north, he might have been able to ski *every* day.

In the Canadian arctic, north of the east-west slot formed by Lancaster Sound, Barrow Strait, Melville Sound, and McClure Strait, it never really gets warm. For seven months of the year, from October through April, mean monthly temperatures are well below zero. (From November 11, 1948, to April 17, 1949, the temperature at Eureka, one of five small settlements in the region, rose above zero on only three occasions.) Snow lies on the ground from the beginning of September to the end of June. Spring, summer, and fall—hardly recognizable by our mid-latitude standards—are telescoped into the remaining two months of the year, namely, July and August; but even during this brief period, the air temperature is more likely to hover around 40°F. than 60°F., and falls of snow are common. The sea temperature seldom gets above 32°F.

Notwithstanding the climatic rigors of the season, there is no lack of life in the high arctic. Though the ground never thaws out more than a couple of inches or so, cranberries, ground willow, sedges, and mosses manage to subsist on the uncertain support of the marshes and muskegs. The cranberries even bloom and bear fruit, despite the fact that their root system is in very cold soil. Lichens grow in profusion over immense areas which at first sight appear to be stretches of only broken, grayish rock but which, in effect, are pastures of vast extent for the wandering herds of caribou and muskox. Birds of many varieties, including the snowy owl, king eider duck, Hutchins's goose, Lapland longspur, and American pipit, breed in the region: and the mosquito population compares favorably, for virility and venom, with that of New Jersey.

One factor which may account for the comparatively abundant plant and animal life in an atmosphere averaging only about 40°F. in the warmest month is the continuous daylight. Because of it or, more directly, because of the solar energy which it betokens, the temperature of the superstructure of plants, lichens, and mosses is raised much higher than that of the ambient air.

Heat waves in the arctic

But to give the devil his due, not all the arctic is like Eureka. Large parts of it do much better. If you happen to be in Fort Yukon, a few miles north of the Arctic Circle in Alaska, in July or August, the chances are that you will be hotter than if you were in Portland, Maine, and much hotter than if you were in San Francisco. For in Fort Yukon the thermometer rises to 70°F., often higher, about fifty days each summer. It has even registered a shade temperature of 100°F. Much the same is true of nearby Fairbanks, where a temperature reading, taken 4 feet above the ground, of 99°F. has been recorded. (Interestingly enough, 4 feet *below* the ground the temperature was 32°F.) The lower Mackenzie Valley of the Northwest Territories has comparable figures to offer. At Aklavik, one of Canada's most northerly townships, the summers are warm enough to permit the raising of lettuce, radishes, oats (for fodder), and potatoes. At Coppermine on Coronation Gulf, the temperature has been known to climb to 87°F., and regularly gets up into the 70s. In a good summer the inhabitants of Coppermine can go swimming. In September, 1948, the Montreal *Daily Star* carried the following news release: "Coppermine, Northwest Territories. Even in this Arctic outpost 1,000 miles north of Edmonton the residents know how to celebrate summer. They had 10 days of swimming in water that reached a temperature of 67°F." Needless to say, this was *not* sea water which even in high summer is likely to be cluttered with ice floes.

If you find these figures hard of belief, it might be as well to remember that at midsummer the sun is above the horizon 22 hours a day at Fairbanks, and continuously at Fort Yukon and Coppermine. There is also the further fact that Fairbanks and Fort Yukon, and Coppermine to a somewhat lesser extent, are sheltered from exposure to the large cold-water bodies which so effectively depress the summer temperatures of localities bordering on Hudson Bay and Davis Strait. (The mean July temperature at Nottingham Island near the outlet of Hudson Bay is only 42°F.)

Upon occasion it can get quite hot at the North Pole. On June 11, 1937, the Russian Arctic Expedition, then located on an ice floe approximately 88° N, reported that "at midnight the weather became calm: in the sky not a single small cloud. The sun warmed our black tent to 75°F. There's the North Pole for you!"

The same Russian expedition reported several showers of rain in the vicinity of the pole—the first of the season on June 28, and the last on August 26. But they reported some snowstorms, too!

That summer of 1816

Sooner or later, somebody is bound to tell you that the weather is not what it used to be and, if he is thinking of the summer of 1816, he is probably right. While making due allowance for the fact that weather stories lose nothing in the retelling, and that five generations of storytellers have worked and reworked the evidence since the events in question, the summer of 1816 was, by modern standards, a melancholy affair. Some would have it that there was no summer at all.

The trouble started early in the June of that year. After an unseasonable incursion of southerly air, with the temperatures in the 90s, the wind shifted on June 5 to the northwest, with highly depressing results. At Salem, Massachusetts, the temperature fell from 92 to 43°F. in 24 hours: at Williamstown in the same state it fell to 35°F. During the next few days there were severe frosts every night from the Canadian border (and beyond) down to Virginia. Snow fell in Ohio, New York State, and all across northern New England. The editor of the Danville (Vermont) *North Star*, writing in the issue of June 15, reported that "on the night of the 6th water froze an inch thick, and on the night of the 7th and morning of the 8th a kind of sleet or exceeding cold snow fell, attended by high wind, and measured in places where it drifted 18 to 20 inches in depth. . . . The shoots of leaves of forest trees which were just putting forth, and corn and garden vegetables that were out of the ground, were mostly killed." Melancholy weather indeed!

Throughout the entire season, temperatures averaged well below normal in the northeastern part of the country. June and July were 3 to 5 degrees below normal: August, September, and October were only slightly less. The Williamstown weather observatory recorded frosts in every month of the year, a state of affairs said to be without parallel in the subsequent history of the place.

But, when all is said and done, the farmers sowed (a little late perhaps), and the farmers reaped (a little less no doubt), and never a one of them "froze to death."

How to tell the temperature—without a thermometer

Human beings are by no means alone in their sensitivity to changes of temperature. Because they are cold-blooded, insects are particularly mercury-minded. One authority claims that he can tell you the temperature of the air any day—to within 1°F.—merely by timing the speed of ants, though he must surely find it difficult to persuade them to keep "on course." Another claims that he can get equally accurate results by pacing a worm. But the neatest method (because it involves no instrumentation) is that devised by a professor of Tufts College some years ago. All you have to do is to take one *Oecanthus fasciatus*, a species of katydid, count the number of chirps in a minute, subtract 40, divide by 4, and add 60. And if you should think it might be difficult to isolate the chirp of a single katydid, the professor assures you that this particular species has a sense of time as well as temperature and is able to synchronize its note with that of all the other members of its class living in the neighborhood.

September

Best month for vacations?

It seems that, for most Americans living north of the Florida state line, summer is more a matter of decrees, sartorial or Federal, than degrees centigrade or Fahrenheit: Memorial Day marks its official opening, Labor Day its closing. On Memorial Day the well-dressed woman casts away her winter furs and woolens and dons the latest fancy of the fashion moguls, most of whom, of course, have never been within 4,000 miles of Sioux City and never read a temperature graph in their lives. But the fiat of Paris must not be denied, even though in the doing of it there is the risk of pneumonia, which there may well be at Sioux City around that time of year. On Labor Day the bright cottons, straw hats, and light footwear of summer disappear from the streets and, lo, the mantle of fall is upon the woman's shoulders, even though the thermometer, like as not, is still hitting the high 80s all the way from Sioux City to Secaucus.

This disposition to regulate our lives by act of Congress and/or Christian Dior is, to a meteorologist's way of thinking, a pity. For one thing, it has the effect of jettisoning half the population of the country onto the lake and shore beaches during the month of August, the last month of summer as officially decreed, and so of inflating hotel prices, slowing down the industrial life of the country, and turning the congested roads into a battleground. (The Labor Day week-end casualties alone average some 400 deaths, to say nothing of many thousands of injured.) For another, it means that over large parts of the country school ends in cool weather and opens in hot, at a time, moreover, when polio is stalking the corridors. And for a third, it means that we deny ourselves the close acquaintance of one of the loveliest months of the year—a month which, whether we spend it by seashore or inland lake, bears itself like a gentleman and dresses like a woman in love. September, over fully three-fourths of the Union, is a month to be embraced, not discarded, lingered over like a vintage wine, not swallowed as a pill.

For whether you consider it from the standpoint of temperature, rainfall, wind, or weather, September is a month of many virtues and few vices. It can be very hot, but seldom as hot, or as humid, as July and August. It can be very wet, but the chances are that it will be drier than its neighbors. It generally has far fewer thunderstorms than the other summer months and fewer days on which sailing is difficult. The sea is still warm—in fact, along many parts of the eastern and southern seaboard the seasonal peak is not reached before late August or early September—and offers good bathing. Because of their small size and terrestrial surroundings, inland bodies of water cool off much more rapidly, but even so many of them maintain temperatures in the mid 60s until late September.

It is true that our northeastern seaboard is capable of chiding the September visitor for his tardiness, but then, it is not always too hospitable in July and August. All the same, it has its friendly side. If its waters are like ice, its air is like wine: the more you take of it, the more anesthetized you become to its rigors. If the nights are cool, the days can be hot: Halifax, Nova Scotia, and Portland, Maine, frequently report higher temperature maxima in September than Atlantic City and Cape Cod. And there is this to be further said in its favor: by late September, the earth of Maine and the Maritimes is

. . . crammed with heaven
And every common bush afire with God.

For the statistically minded, we give herewith some comparisons, for different places in North America, between September and the other summer months. We do not expect these figures to impress the moguls, or their slaves, but they could make rather nice advertising copy for the tourist industry.

MEAN NUMBER OF RAINY DAYS *

	June	July	Aug.	Sept.
New England coast (Boston)	10	11	10	9
Middle Atlantic coast (Norfolk, Va.)	11	12	12	8
Great Lakes (Toronto)	11	9	9	9
Southern California (San Diego)	1	1	1	1
Pacific Northwest (Victoria)	11	7	7	11
Maritime Provinces (Halifax)	14	13	12	12
Florida coast (Miami)	13	15	15	18

* That is, days on which a measurable amount of rain fell.

MEAN TEMPERATURES IN DEGREES FAHRENHEIT

	June	July	Aug.	Sept.
New England coast	66	71	69	63
Middle Atlantic coast	75	78	75	73
Great Lakes	65	69	67	61
Southern California	64	67	69	67
Pacific Northwest	57	60	60	56
Maritime Provinces	58	65	65	59
Florida coast	81	82	82	81

MEAN AMOUNT OF SUNSHINE (PER CENT OF TOTAL POSSIBLE)

	June	July	Aug.	Sept.
New England coast (Portland, Me.)	61	64	63	61
Middle Atlantic coast (Norfolk, Va.)	62	65	64	63
Great Lakes (Chicago)	70	73	69	64
Southern California (San Diego)	62	68	72	73
Florida coast (Miami)	62	67	69	65

Fig. 17. Average number of hours of sunshine per summer day. (Courtesy of Professor S. S. Visher)

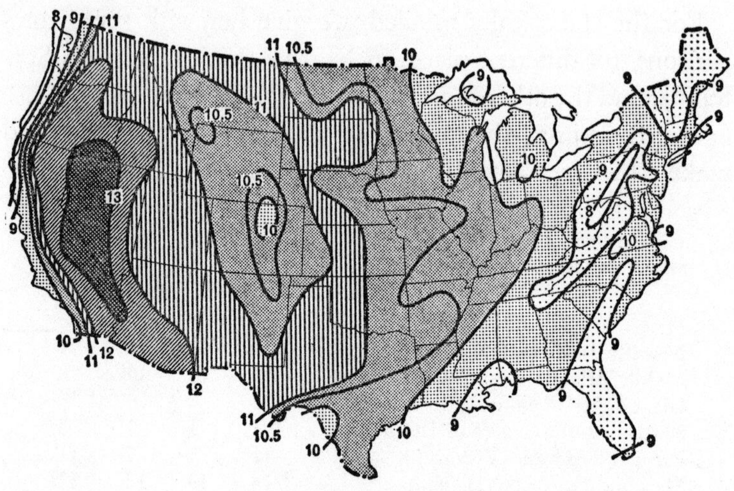

MEAN NUMBER OF DAYS WITH THUNDERSTORMS

	June	July	Aug.	Sept.
New England coast	5	6	4	2
Middle Atlantic coast (Baltimore, Md.)	7	9	7	3
Great Lakes region	8	7	7	5
Southern California	0	0	0	0
Florida coast (Tampa)	16	22	20	13

Hay fever—and how to avoid it

Climatically, then, there's a lot to be said for taking a late summer holiday. But for hundreds of thousands of Americans the most persuasive argument for doing so is not so much climatic as physiologic: their allergy to plant pollen—notably the pollen of the ragweed plant—gets the better of them then.

It is true that there are plenty of earlier pollens to bedevil the life of the unfortunate individual with an allergy, and that some people can get hay fever (as the allergy to pollen is almost universally and most misleadingly called *) from tree pollen in the spring, or from flower pollen in the early summer, without so much as getting a sneeze out of ragweed. It is equally true that the peak period of ragweed pollen may come in August. All things considered, however, the geographical distribution of ragweed pollen tends to be broadest and its atmospheric intensity greatest early in September. By then, it is normally present in almost every state of the Union (though not everywhere in significant amounts), and causing its greatest distress. The most heavily infested areas lie to the east of the Rockies in the northern and central states of the Middle West, the southern Great Lakes region, the Middle Atlantic states, and southern New England. The Southeast, the Southwest, the Mountain states, California, and the Northwest are comparatively free from ragweed pollen (and other pollens as well, for that matter) at that time of the year; so, too, is the greater part of inhabited Canada and most of Maine. Which gives the pollen-allergic holidaymaker plenty of territory to run around in.

Even within the heavily affected areas, it is always possible to come across local pollen-free pockets. The only trouble is

* Compared with the trees, flowers and weeds, grasses are minor contributors to the suffering of hay-fever victims, constituting only about 35 per cent of the causative factors; and fever is not usually one of the major symptoms.

that you can never be really sure where you will find them: they have a habit of changing, even from one day to the next. Furthermore, the annual incidence of pollens in a given locality can vary enormously: hay-fever victims who in one season suffer grave discomfort may in the next experience nothing more trying than an occasional bout of sneezing, and vice versa. For this the weather, it seems, must bear the major responsibility. If the early summer is wet, the plant will grow profusely and produce a large number of flowers with a correspondingly large amount of pollen. If, on the other hand, the early summer is dry, much smaller amounts of pollen will be produced. If the ripening period is sunny, the pollen will stand a better chance of coming to maturity than if it is wet or damp. Heavy dews and early morning showers during the same pollinating period will automatically "ground" a considerable percentage of the pollen dust, and so decrease the supply available for that day's transport.

The biggest variable of all is the wind. Without air movement, the only way pollen can be transported is by direct contact with humans, animals, birds, and insects; the "pollen count" resulting from such agencies is generally too low to be troublesome. On a day of light winds, but strong convection, a large part of the pollen released will be carried aloft, where it may be swept into the speedier air streams of the upper atmosphere and so withdrawn from the haunts of men. On a day of strong winds, the pollen concentrate is likely to be high, and uniform over large areas. On days with light variable winds, the concentration will probably be very high locally, especially if there is a low overcast, for this will tend to act as a ceiling for the pollen. But wind direction can be as important as wind strength. This has been well demonstrated in the pollen counts taken over the New York metropolitan area in recent years. From these it is clear that the highest counts coincide with, or just follow, the arrival, in late summer, of a westerly air current of medium strength and low humidity: such an air current approaches the city via the heavily ragweed-infested areas of New Jersey, Pennsylvania, and the Ohio Valley. The counts decline noticeably when the wind veers to the north and northeast, that is, with winds which are almost entirely pollen-free until they get within 300 miles or so of the city. And they reach their minimum, except for the comparatively few occasions of calm air, when the wind blows from the southeast quarter and has had a sea trajectory for the past several days. It is not merely enough that the wind should be onshore: uncomfortable concentrations of pollen have been found up to 500 miles offshore. Maritime air is unlikely to be pollen-free, unless it has spent a good deal of time over the open ocean.

Which perhaps is another way of saying that the best thing a chronic sufferer from hay fever can do is to take a nice long sea voyage each summer and arrange for the ship to be refueled and revictualed at least 500 miles from the nearest windward shore. Of course, he can always stay at home, shut himself up with an air-filtering and air-conditioning plant, and lay in enough food for about six to eight weeks. Everything will be all right again by the end of October.

The hurricane season

Although hurricanes may occur as early as May and as late as December, they are most liable to occur in September. The accompanying table summarizes the facts of their seasonal distribution:

	May	June	July	Aug.	Sept.	Oct.	Nov.	Dec.
No. of hurricanes (W. Indian–Atlantic region) 1887–1940	4	25	26	80	122	98	24	2
Percentage occurrence	1	7	7	21	32	26	6	0

In action hurricanes are not unlike tornadoes, but their dimensions are very much bigger. Typically they cover a more or less circular area of 300 to 500 miles in diameter, last for several days, and move away from their "breeding" zone in or near the doldrum belt of variable light winds and rain squalls along a roughly parabolic path. In almost every case they move into higher latitudes, and the farther they move, the greater becomes their diameter and the less their intensity. By the time most of them reach middle latitudes, they have either died or taken on the characteristics of a regular extratropical cyclone.

The hurricane is well-named, being derived from the Carib Indian word *huracan* (or *hunraken*), signifying "Big Wind," the evil spirit that was supposed to create stormy weather. How "big" hurricane winds can be is still a matter of some dispute: weather stations lying in their path have a habit of losing their anemometers along with almost everything else. Officially a wind reaches hurricane force when it exceeds 75 miles an hour: there are, however, well-authenticated instances of hurricane winds exceeding 200 miles an hour and, judging from the things hurricanes have been known to do, such as lift pleasure cruisers from their moorings and deposit them inland, much higher velocities must be attained from time to time.

Because of their larger dimensions and longer span of life, hurricanes are much more destructive than tornadoes. They are, indeed, the most lethal weapon in the whole of Nature's armory. The hurricane that hit the New England coast on September 21, 1938—one of the very few on record to retain its pristine fury as far north as 40°N—was responsible for nearly 400 million dollar's worth of property damage. According to the Red Cross, it destroyed 6,933 summer dwellings, 6,965 other dwellings, either partly or completely, and 2,605 boats. Worse still, it claimed the lives of over 500 persons and injured another 1,750.

The origin of such storms is obscure in many details, but their absence from the continental parts of the tropics and their early disintegration after passing from sea to land suggest that they are greatly dependent upon water vapor, which in the doldrum belt is always present in ample amounts. Their predilection, at least in their embryonic stage of development, for the warm waters and unstable atmosphere of the Caribbean Sea and adjacent parts of the Atlantic Ocean also suggests that convection plays a part: it can hardly be more than a "bit player," however, in so far as convection is perennial in and near the heat equator, while hurricanes are seasonal. And, anyway, even during the hurricane season, there is enough latent energy available in the breeding zone to fuel a hundred times as many hurricanes as ever form. Just what else is needed is almost anybody's guess.

There are some who still favor the frontal theory, and who contend that air masses invading the low tropics from mid-latitudes contrive to retain their identity so that they can continue to undercut, or overrun, each other, and indigenous air masses for that matter. It's a little difficult to see how air masses, conservative of their basic properties as they are, can do this, but there is no shrugging off the fact that equatorial fronts can be detected from time to time, and that tropical storms before now have been found to originate in their vicinity,* just as many extratropical storms originate along polar fronts.

The frontal theory has lost ground in recent years to what we might call the disturbance theory. The proponents of this theory maintain that a hurricane, or any other kind of tropical storm, can develop only from a preexisting tropical

* Such fronts are seldom detected within 5 or 6 degrees of the equator, and it is worthy of remark that tropical storms have scarcely ever been found breeding nearer the equator than that.

disturbance. This disturbance may take the form of a pressure trough or wave (showing up on a pressure chart as a slight kink or sinuosity in the run of an isobar) or a wind discontinuity in a horizontal plane—generally known as a wind shear. But, you will surely ask, what makes the pressure trough, wave, and wind shear that make the hurricane? And why do we get so many more "disturbances" than hurricanes? Or, to put it another way, what causes some of the disturbances to intensify into hurricanes, and others to die stillborn?

Answers to these questions are still being sought. Among the many likely guesses are the following: that two tropical disturbances collide or, if moving at different elevations, become conjoined; that a high-level cyclonic disturbance moves down from middle latitudes and becomes superposed on a low-level tropical disturbance, thus intensifying the vorticity of the lower disturbance; that a high-level anticyclonic system becomes superposed on a low-level cyclone already active (such an anticyclone being cold in relation to its surroundings would have the effect of steepening the lapse rate in the cyclone and so of encouraging any convective propensities it might have); and, lastly, any dynamic situation in the atmosphere that would promote any of the foregoing developments. Which leaves us with only one important question: what produces the dynamic situation that produces the wave, trough, or shear that produces the cyclonic disturbance that produces the hurricane?

Hurricane prognostics

The northward passage of a hurricane is generally preceded by a short spell of bright, cloudless weather, in which the barometer rises above normal and the wind is very light and variable in direction. These conditions need not arouse any anxiety unless they give place to a period of showery or squally weather lasting 24 hours or so, and these in turn are superseded by a state of affairs reminiscent of an approaching warm front: that is, the sky clouds up with feathery cirrus and cirrostratus, giving unusually brilliant solar and lunar halos; the barometer starts to fall, and the wind to blow from a more or less constant direction, very lightly at first and slowly increasing. As the cirrus clouds travel in the same general direction as the storm, the skilled observer should be able to gauge roughly, at all events, whether or not he is situated along its line of advance. At sea, an equally useful portent is the appearance of a long low swell which breaks into a heavy surf on reaching an exposed beach.

As the storm center approaches, the barometer continues to fall (at a unique rate within 300 to 400 miles of the vortex), the wind freshens and becomes more gusty, the high clouds thicken, blotting out sun and moon, and storm clouds begin to form at lower levels. If this stage of the storm development should coincide with sunrise or sunset, the sky takes on a most unusual and sinister coloration, with a marked preference for yellow, orange, and green tints. Closely following the appearance of the heavy storm cloud (nimbostratus) that surrounds the eye of the storm, the barograph trace becomes almost vertical, and the atmosphere is filled with the furious sound of wind, rain, and thunder, and "the scattered waters rave." As the center of the storm passes overhead, the wind falls, the rain ceases, and the clouds lift and may even disperse completely. The period of uneasy calm associated with the eye of the storm —"the whirlwind's heart of peace," as Tennyson puts it—is not likely to last more than half an hour or so. It is followed by another howling tempest blowing from the opposite quarter, and another spell of blinding rain and low cloud, during which the barometer rises sharply. Twelve to twenty-four hours later the weather clears, and the wind is gone.

What can be done about the hurricane?

About the only thing anyone can do at present is to get out of its way. Thanks to the very fine U.S. Weather Bureau's Hurricane Warning Service, it is usually possible to give ships at sea two or three days' warning of the presence of a hurricane, and because hurricanes invariably start life in the open ocean and move slowly in their incipient stages, islands and mainlands lying near their assumed paths normally get even longer notice.* Maybe it is cold comfort to the inhabitants of Jamaica or Jacksonville to know that a hurricane is heading straight for them, but at least it gives them a chance to "batten down," and take cover. In the more than fifty years it has been going (authority to operate reporting stations in the West Indies was first given by Congress during the Spanish-American War with a view to protecting our forces from hurricane damage), the Warning Service has earned its keep many times over. In the five-year period 1926–1930 there were 161 hurricane fatalities per 10 million dollars of property damage; the corresponding figure for 1931–1935 was 81, for 1936–1940, 26, and for 1941–1945, only 4.

While it would be foolish to expect any comparable decline in the toll of damage to land, property, and equipment, even here the decline is far from negligible. Thus the U.S. Air Force has been able to save hundreds of millions of taxpayers' dollars

* The hurricane that hit New England on September 21, 1938, was one of the few the service miscalculated: which may help to explain why a Long Island farmer who, that very morning, received through the mail a barometer reading "Hurricane" had it immediately shipped back to the makers. Twenty-four hours later, he realized the makers had built better than he knew.

by flying aircraft from bases lying on the indicated path of a hurricane to airfields located at a safe distance from it. And in other ways, such as the development of housing that is "hurricane-resistant," the use of glass jalousies and light metals in industrial plants, and the siting of dwellings beyond the reach of tidal waves, the hazards of the "big wind" are undergoing a slow but sure attrition.

But, you may ask, are avoiding action and passive resistance our only weapons against the hurricane? Do we not have some more positive—aggressive—means of dealing with it? What of the possibility of disintegrating a hurricane with the help of an atomic bomb, for instance? As we saw earlier,* there is a growing disposition on the part of many people, and not just publicity seekers either, to try and change what they don't like about the weather of a given place or season. Having discovered that it is possible (under certain circumstances) to dissipate a cloud (of restricted dimensions) for a period of time (quite limited), what could be more natural than that they should want to dissipate a storm, or even a hurricane? So far they haven't done much except talk about the possibilities, which, to be quite honest, we do not rate too highly. Even if a bomb could be made to explode in mid-air right in the eye of the storm, it is doubtful whether it would seriously affect the vitality of the storm. Compared to a fully fledged hurricane, which in a single day expends as much energy as would be needed to drive all the machinery in the world for three to four years, an atom bomb is little more than a puff of wind.

More promising on the face of it is the contention of the "neutralizers." These point out that Nature is very fond of employing the "trigger" technique when she wants to get things moving. By this they simply mean that her mighty ends are often accomplished by a sequence of quite small means. To

* See May, pp. 113–116.

take an example; an avalanche is usually started up by the displacement of small pieces of rock or ice, which, in turn, displace others until half a mountainside is in motion. It is known to be the same with the atmosphere; a single convective "cell" frequently supplies the trigger that sets the whole countryside reverberating with the noise of thunder. So what these neutralizers would like to do is to kill the hurricanes before they really get going. This would mean seeking them out while they are still nothing more than good-sized thunderstorms located in or near the doldrum belt. The "killing," they say, could be done by pouring oil over the sea beneath the budding storm and then igniting it. This, it is argued, would lead to a rapid updraft of air which would cause so much of the energy of the storm to be devoted to rain making that it would forget its real business. Alternatively, the same result might be obtained, they think, by bombarding the atmosphere above the storm with a fine powder such as coal dust, thereby cutting the thundercloud off from its supply of incoming solar heat. Neither view is without its difficulties. In a region of unstable air, such as the doldrums, there would seem to be an excellent chance of the ignited oil acting as a tonic rather than a dope to an incipient hurricane. As for the coal-dust notion, much would depend upon whether or not the stuff stayed in suspension: if it happened to fall through the atmosphere to the surface, the effect would almost certainly be disastrous, but not to the hurricane. And even if the dust did remain aloft and so formed a barrier to incoming radiation, there would still be one serious problem to overcome, namely, how to tell which of the thousand and one thunderstorms harbored by the doldrum belt at any one time would produce the hurricane!

Wind and wave

Greatly feared as the winds of a hurricane are, it is the waves raised by a hurricane, often mistakenly referred to as tidal waves,* that usually do most of the killing. It has been estimated that "more than three-fourths of all the loss of human lives in tropical cyclones has been caused by these inundations and not by the winds directly." †

Prior to World War II most meteorologists knew scarcely more about waves than song writers. They knew very roughly the size of waves corresponding to various wind speeds in the open ocean; they knew, too, that wind waves, when long, continued as swell waves for considerable distances away from the area in which they originated; but they had only a very hazy idea of the changes in height, length, and rate of travel which these waves underwent with the passage of time. With the war came amphibious operations involving landings of completely equipped armies on open beaches. On such beaches it was not enough to know the force and direction of the wind, but also the kind of seas which would break on them, for experience in some of the early Commando raids showed that even a miscalculation of the height of a breaking wave by as little as one foot could be very costly.

Today the marine meteorologist is much better informed on such matters, though that is not to say that he knows all he would like to know: for him, as for the rest of us, the multitudinous seas that one day "boil like a pot" and the next are "like ointment" will long retain an element of mystery and wonderment.

* It is, of course, possible for storm waves to be reinforced by the astronomical tide, but no tide, *of itself*, is capable of the destructive force of a storm wave.

† *Weather Glossary*, U.S. Department of Commerce (Weather Bureau), p. 255.

According to the dictionary, a wave is "any regular periodic oscillation," but a wave on the sea is more than an oscillation, as anybody knows who has watched a cork bobbing up and down on the sea surface. There is progression of wave form across the surface, and there is also actual movement of the water particles manifested by the floating cork that moves a short distance in the direction in which the wave is progressing while it is on the crest of the wave, and back again approximately the same distance when it is in the trough. (I say "approximately" because the water particles in deep-sea wind waves are subject to a very slight progressive motion in addition to their cyclical motion.)

For waves to begin at all, it seems that there must be a vertical component in the flow of air near the sea surface. If the flow of air over water were as frictionless as it is over glass, and there were no exchange of heat between air and water, the air would have a streamlike motion, and turbulence—eddy motion which provides for the upward and downward transfer of air—would be almost nonexistent. Because the surface of the sea is seldom as smooth as the proverbial millpond, and because air streams easily acquire up-and-down components of velocity or gustiness when the temperature of the sea differs from that of the air (which is usually the case), this condition of equilibrium is rare. Even with winds of forces 1 and 2, that is, winds less than 8 miles an hour, there is commonly a well-defined, gusty, turbulent layer. As soon as this equilibrium is disturbed—and it is so delicate that in almost still air the flight of a bird may disturb it—ripples begin to form. "Ripples" in the layer of air adjacent to the water surface produce sympathetic ripples in the water.

When a wave system is well developed, it begins to influence the motion of the air immediately above. Thus, on the weather side of a wave the air-flow lines conform to the wave profile and the air particles are accelerated, as friction is reduced to a minimum and air and water particles work together in "double harness," so to speak. At the crest the accelerated air particles tend to be shot forward on account of their inertia and to retain, at first, a small upward velocity. (This can be deduced from the motion of sea birds: thus gulls allow waves to advance underneath them in order to have themselves lifted by the air flow at the crests.) Once over the crest, the moving air particles may break away from the wave profile and shoot forward, allowing eddies to form in the lee of the crest. It is these eddies, coupled with the greater wind pressure exerted on the weather side of the wave, that help to give sea waves their characteristically asymmetrical shape. However, the presence of such lee eddies cannot always be assumed: a lot depends on the angle at which the downward components of the air stream strike the water. This angle is largely a function of the wind velocity and the temperature relation between air and water. When the temperature of the air is below that of the sea—as is normal in the winter half of the year—the vertical component is greater than when the reverse temperature relation holds, as it does on the average in summer. Eddy motion is encouraged by the vertical temperature gradient in the former case, and discouraged in the latter. Given the same horizontal wind force, the downward eddies in air that is colder than the sea tend to hit the water surface at a higher angle and with greater velocity than in air that is warmer than the sea, and so more kinetic energy is available for the building up of waves. This fact partly explains why a given wind can usually raise a rougher sea in winter than in summer.

Two other wave-making factors, and very important ones, are (1) the length of fetch, that is, the distance upwind over which the air stream remains roughly constant in force and direction, and (2) the duration of the blow. Anybody who has ever gone sailing in a stiff breeze will know that there is a world of difference between wave conditions on the lee and windward shores of even a mile-wide sound, and that the sea becomes choppier as time passes.

Given the wind force and the fetch, it is possible to determine, within a tolerance of, say, 20 per cent, what the height, length, and period of a train of waves will be, and it is possible to do the same, given the wind force and the duration of the blow.* The accompanying tables (for which I am indebted to my friend and former "chief," Commander C. R. Burgess, O.B.E., R.N., whose *Meteorology for Seamen* should be prescribed reading for all boatowners) may not enable the curious reader to work out his chances of survival in a hurricane, but they will at least warn him to keep as far away from one as possible.

Just what is the wave-raising potential of a hurricane, nobody quite knows, but it is certainly well in excess of the figures in the last line of the first table (below), since a hurricane, by definition, signifies a wind of over 75 miles per hour. Mariners have frequently reported waves 40 to 50 feet high in the "dangerous quadrant," and there are authentic cases of winter storms in mid-Atlantic raising waves to a height of 80 feet (S.S. *Majestic* reported "mountainous seas" of this order on December 29, 1922). Fortunately, hurricanes are fairly fast-moving, so that while they have the velocity to raise such waves, they do not stay long enough in one place to satisfy either the fetch or duration-of-blow requirement for an 80-foot wave. However, this does not prevent them from propagating trains of waves that can travel from one side of the Atlantic to

* The height of a wave is the vertical distance of its crest above the troughs on either side. The length of a wave is the horizontal distance from one crest to the next. The period of a wave is the interval of time elapsing between the passage of two successive crests past a fixed point.

Table giving (a) height in feet, (b) length in feet, and (c) period in seconds, of waves produced by winds of different velocities and durations (all values approximate)

Wind velocity (in m.p.h.)	Duration of blow * (in hours)											
	6			12			24			48		
	(a)	(b)	(c)	(a)	(b)	(c)	(a)	(b)	(c)	(a)	(b)	(c)
19–24 (Force 5)	3½	140	5	4½	180	6	5½	280	7½	7	380	8½
25–31 (Force 6)	5	180	6	6	270	7	8	360	8½	10	530	10
32–38 (Force 7)	7	250	7	8	360	8½	11	520	10	14	730	12
39–46 (Force 8)	9	340	8	12	480	9½	15	680	11½	20	1000	14
47–54 (Force 9)	13	450	9½	17	630	11	21	900	13	27	1300	16

Table giving (a) height in feet, (b) length in feet, and (c) period in seconds, of waves produced by winds of different velocities and fetches (all values approximate)

Wind velocity (in m.p.h.)	Fetch of Wind * (in miles)											
	50			100			200			500		
	(a)	(b)	(c)	(a)	(b)	(c)	(a)	(b)	(c)	(a)	(b)	(c)
19–24	3½	120	5	4½	180	6	5½	250	7	7	360	8½
25–31	5	140	5	6	250	7	7	320	8	9	450	9½
32–38	7	180	6	8	330	8	10	400	9	12	500	10
39–46	9	250	7	11	400	9	13	520	10	17	700	11½
47–54	12	300	7½	14	500	10	17	650	11	22	900	13

* In any given set of circumstances, the waves generated will be those from the table which gives the smaller length and period. For example, a wind of 45 m.p.h. blowing over a fetch of 100 miles for 6 hours will generate waves of only 9 feet in height, 340 feet in length, and an 8-second period. A longer blow (up to 12 hours) would be needed to bring the wave values to those given in the appropriate column in the second table.

the other: these swell waves take up to four or five days to make the crossing, but at the end of it they may still have enough momentum to break up beach huts, destroy harbor installations, and flood low-lying back country.

On one such occasion (January, 1913) a series of long swell waves originating somewhere off Newfoundland—and hence not the work of the usual kind of hurricane—paralyzed the commercial life of Casablanca for several months. But at least one good thing came out of this disaster: the French authorities began investigating the occurrence of heavy swell along the coast of Morocco. By the time—some thirty years later—the American landings took place, we weren't quite so ignorant as we might have been about the chances of our living to tell the tale.

The onset of autumn

As with the other seasons, there are various ways of timing the onset of autumn. If you go by the newspapermen (who go by the astronomers, who go by the apparent motions of the sun), you will probably say that autumn arrives with the September equinox, that is, around the twenty-second to twenty-third of the month. At that time the noonday sun is vertically overhead at the equator and takes its leave of the Northern Hemisphere until the following March when the ecliptic, as the annual path of the sun is called, once more intersects the equator.

But while

The Sun with his Planets in chime
Marketh the going of Time,

as a marker of the going of heat, the sun is much less useful. Here, for instance, are the mean temperatures, on or about September 22, for half a dozen inhabited places in North America:

Dawson City, Yukon	40°F.
Nain, Labrador	39°F.
Calgary, Alberta	49°F.
San Francisco, Calif.	59°F.
New York, N.Y.	64°F.
Miami, Fla.	80°F.

The range is striking: there is more than a 30°F. difference between Calgary and Miami, while the difference between

Nain and Miami is more than 40°F., that is, approximately the difference between the summer and winter temperatures of New York. By the standards of the warm-blooded Miamian, winter has already arrived in Labrador and the Yukon, and by anybody's standards, summer is still going strong in Florida.

So, true as it may be astronomically that "four seasons fill the measure of the year" and equally true, if we may go on to *mis*apply the next line of John Keats's famous sonnet, "The Human Seasons," that "There are four seasons in the mind of man," it is by no means true that we can equate the coming of one with the other.

For most ordinary folk, the march of temperature provides a more satisfactory criterion of seasonal change than the march of the sun. The only trouble is that most ordinary folk cannot agree on what constitutes the "threshold" temperatures of a given season. Earlier in this book * we suggested that there was

Fig. 18(a). Beginning of fall, as measured by the southward retreat of the 68°F. isotherm.

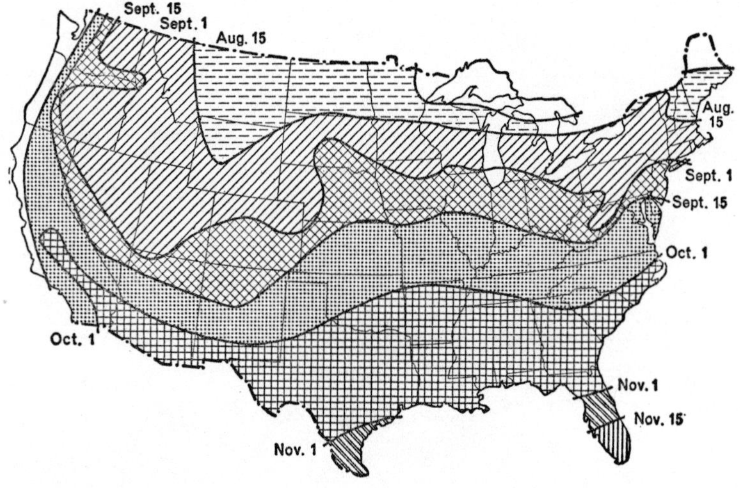

* See June, p. 144.

something to be said for using the figure of 68°F. as the threshold temperature of summer, and we showed how the 68°F. isotherm advanced northward during the three months of May, June, and July. By the same token, the southward recession of the 68°F. isotherm gives us a means of dating the onset of autumn. Using this figure, Prof. Stephen Visher, America's most assiduous student of climatic distributions, has shown (in a map which we are pleased to be able to reproduce here with his permission) that the regional differences in the onset of autumn are as great as, if not greater than, the regional differences in the onset of summer. In northern Vermont and round the shores of the northern Great Lakes, the 68°F. isotherm begins to recede southward in mid-August. It reaches Long Island and the southern fringes of the Great Lakes by September 1. By October 1 it has traveled southward

Fig. 18(b). Beginning of fall, as measured by the date of the end of the warmest 3 months of the year. (Figs. 18(a) and (b) courtesy of Professor S. S. Visher)

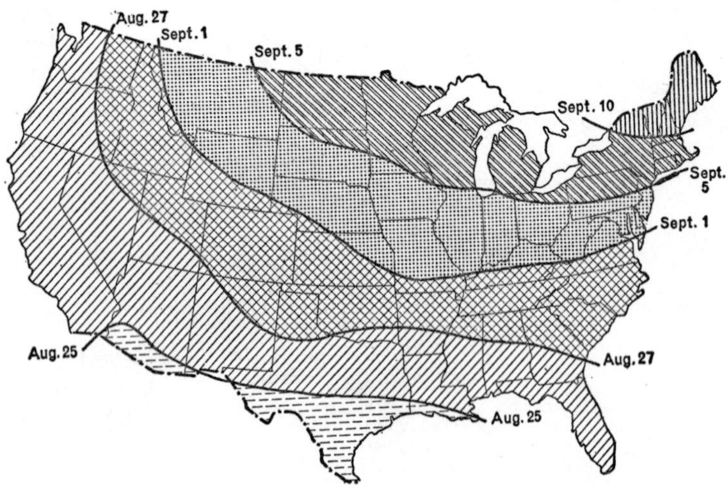

as far as Cape Hatteras, southern Tennessee, and the Texas Panhandle. By November 1 only the Florida peninsula and the extreme southern end of Texas lie south of it; by the end of that month only the Keys remain to the south of it. In other words, a full four-months' interval separates its departure from central Maine and its arrival in southern Florida.

However, we can hardly expect the inhabitants of the Pacific coast from Long Beach, California, northward to see eye to eye with Professor Visher whose map as good as tells them that it is later than they think, that what they call summer is really already autumn, since they never do make the threshold temperature of 68°F. In this respect, the Pacific coast is not entirely alone: northern Maine, northern Michigan, and the lake fringes of Minnesota and Wisconsin keep them company.

Perhaps the simplest and least equivocal way of settling the question of the "fall" of fall is to divide the year into four equal parts of 91¼ days, and call the hottest of the four periods summer, the coldest of the four winter, and the period in between the hottest and the coldest, fall. If we do this everybody, even the Eskimo and the coastal Californian, gets a summer and a fall, and gets them at roughly the same times. On this basis the change-over from summer to fall occurs somewhere between late August in the South and West and mid-September in the Northeast.

Dew on the grass

The countryman will probably tell you that there is a much simpler way of deciding the question: that it's not a matter of temperatures, let alone dates, but dew, that when you

Get up . . . and see
The Dew bespangling Herbe and Tree,

the fall is but a handbreadth away.

And, in a manner of speaking, he is right, for although it is possible to get a fall of dew in any season of the year, the state of the atmosphere is particularly favorable to its formation in late summer. For then the air is warm and capable of absorbing water vapor in generous amounts, winds are light, and turbulent mixing of the moist surface layers of air with the drier layers aloft is at a minimum. If to these circumstances there is added another, namely, high pressure, with its characteristic accompaniment of clear night skies, then the stage is set for rapid loss of daytime heat and chilling of all radiating surfaces; if the chilling process is given enough time (and by September the nights are almost as long as the days), and the air is moist enough to start with, the water vapor in immediate contact with the coldest surfaces will begin to condense—in much the same way as it condenses onto the outside of a glass of ice water. The longer the condensing process is given, the heavier the deposit of dew. While there is no guarantee that the weather will turn colder after a heavy dew in late summer, let alone usher in the fall, most countryfolk can remember enough instances of this happening to feel entitled to their conviction. And it has to be admitted, in fairness to them, that the breakup of a warm anticyclone in late summer often paves the way for the "first clash of autumn's cymbals" and the incursion of cold air from the northlands.

However, in the context of day-to-day weather changes, dew must be regarded as an augury of fair weather rather than bad, since its presence betokens not only high pressure but the absence of prefrontal cloud during the night. By the same token, the absence of dew on the ground in the early morning can sometimes be taken to mean that the sky became clouded over during the night (thereby blanketing in the previous day's heat) and that frontal rain is on its way. Hence the sayings:

When the dew is on the grass,
Rain will never come to pass.

(at least "never" before the following evening), and

When the grass is dry at morning light,
Look for rain before the night.

Frost on the pumpkin

In some parts of the country, the first fall frost follows hard on the heels of the first fall dew. In northern Michigan, the two may even coincide—in the guise of rime, or hoarfrost, which, after all, is only a rather special form of dew, the temperature alone deciding whether the condensing water vapor turns into the one or the other. Farther south there may be anything up to a three-month interval between the two; and in the extreme south there are a few localities which, while no stranger to dew, have yet to see their first white frost.

The map on page 220 shows when the first killing frost may be expected to hit the different parts of the country. Not that all hoarfrosts are killing frosts, nor yet that all killing frosts reveal their presence as hoarfrost does: nevertheless, the growing season is as good as over "when the frost is on the punkin" or when your minimum grass thermometer first registers 30°F. or less.

The expectations, it will readily be seen, vary widely from place to place. In the high country of Nevada and Idaho, you can reckon on frost by the end of August. In southern Texas, you may not get it before Christmas Day: in southern Florida, you may not get it at all. But it is not necessary to walk across half a continent to find striking contrasts: you can find them sometimes between one part of a state and another. Thus, in northern Maine frost is likely to come in early September, in southern Maine, not before the end of October. In some parts of Colorado frost may come as early as August, in others as late as mid-October. On the other hand, large parts of the country exhibit remarkable uniformity of frost occurrence. The average dates of the first killing frost in the north of North Dakota and the Texas Panhandle differ by less than a month, those of northwest Washington and southern California by less than a week (in neither locality is frost likely to strike before the end of November).

But perhaps the most impressive thing about the map is the witness it bears to the heat-conserving property of large water bodies and their consequent ability to ward off the early frost. This is seen to excellent advantage along the southern shores of Lakes Erie and Ontario, the middle Atlantic seaboard, and the coasts of Washington and Oregon where, in every case, the prevailing winds at that season of the year are onshore. In the

Fig. 19. Average dates of first killing frost in fall. (*Courtesy of the Weather Bureau, U.S. Department of Commerce*)

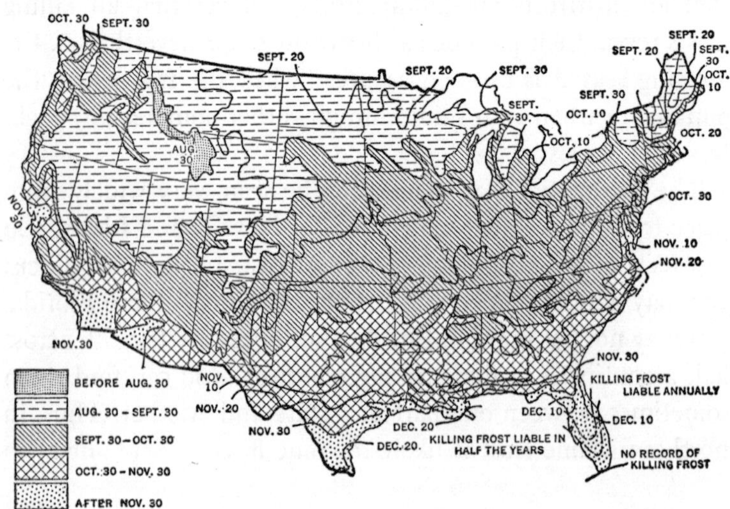

case of the Lakes, the tempering effect of the onshore winds is such that it temporarily reverses the normal southward advance of the frost line. Which means to say that if you should happen to live in Springfield, Ohio, you would be more likely to find frost in October by going *south* than you would by going north.

Equinoctial weather

Among the many meteorological notions for which influential supporters can still be found, none has had a longer inning than that of the equinoctial storm. Originally confined to the autumnal equinox in point of time and to the North Atlantic and its bordering lands in point of place, the equinoctial storm later spread, in human imagination, to the vernal equinox and, by the European emigrant and seafarer, to the ends of the earth. And many ponderous attempts to account for it have been made, none more so, perhaps, than that made by Rear Admiral Robert FitzRoy, the first head of the British meteorological service. "What causes such equinoctial disturbances? Not the mere fact of the sun's astronomical position? No: the united tidal action of moon and sun upon the whole atmosphere which then is a maximum force. Lateral offsets, streams overflowing toward each pole and, as they go, preserving more or less momentum, are at those times more powerful, and their effects are more felt everywhere. . . . The manner in which such lunitidal effects accord with apparent atmospheric waves, supposed to move from west to east, and by some persons said to cause storms, seems to the writer satisfactory, because it appears to unite facts and reasonings (of the highest meteorologic authorities) about tides, waves of air, and storms—by a chain of theory, deduced from observations, sufficiently strong to bear even a crucial strain." *

* *The Weather Book,* 1863, pp. 253–254.

Alas, there was more theory than observation behind Fitz-Roy's reasoning. That there is likely to be a storm around the end of September, or March for that matter, is conceded, for extratropical storms occur at frequent intervals throughout the winter half of the year, but from the body of observation now at our command, it is quite clear that the frequency is no higher on or about September 23, or March 21, than it is immediately before or after.

Actually, hurricanes apart, and they do not show any special partiality for the autumnal equinox either, September on this continent is notable for its light winds. At places as wide-flung as Los Angeles, Galveston, North Head (Washington), Montreal, and Portland (Maine), September ranks as one of the two quietest months of the year. So it looks as if yet another chain of theory has snapped under the "crucial strain" of the facts and that the belief rests upon nothing more substantial than an occasional chance coincidence.

Incidentally, modern meteorologists have been quite unable to find any good reason why the atmosphere should be disturbed more when the sun is overhead at the equator than when it is north or south of it.

October

Fall is warmer than spring

TAKE THE MONTHLY temperature averages of almost any weather station in North America, and you will find that the three autumn months of September, October, and November are warmer than the spring months of March, April, and May. At St. Louis, for instance, October is 2 degrees warmer than April, November is 1 degree warmer than March, and September is 4 degrees warmer than May. Observing stations as far apart as Denver, Duluth, Calgary, Montreal, Pittsburgh, and Pikes Peak tell the same story. Round the coasts the contrast is even more marked. Thus, at San Diego the average autumn temperature is 63°F. against 58.4°F. for the spring months. At Halifax, September and October are fully 9 degrees warmer than April and May.

The explanation of this difference is bound up with the annual variation of sea temperatures. As we saw earlier,* the sea warms up and cools off much more slowly than the land. Whereas the land experiences its greatest heat in July (or

* See pp. 177–178.

August at the latest), the sea does not reach its peak of warmth until late August or early September. Similarly with the minimum temperatures: over land these occur usually in January (or February at the latest), over the sea, not much before the middle or end of February. It is obvious, therefore, that the *sea* is warmer in autumn than in spring; the difference between autumn and spring sea temperatures averages approximately 5 degrees off the California coast and 10 degrees off the Nova Scotia coast, that is, practically the same as the difference between the spring and autumn *air* temperatures.

However, this is not the complete story. The dominant air masses, polar and tropical, are a contributory factor of some importance. In the spring the tropical air masses are seldom able to penetrate very far into the heart of the continent before finding their progress stopped by cold waves—those atmospheric "icebergs" that are continually "calving" from the glacierlike anticyclone that then holds the western arctic in thrall. These cold waves are still very cold at that season, and over the continent as a whole are more likely to send the mercury shooting down to winter levels than the warm waves are likely to send it soaring up to summer levels. In the fall, the northern half of the continent is enjoying the afterglow of its short summer day: its rivers and lakes are still for the most part unfrozen, and although there may be snow on much of the ground, by November at least, cold waves are uncommon. Furthermore, when they do occur they are nothing like as cold as those coming at the winter's end when the land is still numb from its exposure to the long arctic night. And because as yet no formidable anticyclone has arisen to fend off all would-be intruders, tropical air masses stand more chance of penetrating into middle latitudes than in spring. And because they originate over the still warm seas of the Caribbean and Gulf of Mexico, their arrival is more likely to produce a spell of belated summery weather than the arrival of a cold wave is likely to produce a spell of premature wintry weather.

Indian summer

The weather year is full of oddities, unexpected changes, sharp reverses, misplaced days, quite out of tune with the month, and even, so we are sometimes tempted to think, misplaced seasons.

Indian summer is such an oddity, a most agreeable one to be sure, for it comes, usually in the latter half of October or the first half of November, after we have already felt the first chill winds of autumn and awakened to see the hoarfrost lying thick on the ground. It comes, as a *New York Times* editorial writer once put it, "as a final reprieve, as a sad last look at the world in congenial colors before the ground becomes hard again, the gutters gray with sleet, the skies barren and flat like dirty metal." It may not even be the final reprieve, either, for many an October conjures up two distinct spells of balmy weather separated by a colder spell, and it is by no means unknown for a fall to produce three or even four.

While there is no knowing precisely when such spells will occur, the chances are that, in any given locality, they will be more partial to certain dates than to others. In the region of Montreal and the lower St. Lawrence, for instance, Indian summer is more likely to come during the five-day period from October 5 to 9 than at any other time of the month, and least likely to come between October 15 and 19 and between October 23 and 27.*

* However, even when the expectation of an Indian summer is greatest at Montreal, the chances that the city will get a cold spell are formidable, for the trouble with Montreal is that even in midsummer it is never so far away from the source of cold air as it is of warm air; by the fall, the cold air is practically on its doorstep. (During a thirty-eight-year period, the McGill Meteorologi-

In our uncertain North American climate, temperature relapses to the previous season are of course not confined to any particular time of the year. All the same, they seem to show a marked preference for autumn and spring, that is, for the periods when the semipermanent highs which play such a large part in our weather economy are jockeying for their favorite winter and summer positions. And of the two transition seasons, autumn is the more likely to experience a prolonged "relapse" than spring. In autumn the atmosphere is less subject to violent territorial exchanges of air than in spring, when, as we have seen, there is often a strong southward flow of cold air from the snow-covered barrens of northern Canada: the weather is, on this account, more stable and less given to spasm. Further, when a part of the Bermuda high stagnates over the continent in autumn, it is less likely to give dull weather than in midsummer when the greater power of the sun makes for more vigorous convection, and so more rapid cloud formation.

Many theories, none of them very convincing, have been advanced to account for the name "Indian summer." Most of the pundits seem to lean toward the view advanced by a writer in the *Boston Transcript* more than a hundred years ago (June 8, 1832), namely, that, "The Indian summer is so called because, at the particular period of the year in which it obtains, the Indians break up their village communities, and go to the interior to prepare for their winter hunting." Another possibility is that the early settlers in the interior attributed the blue haze which commonly characterizes the Indian summer to the smoke of the prairie fires set by the Indians at that season, and named it accordingly. A third explanation, less likely but by no means impossible in view of the trans-Atlantic

cal Observatory in Montreal reported 300 days in October and November when the temperature was at least 10°F. below the mean, and only 114 days when it was at least 10°F. above the mean.)

origin of so many of our weather sayings, is that the name was given by some early European explorer who saw in these spells of dry, hazy weather a similarity to atmospheric conditions in India during the same months. British sailors have long been in the habit of speaking of the period of the retreating southwest monsoon as "Indian summer." Or maybe we need to look no further than another phrase in common parlance, namely, "Indian giver," the giver who is fickle and something of a sham; for such is Indian summer, the time when one feels, in William Morris's words,

. . . the treachery of the sun
And knows the pleasant time is well-nigh done.

But what matter if the origin of the name remains as hazy as the weather it designates? Indian summer is to be enjoyed, rather than explained, accepted as a suitor, not questioned as a delinquent!

Fire weather

But we must not allow our enthusiasm for the Indian summer to run away with us. It is possible to have too much of a good thing, and an Indian summer that lasts more than a week or so can easily become a bad thing. Because it is conceived in the rainless womb of an anticyclone, cradled in the lap of "the sere, the yellow leaf," and nourished by sunshine, it is a fire hazard almost from the very start. With each day of low humidity, clear skies, and drying breezes, the hazard grows: if, as sometimes happens—for instance, in 1952 and again in 1953—the ground is already parched from summer drought, the forest-fire hazard during a belated spell of warm weather is likely to reach its seasonal peak. Late spring may run it a very close second, especially if the previous winter was on the dry side, but the chances are that there will be higher ground humidities then than in the fall on account of the lower air temperatures, the correspondingly slower rate of moisture evaporation from the ground, and the smaller amount of loose "duff," that is, inflammable leaves and twigs, on the forest floor and the absence of leaves from the trees.

Of all the factors in the fire-hazard equation, relative humidity is the most critical. Generally, fires do not stand much chance of spreading if the relative humidity of the air is more than 60 per cent. If the figure drops to between 40 and 50 per cent, the chances are much greater, and if it drops below 40 per cent, even small fires become difficult to manage. (It has been estimated that more than 90 per cent of the damage done to our eastern forests by fires began on days when the relative humidity fell below 40 per cent.) Almost as important—perhaps even more important in determining the "starting odds," is the relative humidity of the top layer of duff. This, of course, is a function not only of the relative humidity of the air, but of the lapse of time since the last wetting rain, the nature of the underlying soil (for instance, its power to shed water, and hold it), the type of forest (an open forest is likely to be better ventilated than a close-canopied forest), and the time of year. There are several ways of measuring the moisture content of the litter layer. One of the simplest and best is provided by the duff hygrometer, which registers on a dial the contractions and expansions of a piece of rattan enclosed in a ventilated tube. An even simpler device is used in the forests of the Northwest: all the forest ranger has to do is to measure the variations in weight of a given piece of the moisture-loving moss that abounds in that part of the world. Duff humidities of 25 per cent and over mean that fires are unlikely to get started in the ordinary course of events: duff humidities below 15 per cent call for great watchfulness: below 10 per cent they spell almost certain trouble. As they seldom drop below this level before about nine or ten in the morning or remain below it after sundown, the chances of serious outbreaks occurring during the hours of darkness are much smaller than they are during the middle hours of daylight.

Once a fire has taken hold on a forest, humidities are of less importance than wind force and direction. A well-established conflagration fanned by a strong wind can even "ride out" a rainstorm, though admittedly in the long run there's nothing like a good soaking rain to assuage the fury of a forest fire. Nor should we forget that a large fire is capable of making its own wind—a wind, moreover, of tornadic intensity. Every leaf-burning gardener is familiar with the phenomenon of inblowing air to replace the air carried aloft by convection and has seen dried leaves on the perimeter of his pile drawn fireward by the draft: he may often have seen the beginnings even of a circulatory system in the ascending smoke and flame. Multiply this a millionfold and the ferocity of the winds round the edge of a blazing pine forest can be imagined. In the great Minnesota fire of 1918, the fire-fighters' wagons were overturned by the wind, and tall trees were snapped in two: in the Tillamook, Oregon, burn of 1933, giant Douglas firs were pulled right out of the ground by twisterlike winds.

The role of the forecaster in all this can readily be seen—not that he can stop a fire once it has started; however, he can frequently give 24 (even more) hours' notice of the onset of critical conditions of humidity, wind, and atmospheric electricity.* This is usually time enough for the fire fighters to get their stations manned, to close the fire-hazard areas to the public, to enable logging companies to suspend their slash-burning operations and put forest-patrol systems into effect. And even after a fire has started, the forecaster is still the key

* Lightning is believed to be the cause of about 18 per cent of all forest fires.

strategist. By correlating fire behavior and fuel types * with expected weather changes, the forecaster who operates near or at the scene of a fire is in a unique position to decide where reinforcements will be needed, where men and equipment can be used to best advantage, and what fire-fighting techniques are most appropriate. For example, if he knows that the characteristic downslope winds of the night are not going to materialize in a certain mountainous locality, plans must be made to reinforce fire fronts that would not ordinarily be very active. Advance intelligence of a major wind shift can be even more rewarding, for this will enable the fire-control teams to anticipate the change in direction of travel of the fire by reinforcing the flank from which the fire is likely to escape.

A measure of the growing significance of the U.S. Weather Bureau's Fire-Weather Service (which now operates over more than half of the country) is contained in the following statistics of fire damage in the State of Washington. Whereas in the decade 1926–1935 there were 8,143 fires involving 730,476 acres, *i.e.*, the area affected by a fire averaged 89.7 acres, in the decade 1936–1945 there were 10,361 fires involving 76,177 acres, *i.e.*, the area affected by a fire averaged only 7.3 acres. Admittedly, the meteorologist cannot take all the credit for this: much of it, perhaps most, belongs to the men who are forever improving our fire-warning and fire-fighting techniques, but it is so seldom that the meteorologist gets a chance to rise to his full height and take a bow that you must forgive him if, on this occasion, he does so.

All the same, "blowing one's own balloon" is a very risky thing for the meteorologist to do at the best of times, and fire weather is *not* the best of times! No sooner is one fire brought under control than half a dozen others will erupt to bedevil

* Variations in the inflammability of different species of timber, even of different age groups within the same species, are considerable.

his life and test his knowledge not only of the principles of large-scale forecasting, but also of micro-meteorology—and every forested hill and vale has its own meteorological idiosyncrasies. As if there were not problems enough for him here, he will be expected to forecast the drift of the smoke from the fires and their effect on both vertical and horizontal visibility. And there are times when the smoke will drift for thousands of miles before finally dissipating. In late September, 1950, the smoke from a series of forest fires in northern Alberta and the Northwest Territories traveled southeastward across the Prairie Provinces, the Great Lakes region, and the mid-Atlantic seaboard, darkening the noonday skies as it went. Afternoon baseball matches had to be played under night lights, automatically controlled street lighting came on in many cities, airline pilots reported the smell of smoke to be so strong that their passengers kept inquiring if everything was all right, and in many towns the strange red haze produced something approaching panic. Unfortunately, there wasn't a meteorologist who knew what was happening far enough ahead of time to be able to ease the minds of the fearful. Farmyard animals took a more philosophical view of things: they simply retired, as if for the night.

The durability of spells

One of the toughest jobs a meteorologist has is to tell when a spell of weather, such as Indian summer, will break up, and how. For when Dame Nature takes a fancy to a weather style, she is hard to budge. In most parts of North America a fine day is more likely to follow a fine day than a wet day: a fine week is more likely to follow a fine week than a wet week. In Montreal, for instance, the probability of a change to wet weather after a string of seven fine days is only 30 per cent.

And the same tendency is shown by other places in similar latitudes, not only on this continent, but in Europe: thus, in Kew (near London) the probability of a rainy day after one fine day is 45 per cent; after two fine days, it is 34 per cent; after four, 32 per cent; and after eight, only 22 per cent. And much the same is true of rainy spells: the longer they last, the greater their chances of continuing—at least up to ten days or so.

The reasons for this phenomenon, commonly referred to as persistence of type, are plain enough.

Fundamentally, every weather type is the expression of a distinctive combination of air-mass conditions, such as moisture content, vertical lapse rate (that is, rate of change of temperature with height), and characteristic surface temperature. All the time a given air mass retains its native qualities, that is, all the time the pressure situation in the air mass remains steady, the day-to-day weather will tend to follow the same pattern. During the North American summer and early fall, the all-important air-mass controls are the Bermuda and Pacific highs. In contrast to the small, shallow lows which form sporadically over the Gulf of Mexico and along the eastern flanks of the Rockies and move Atlantic-ward across the continent, and the equally small-scale and mobile ridges of high pressure which separate them, these larger systems change their positions and appearances quite slowly. As the relative position of these high-pressure areas determines the tracks (and to some extent the intensity) of the low-pressure areas separating them, there is consequently a predisposition for a given weather type, be it fair or foul, to continue for several days, or even for weeks. This predisposition is strengthened by the fact that the amount of heat received from the sun changes only gradually with the seasons. The resulting temperatures of the continents and oceans also change slowly—in the case of the ocean surface, even more slowly than the incoming radiation does. When, then, in October, the general pressure situation favors the poleward flow of "Gulf" air up the Mississippi and Ohio Valleys, the inhabitants of the eastern half of the United States are quite likely to find themselves basking in unseasonable warmth for days on end. On the other hand, when the Bermuda high is jockeyed out of this position by a landward extension of the Pacific high or a prematurely developed arctic high, the chances are that the Mississippi and Ohio Valleys will become the arena of a fiercely fought series of cyclonic skirmishes that may likewise last for days and leave behind them a trail of rain-sodden earth. The literal truth of the saying, "It never rains but it pours" will then be only too apparent.

This habit-forming tendency of our middle-latitude weather has long been appreciated both in North America and Europe. It is what the old farmer had in mind when asked about the likelihood of rain during a drought. "Rain, sir? Why, I tell you it's not going to rain till the ground gets wet: *then* we shall have plenty of it." It is what the Shepherd of Banbury (near Oxford in England) was thinking of when he declared, more than 200 years ago, that if "the wind turns to northeast and it continues two days without rain, and does not turn south the third day, nor rain the third day, it is likely to continue northeast for eight or nine days, all fair; and then come to the south again." * And, although he may never have known the reason, there was more than a particle of truth in the Shepherd's contention. For when a depression is succeeded by a ridge of high pressure, to be followed in due course by a new depression—a common enough sequence—the most that can be hoped for by way of relief from strong westerly winds and heavy rain is

* The same idea has been expressed rather more economically in couplet form, thus:

If the wind is northeast three days without rain,
Eight days will pass before south wind again.

a day or so of fair weather with a northerly (northwest-northeast) wind. If this interlude is prolonged, it probably means that the area has come under the stabilizing influence of a larger high-pressure system; a slowly moving high of this sort, composed of heavy, subsiding air, is generally in no mood to be bustled about by fussy depressions and may well be able to hold its own against all comers for eight or nine days—perhaps longer. Such a spell of anticyclonic weather is quite likely to be "all fair" in summer and early fall, if not later in the year when, as we shall see, anticyclones have a habit of breeding fog.

To change or not to change?

So, then, when we come to put the question "What's the weather going to do?" we need to remember there is always a good chance that it will remain the same, especially if it has not changed much during the past few days. I once knew a forecaster whose reputation—by no means inconsiderable—was said to be largely derived from the fact that whenever he was in doubt, he predicted a continuation of the existing conditions. Others of us have, alas, been rather less successful in playing our hunches. After all, every weather spell must break sooner or later.

The art of detecting the "break" ahead of time—even 24 hours ahead—is no small part of the art of forecasting. And I use the word "art" rather than "science" because judgment is as important a tool in the kitbag of the meteorologist as it is in that of the doctor: and judgment, while it is not opposed to logic or dialectic and soon falters if it is not supported by sound learning, is something that does not reside in a slide rule nor yet in an isobaric chart. And, furthermore, scientific answers to some weather questions take so long that the weather change can occur before it is forecast. If all the variables in a day's weather were properly considered, it would take a crew of mathematicians several weeks to compute their aggregate effect—by which time the weather of the day in question would have ceased to matter. No doubt electronic computers will be able to cut down the time consumption from weeks to minutes, but even so there will aways be need of judgment in applying the forecasts to different localities. Meanwhile, there's still much to be said for cultivating a "weather sense," something our forefathers, who lived closer to the earth (and to heaven?) than most of us city-bred dwellers in semidarkness, had in abundant measure.

The indicators of change are of many kinds. They may be seen in the sky, in the air, and on the ground; in the face of a barometer, on the drum of a hygrograph, and in the column of a mercury thermometer; and, for those more technically inclined, they may be read in a lapse rate, on a synoptic chart, in an upper air sounding, and even in a radio receiver (for "static" provides a clue to the amount and proximity of thunderstorm activity). And because the atmosphere is what it is—a balance of many forces, delicately contrived and easily disturbed—a change in any of its components is something to be watched with care.

Two signs are better than one

A change in two or more of its components should be watched with even more care.

No matter how indicative of an imminent change of weather a change in the barometer, the state of the sky, or the feel of the air may be thought to be, it is asking for disappointment to base a forecast on it, unless there are concurrent indications forthcoming from other weather elements.

It is the concurrence of changes in the weather elements that really matters. Because air masses are the product of the slow interaction of *many* atmospheric components—all of them liable to variations, the nature and extent of which are often in doubt—and because weather changes are so closely identified with changes of air mass, the forecaster is not in a position to predict the course of the weather from single lines of evidence. Perhaps we can best bring home the need for thinking in terms of associated rather than isolated changes by tabulating the modifications that are likely to take place in the various components at or near fronts between well-marked air masses.

Spotting fronts

Fronts, the real troublemakers of our North American atmosphere, are of three main kinds: warm, cold, and occluded.

A. WARM FRONT

This is officially defined (by the U.S. Weather Bureau) as a "line of discontinuity along the earth's surface, or a horizontal plane aloft, where the forward edge of an advancing current of relatively warm air is replacing a retreating colder air mass."

Fig. 20(a). Warm front.

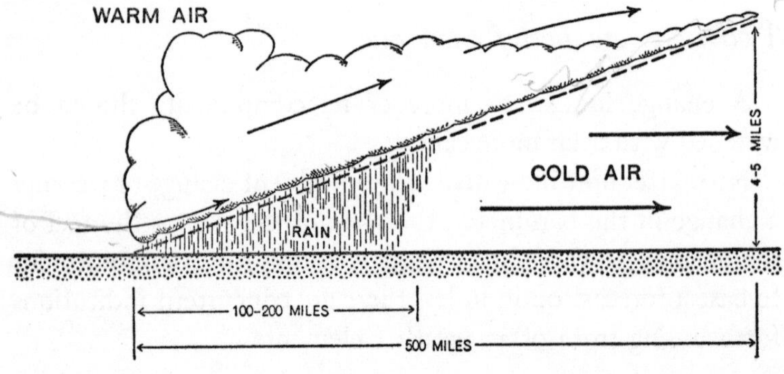

While no two warm fronts are identical (and the same applies to the other types), the chances are that their approach and passage will be marked by some, if not all, of the following phenomena:

Element	In advance	At the passage	In the rear
Barometer	Falling	Fall arrested	Little change or only slow fall
Wind	Backing and increasing in speed	Veer, e.g., from S to SW	Steady direction, perhaps increased speed
Temperature	Steady	Rise, but not usually very sharp	Little change
Humidity	Gradual increase	Rapid rise to (near) saturation point	Little change
Visibility	Good at first, slowly deteriorating	Poor, often mist or fog	Slight improvement, though mist or fog may persist
Sky	Gradually becomes overcast; usual cloud sequence being cirrus, cirrostratus, altostratus, stratus, nimbostratus	Low nimbostratus and fractostratus	Cloudy or overcast with stratus, stratocumulus, even nimbostratus
Weather	Drizzle, turning to rain	Rain either stops or reverts to drizzle	Little change, but continuous rain unlikely

B. COLD FRONT

This, also in the language of the U.S. Weather Bureau, is defined as a "line of discontinuity at the earth's surface (or at the intersection of the cold frontal surface with a horizontal plane in the atmosphere) along which a wedge of cold air is underrunning and displacing a warmer air mass." As with the warm front, its manifestations are many and by no means always the same. In summary form, which suggests a "tidiness" not always practiced by Nature, these are as follows:

Element	In advance	At the passage	In the rear
Barometer	Falling slowly or steady	Sudden rise	Rise continues, but rather more steadily
Wind	Backing or steady, becoming more squally	Sudden veer, *e.g.*, from SW to WNW, frequently accompanied by heavy squalls	May back a little after frontal squall, then steady or veering in later squalls
Temperature	Steady, or slight fall if raining	Usually well-marked drop	Little change
Humidity	Steady	Decreases, often sharply, at front	Variable in showers, but usually low
Visibility	Usually poor, even mist or fog	May be poor in heavy rain, but improves once front has passed	Very good
Sky	Altocumulus, stratus, or stratocumulus, with heavy cumulonimbus in immediate vicinity of front	Cumulonimbus, with fractostratus, or scud (usually very low)	Clouds usually show break and lift. Cumulus, altocumulus, with only occasional cumulonimbus
Weather	Intermittent rain or drizzle; perhaps distant thunder and lightning	Heavy rain or hail, accompanied often by thunderstorm	Rain generally eases off within an hour or so of passage. Then "scattered showers with bright intervals"

C. OCCLUDED FRONT

This is defined as "the front formed when and where the cold front overtakes the warm front in an extratropical cyclone." When this happens, the warm sector which hitherto separated the warm front from the cold front is lifted off the surface and continues to exist only as a trough of warm air aloft.

Fig. 20(b). Cold front.

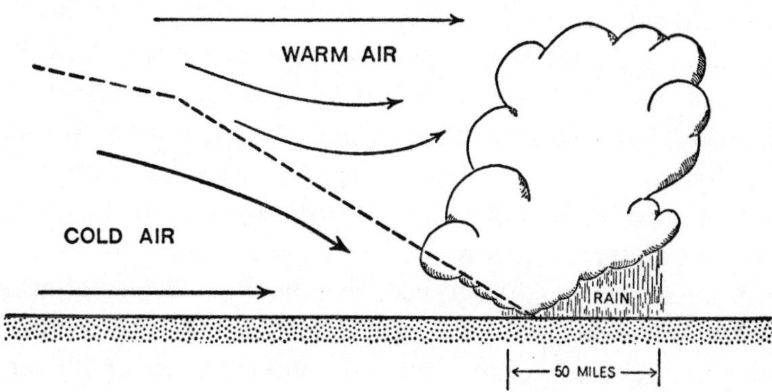

It is possible to identify three different occlusions: the warm-front occlusion in which the *prefrontal* and passage phenomena tabulated under (A) are likely to occur because the air behind the front is warmer than the air in advance of it; the cold-front occlusion in which the passage and *postfrontal* phenomena tabulated under (B) are likely to occur because the air behind the front is colder than the air in advance of it; and the combined warm-front–cold-front occlusion in which the prefrontal phenomena of a warm front are likely to be followed by the passage and postfrontal phenomena of a cold front: in this case the precise sequence and intensity of the frontal phenomena

Fig. 20(c). Warm occlusion.

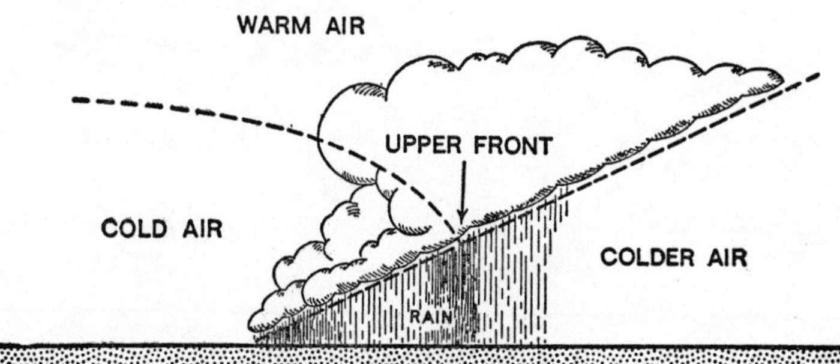

will depend largely on the proximity to the surface of the squeezed-out warm sector.

With the exception perhaps of temperature and humidity, it is usually possible to spot these frontal signs without too much difficulty. Unfortunately, the thermometer (both the wet- and the dry-bulb kind) responds too readily to local and diurnal factors to be the best of front detectors. Apart from the question of exposure, which is likely to be satisfactory only if the instrument is properly screened, there is the difficulty of getting it to record the representative temperature, that is, the temperature which characterizes the surface layers of the air mass as a whole. The diurnal variation of temperature can be so considerable that it will quite frequently conceal the changes of temperature and moisture content due to change of air mass. In fact, unless the sky is overcast and the wind is blowing at least force 4, say 15 miles an hour, the chances of discovering the representative temperature and humidity of the air on either side of the front are small. Then, again, as far as the dry-bulb reading is concerned, the most significant rises and falls take place *after* a front has passed, that is, after the change in the weather has already become apparent.

Fig. 20(d). Cold occlusion.

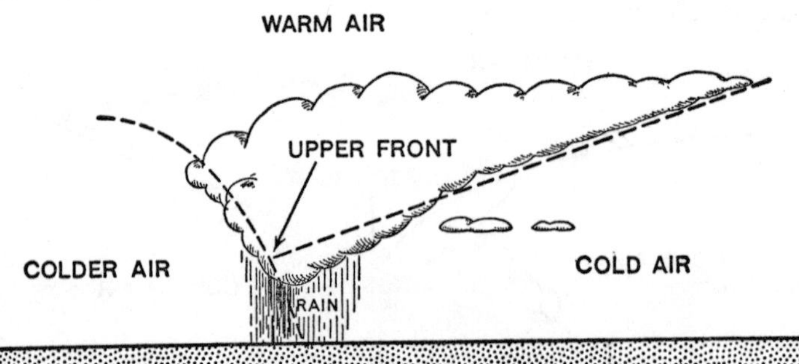

"Something in the wind"

Similar caution needs to be observed in interpreting changes in wind direction and velocity. These can be very useful indicators of changes in the weather, but there are times when they are no more indicative than the diurnal variations of temperature and relative humidity.

To begin with, there are next to no foolproof weather rules based solely on wind. Perhaps the nearest approach to such a rule is found in the saying:

A veering wind, fair weather,
A backing wind, foul weather.

A great deal of our weather in North America travels, as we have seen, from a western point to an eastern point in the form of alternating highs and lows. If you care to sketch such a succession, keeping the center of the depressions to the north of the Canadian border (as they frequently are), and remembering that the circulation is clockwise round the highs and counterclockwise round the lows, you will readily see that the wind must back, that is, shift against the direction of the sun's apparent motion, as the low advances with its assorted samples of bad weather, and veer, that is, shift with the sun, as it passes off to the east. You will also see from your sketch why, "A northwester is not long in debt to a southwester" when low succeeds high at fairly regular intervals. Clearly, though, the rule breaks down as soon as one or other pressure system slows up or stagnates.

But over a continent as large as North America, with its almost never-ending variety of terrain, wind shifts are influenced by many factors: by mechanical eddies forming in the lee of hills; by valley and mountain breezes; by the orientation of mountain ranges in relation to the general wind direction;

by land and sea breezes which, near coasts, can make things still more complicated, and by thunderclouds which, because of the mighty indrafts of air continually feeding their convectional "fires," are notorious for their capricious winds. Any one of these things can make the mere fact of veering, or backing, of wind quite meaningless from a prognostic point of view. It is only when wind shifts are associated with rises and falls in the barometer that they need to be carefully watched. Thus, when, during a spell of Indian summer, a backing wind—particularly a southerly wind—synchronizes with a falling barometer, the odds are that a cyclonic disturbance is on the way. The seaman, whose prowess as a weather prophet is traditional, will go further and assure you that:

When the wind backs and the weatherglass falls,
Then be on your guard against gales and squalls.

But this takes rather too pessimistic a view of the portents, for even over the sea where winds in a cyclone habitually blow harder than they do over the land, gales and squalls are nothing like so common as falling barometers and backing winds. Whether there is a gale or not will largely depend on how far the barometer falls in a given time, and as a working rule you can assume that it falls lower and faster for wind than for rain.

Signs in the sky

But of all the indicators of change, none is more revealing than the sky. Shakespeare commended the practice of judging "The state and inclination of the day" from "the complexion of the sky," and we can only lament that the circumstances of life make it increasingly impossible for the majority of Americans to honor the custom: neither a city street nor yet a moving sedan is any place in which to see what the weather is doing.

Even professional meteorologists are wont to pay more attention to indoor analysis than outdoor observation: and those who do look out of their windows have, before now, been known to attach greater importance to the state of the road than the state of the sky. A distinguished meteorologist of my acquaintance once confessed that he felt sufficiently dubious about a "continuing fair and mild" forecast to take a look outside. Noticing that the street in front of his office was wet, he amended the forecast accordingly—only to discover later that the "rain" had been produced by a water truck!

One reason why clouds are so useful in this connection is because weather is largely a product of air mass; change the air mass, either at the surface or aloft, and you stand to change the weather. Change of air mass implies change of the moisture content of the air at different levels and change in the vertical temperature gradient, or lapse rate. Now although it is true that the *amount* of cloud can change as a result of local geographical causes, the *type* of cloud can change only if the lapse rate and moisture content change, that is, if the origin and history of the air change. Therefore, as soon as you see a new type of cloud appearing—say cirrus or cirrostratus overrunning fair-weather cumulus—you will be right in assuming that a new air mass is in the offing. This, of course, does not necessarily mean that the weather will break up in your particular part of the country: it will do this only if you happen to be in the direct track of the depression which the cirrus and cirrostratus clouds herald. In this event the sky will soon provide further indications of the weather's intentions.

Naturally, not all clouds are of equal prognostic value. Stratocumulus, for instance, is generally regarded as telling the forecaster very little. But as the modern trend in meteorology is to look increasingly to the distribution of moisture and temperature in the upper air (that is, in the cloud levels) for the key to tomorrow's weather, it may well be that we shall eventually find that the clouds themselves declare more about the weather to come than office-bound professionals have been willing to admit. As things are, most of us know less of cloud lore than men did 200 years ago. The Shepherd of Banbury could certainly have told us a thing or two. Here are a few of his cloud signs. We leave the assessment of their reliability to the reader.

If cloudy, and it soon decrease, certain fair weather.

If small clouds increase, much rain.

If large clouds decrease, fair weather.

In summer or harvest, when the wind has been south two or three days, and it grows very hot, and you see clouds rise with great white tops like towers, as if one were upon the top of another, and joined together with black on the nether side, there will be thunder and rain suddenly.

If two such clouds arise, one on either hand, it is time to make haste to shelter.

Here are some others of greater antiquity—and no less merit when they find corroboration in other weather elements.

*Hens' scarts * and filly tails †*
Make lofty ships carry low sails.

A dappled sky, like a painted woman, soon changes its face.

A mackerel sky
Is as much for wet as 'tis for dry.‡

If woollen fleeces spread the heavenly way,
Be sure no rain disturbs the summer day.

* That is, scratchings.

† These refer to the delicate, featherlike plumes of cirrus cloud that frequently presage the approach of a vigorous cyclone.

‡ Cirrocumulus clouds frequently forbode thundery weather, which is characteristically capricious, if not downright treacherous.

When the mists begin to nod,
Fisher, then put by your rod.

When the clouds are upon the hills
*They'll come down by the mills.**

And we could extend the list greatly, for there are many more time-tested cloud rules than there are rules for pressure, wind, temperature, and humidity. Incidentally, the best amateur weather prophets still seem to be shepherds and seamen whose acquaintance with the heavens is more intimate than most, and from whose stock in trade the barometer is often absent.

But "the complexion of the sky" is more than a matter of cloud cover. It is also a matter of color. In order to appreciate the prognostic possibilities of sky color, it may be as well for us to call to mind how the sky acquires its color. Rays of "white" sunlight passing through a dusty or moisture-laden atmosphere are broken up, or scattered, into their component colors in much the same way as they are when they pass through a prism. At any moment in any given part of the sky the dominant color depends on the amount of scattering to which each color is subjected, and this in turn depends on the size and number of the dust and moisture particles in the atmosphere. When the atmosphere through which the sun's rays pass contains very fine dust, the rays are partly scattered, the blue rays being scattered more widely than the other colors. Tobacco smoke provides a good illustration of this greater scattering of blue light, for although it consists of small drops of a yellow liquid (as can easily be seen by watching what happens to a white handkerchief when the smoke is blown through it), the color of the smoke is predominantly blue. In their passage through a dusty

* The significance of stratus cloud forming on hilltops is appreciated the world over: while there are plenty of summer mornings when a capping of such cloud betokens a fine day, it more often betokens rain, especially when it follows in the train of cirriform and altostratus cloud.

atmosphere the sun's rays lose their blue component, and to a lesser extent their green and yellow components: the only rays which completely succeed in getting through the atmosphere are the red rays, which explains the dominantly red coloration of the clouds and sky in such circumstances. However, only particles which have diameters smaller than the wavelength of light, that is, somewhat less than 1/50,000 inch, can scatter light in this way. Normally, the vapor droplets in cigarette smoke are of the required order (about 1/100,000 inch). Cloud and fog particles, on the other hand, are much bigger, characteristically being between 1/2,500 and 1/250 inch across. Thus, while the sun seen through a smoke fog looks red, it looks white through a water fog.

If we bear this important distinction in mind, it will help us to understand why sky colors are regarded, almost everywhere in the world, as having prognostic significance. Here are two of the more trustworthy "color" rules:

Evening red and morning grey
Help the traveller on his way.
Evening grey and morning red
Bring down rain upon his head.

Or, in its scriptural form,

When it is evening, ye say, It will be fair weather: for the sky is red. And in the morning, It will be foul weather to day: for the sky is red and lowring.*

The justification of these rules becomes apparent when we recall the atmospheric conditions under which our weather, good and bad, is normally produced. Most of our North American weather travels, as we have had occasion to remark more than once, from west to east. Accordingly, when the sky is red

* Matthew 16:2–3.

at sunset, we can infer that the air to the west of us is dry (since it is only in dry weather that the air contains large numbers of particles sufficiently small to scatter light effectively), and also that there is no heavy cloud to obscure the sun. We may therefore conclude that fine weather is coming along from the west. If, on the other hand, the western sky is a dull gray at sunset, we may reasonably infer that the air to the west of us is moisture-laden, and that some bad weather is on its way. A red sky about the time of sunrise means that there are plenty of very small particles near the surface, and also that there is some cloud near the western horizon to pick up the scattered light rays. Such a situation is most likely to prevail at the end of a quiet anticyclonic spell of fine weather when the lower atmosphere has become highly charged with dust particles, and the upper atmosphere has begun to be invaded by a warm front.

The reliability of these rules, long affirmed by countrymen and townsfolk alike, was investigated statistically some time ago for the south of England with the following results: a red sunrise was found to be followed by rain (or snow) within 24 hours seven times out of ten, and a red sunset by 24 hours' good weather on at least two occasions out of every three.

Red is probably the most significant sky color in amateur forecasting, but a pale yellow sky around sunset runs it pretty close, for in winter this is attended by a 60 per cent risk of rain within 24 hours. When the sky above the western horizon is tinged with green soon after sundown, the chances are even better—roughly 80 per cent—that the following day will be wet and stormy. The only trouble about forecasting from a green sky is that a lot of weather can happen while you are waiting for it!

"When the moon comes over Brooklyn"

Clouds and colors are also responsible for most of the useful weather lore associated with the moon. The following aphorisms, express in rhyming form beliefs that have traveled far, but changed little, since they were first framed in the mind of Mediterranean man:

Pale moon doth rain,
Red moon doth blow,
White moon doth neither rain nor snow.

If the moon show a silver shield,
Be not afraid to reap your field;
But if she rises haloed round,
Soon we'll tread on deluged ground.

And there is much truth in them, whether the moon comes up over Brooklyn, or the borough clock, Palmyra, or Antioch. "Pale moon" and moon "haloed round" both imply the presence of thin cirrostratus cloud, such as runs ahead of a depression; "red moon," like "red sun," frequently implies a high relative humidity in the atmosphere, a common enough state of affairs immediately prior to a rainy spell. "White moon" and moon with a "silver shield" point to cloudless skies and a comparatively dry atmosphere.

Sayings concerning the clarity of the moon likewise rest on a rational foundation. Take, for instance, these two:

Clear moon
Frost soon.

Sharp horns do threaten windy weather.

Because the rate of nocturnal cooling of the earth's surface tends to be a function of the amount of low cloud, low ground temperatures are more likely to occur, other things being equal (and they aren't always), when the sky is clear: in the absence of a cloud cover, the ground quickly radiates skyward the day's income of solar heat. The degree of definition of the moon's margins is a function as much of pressure as of temperature gradient. When there is little or no wind, that is, when the horizontal pressure gradient is slack, the vertical gradient of temperature tends to be irregular, often to the point of being inverted. These irregularities lead to density differences between one level of the atmosphere and the next, which in turn lead to different amounts of refraction of the moon's rays: when this happens, the outline of the moon often gives the impression of being out of focus. When, on the other hand, there are strong winds aloft, these irregularities of temperature gradient and, so, of density gradient get smoothed out. Under such circumstances, the refraction of the moon's beams is greatly reduced, with the result that the horns of the crescent moon tend to be much better defined. The prognostic value of strong upper winds (as deduced from the rate of progress of cirriform clouds across a clear sky *) has long been appreciated by seafarers, and is neatly expressed in the following couplet:

Trace in the sky the painter's brush †
Then winds around you soon will rush.

There are, however, some sayings about the moon that are of a very different kind. To distinguish these from the optical kind described above, we shall call them astrological. Such sayings ask us to believe that meteorological significance attaches to the horns of the new moon being upward or downward, to the moon lying on its back, and to the coincidence of types of weather with lunar phases. These, we venture to sug-

* It has been estimated, by the late H. H. Clayton, that the average speed of cirrus cloud is about 80 miles an hour.

† The more fibrous forms of cirrus cloud give the impression of being the creation of a master artist working in white oils on a blue canvas.

gest, belong, not to weather lore, but to folk lore, because what is visible of the moon depends (apart from the cloud factor) solely upon its position relative to the sun. Admittedly, it is not difficult to see how the tradition arose. As the moon is chiefly responsible for the rise and fall of the tides, it was only natural to suppose that the earth's atmosphere is affected in the same way. Such atmospheric tides have been detected, but they represent a difference of less than 1/1,000 inch on a mercury barometer, and they are inappreciable as a factor in weather change. As, on the average, our North American weather alters significantly every four or five days, it is not surprising that the changes should sometimes coincide with phases of the moon, which alter every seven days. Any success achieved by prophets who base their predictions upon phases of the moon must, we feel, be ascribed to the laws of chance. The trouble with most of us, in this and other similar matters, is that we are delighted to seize upon coincidences and magnify them into laws. A few examples of the change of the weather with the moon, especially when change is very much desired, are normally sufficient to counterbalance those far more numerous and (to us) unimportant occasions when no such change occurs.*

Reading between the millibars

In the popular esteem, the barometer has long enjoyed a prognostic reputation equaled only by Nostradamus, the *Farmer's Almanac*, and the woolly bear caterpillar. The esteem is

* The "doubting Thomases" among us might be interested to read an article on the subject written by K. G. Collier in *Science News*, No. 11 (1949), pp. 32–38 (Penguin Books). In this—"The Moon and the Weather"—he claims that in a test period of 1,230 days there were only 10 coincident changes of moon and weather, that is, 1 in 123 days, while the chance expectation of such coincidences over that same period would have been 1 in 100—that is, higher!

partly deserved, if for no other reason than that high-pressure systems are usually characterized by quite different types of weather from low-pressure systems; and certain it is that no professional meteorologist could do without his barometer, for with enough simultaneously taken barometric readings, he can fashion a synoptic chart that will tell him where the significant pressure systems are located, how they are developing, and where they are likely to travel in the next few hours. But the utility of the hall barometer to the ordinary householder is strictly limited—no matter how impressed he may be by the confidence of its maker that the weather will be "settled fair" when the reading is high, "stormy" when it is low, and "unsettled" when it is midway between. It is probably safe to say that these assurances have been responsible for more mistimed outdoor enterprise, including everything from haymaking to hill climbing, than all the backfiring forecasts of the U.S. Weather Bureau. The fact that the pressure of the atmosphere is, let us say, 1,020 millibars * has next to no prognostic value; many of our choicest winter fogs and not a few of our heaviest summer storms occur when the barometer is round about that pressure. Furthermore, it can rain just as hard, and for just as long, when the barometer reads 1,010 millibars, as when it reads 980 millibars.

Far more indicative than the actual pressure reading is the pressure *tendency*, that is, the amount the barometer has risen or fallen in a given period. This provides the observer with a

* We hope our readers won't object too strongly to our using the appropriate unit of measurement. To weigh pressure in *inches* is just about as silly as measuring elevation in foot-pounds, or distance in decibels. A millibar is the meteorological unit of pressure on the centimeter-gram-second system and is equal to a force of 1,000 dynes per square centimeter: the pressure of 1,000 millibars (which is not far removed from the mean surface pressure over North America) is equivalent to the pressure exerted by a column of mercury 29.531 inches high at 32°F. in latitude 45°. Actually, sea-level pressures over the continent oscillate about 50 millibars or so on either side of the 1,000-millibar level.

measure of the development and displacement which the pressure system in his locality is undergoing,* which in turn provides, especially if it is associated with changes in one or more of the other elements, a measure of the pace of atmospheric change. And pace of change is what matters most in appraising almost any weather situation. If there is such a thing as a foolproof rule in forecasting, then the following couplet comes as near as any to providing it:

Long foretold, long last:
Short notice, soon past.

What it is saying (and its application is not restricted to pressure), is simply that a forecast of settled fair weather based on a sudden rise of pressure after a storm is less likely to "come off" than one based on a slow and steady rise of pressure, and similarly with a falling barometer—which is reasonable enough. When the barometer recovers sharply after a storm, all it usually means is that a narrow ridge of high pressure has become sandwiched in between two fast-moving cyclonic disturbances. In this event, no sooner does the "weatherglass" register "set fair," or "fine," or "dry" than it will start to fall again, with the result that a day's sunshine is about all you are likely to get before the next disturbance arrives. If, on the other hand, the barometer recovers slowly after a storm, or falls slowly after a prolonged spell of good weather, the chances are that a more substantial and longer-lasting change is indicated. Large anticyclones are concerned with the transport of anything up to 20 trillion tons of air. Because of this they move slowly and give due notice of their arrival and departure. Further, they can usually be relied upon to stay around for a while. When they do settle down over an area, you will be

* This does *not* apply to low latitudes however: there the diurnal and semidiurnal rhythms of pressure are so large that pressure changes due to air-mass movements and frontal passages are often completely masked.

right nine times out of ten if you gamble on the weather continuing as it began.

Once in a while, however, a steady high barometer will deceive you badly, for violent and persistent rain can occur in the middle of an otherwise fine anticyclonic spell without any noticeable drop in pressure. Such rain is the work of fronts that have stagnated in the high. Stationary fronts, as these are often called, are not easily detectable on the barometer, particularly in summer when fronts of every description tend to be rather more diffuse than in winter. At the same time the physical processes associated with the front—the upward flow of warm air, or the undercutting of cold air, with the consequent formation of frontal cloud and precipitation over a wide area—are at least as pronounced as in winter on account of the much greater moisture content of the warm air in summertime. In such circumstances the best thing to do is watch the sky for signs of impending change.

If you happen to live in New England or its vicinity, it is also easy to be deceived under rather different circumstances, namely, when the wind is in the northeast and it is raining or snowing. Then it sometimes happens that, although the barometer will go on rising day after day, the precipitation will go on falling, and the fair weather which eventually follows proves to be little more than a brief intermission between acts of atmospheric violence. This state of affairs is associated with a disturbance off the northeast coast that is either moving slowly out to sea or slowly dissolving.

Poor man's weatherglass

There are indirect as well as direct manifestations of weather change, and the indirect are often easier of observation. The natural realm abounds in sensitive mechanisms that register changes of temperature and humidity, and even of pressure, with as much precision as meteorological instruments—the big difference being that to use them knowingly the observer has to do his own calibrating. It is true that these mechanisms register only current conditions, or conditions in the immediate past, but because Nature makes a habit of accomplishing her ends by means of sequences and cycles which, once begun, are seldom interrupted, it is frequently possible to put these mechanisms to prognostic use.

Take, for example, the sensitivity of certain kinds of flowers to changes of humidity. The English pink-eyed pimpernel habitually closes its petals by day when the relative humidity of the air exceeds 80 per cent. Daisy and chickweed do the same when it rises above 82 per cent. More sensitive still are the so-called everlasting flowers, especially the varieties *Acroclinium roseum* and *Acroclinium album*. The petals of these flowers have, near their base, a kind of elbow joint consisting of a hygroscopic substance which causes the main part of the petal to change its position with changes in the dampness of the air. Given a pin, a piece of cardboard, a pencil, and some patience, it is possible to calibrate the changes of direction in which a petal points against changes in the relative humidity. Now while there is no precise correlation between relative humidity and weather, we do at least know that there is more chance of frontal rain occurring when the relative humidity is high and rising than when it is high and falling, let alone when it is low and falling. It was in recognition of this fact that John Gerard, the author of the famous sixteenth-century English *Herbal*, wrote of the pimpernel that the closing of its petals during daytime, "betokeneth rain and foul weather: contrariwise, if they be spread abroad, fair weather." No doubt the flower came to be known as the "poor man's weatherglass" for the same reason.

Similar assumed, and in many cases demonstrable, associations between the behavior of living things and impending weather change are to be found in the literature, ancient and modern, of Europe, whence most of our American weather lore is derived. Virgil in his *Georgics* speaks thus of the prospects of rain:

The wary crane foresees it first, and sails
Above the storm, and leaves the lowly vales;
The cow looks up, and from afar can find
The change of heaven, and snuffs it in the wind;
The swallow skims the river's watery face;
The frogs renew the croaks of their loquacious race;
The careful ant her secret cell foresakes,
And drags her eggs along the narrow tracks;

. . . . .

Huge flocks of rising rooks foresake their food,
*And, crying, seek the shelter of the wood.**

Sir Alan Herbert has a more humorous treatment of the theme:

But I know ladies by the score
Whose hair, like seaweed, scents the storm:
Long, long before it starts to pour
Their locks assume a baneful form:
Ah, who has not with Muriel rejoiced
One morning when her hair was much less moist,
Meaning it must *be warm?*

And I believe, with brush and comb,
Some damsel in an inner shrine
Sits always at the prophet's home
While sages all around recline

* Dryden's translation.

Or wait with reverence on the outer mat
Until in ecstasy she pins a plait
And shrieks "It will be fine." *

Sir Alan may not be so sure of his meteorology as the meteorologists he is satirizing, but he has a point, as every woman knows: for when the atmosphere is gathering moisture, as it does during the approach of a warm front, even the best head of hair in the world is apt to give its owner trouble.

And while we are talking of trouble, let us not forget all those "old sinners" (and saints for the matter of that) who

. . . have all points
O' the compass in their bones and joints.

For who that is sick among us would not readily swear that

A coming storm your shooting corns presage
And aches will throb, your hollow tooth will rage.

* By courtesy of the publishers of *Punch* and Sir Alan Herbert's agents, Messrs A. P. Watt & Son.

November

. . . No road—
No street—
No t'other side the way.

Of the many kinds of bad weather that from time to time afflict the inhabitants of this continent, few give so much trouble as fog. Cold weather can be offset with warm fires and clothing, rain with umbrellas and raincoats, only in the worst storms does wind work serious havoc, and lightning does much less harm than in the days before ferroconcrete and conductor rods. But against fog man has been able to do almost nothing—except make it worse by belching millions of tons of smoke into the atmosphere. Fog still grounds his air armadas, immobilizes his fleets, and vies with a blackout in raising road-accident rates. And all because a few hundred tons of water get distributed in the wrong place.

Although fogs can occur at almost any time of the year, provided the air is heavy with moisture and the nights are cool, clear, and practically calm, they are most likely to be troublesome in fall and winter. By late autumn the sun has lost much of its strength: on this account it is less able to "burn off" the early morning shroud of moisture and set the air in turbulent —or convective—motion than it was during the summer. This means that even in the most favorable circumstances the time taken for a night fog to clear increases as the season advances. Furthermore, the nights get longer as the sun gets weaker, so that stagnating air has more chance of cooling to its dew point and of building up a layer of fog. The deeper it becomes, the smaller the chances of its daytime dispersal, for fog is a very poor carrier of heat and seldom gets far with the job of converting the incoming short-wave light rays into long-wave heat rays, which are the immediate source of all our terrestrial warmth. Instead, most of the short waves get reflected straight back into space from the upper surface of the fog: only very few manage to reach the ground, where they can be used to heat the water droplets in the enveloping fog and so cause them to vanish into thin air.

From this it might be thought that our worst ground fogs would occur in the depth of winter. Actually the fall is rather more liable to have *bad* fogs than winter. The reason for this is partly that the winds are generally lighter at that season, partly that maritime air masses—the most fecund fog breeders—have, on the average, a somewhat higher water content then than in winter when the sea is cooler, and partly that in the fall the sea is warmest relative to the land, with the result that air coming off the sea stands more chance of cooling, and so of condensing, then than at other times.

What is fog?

In essence, there is no real difference between a cloud and a fog. Both are the result of the cooling of the atmosphere to a temperature below its dew point which, as we saw earlier,* is the name given to the temperature at which air becomes

* See February, p. 40.

saturated and the moisture in it starts to condense; that is, they are both suspended forms of dew or hoarfrost. The only difference between them is that of location: whereas fog consists of water droplets condensed from, and floating in, the air near the surface, cloud consists of water droplets (or ice particles) condensed from, or floating in, the air well above the surface.

There are two main types of fog: that produced by evaporation of warm water into cold air, and that produced by cooling of warm air in contact with a cold surface.

Fogs of the first type form only when cold air passes over water at least 20 to 25°F. warmer, or when warm rain falls through cold air. When you turn on the hot-water tap in a cold bathroom (an unlikely circumstance, to be sure, in our overheated American homes), you reproduce the former state of affairs and get what, in nature, is known as steaming fog or sea smoke. The latter state of affairs exists sometimes in a depression when warm saturated air overruns, or is undercut by, colder air.

Fogs due to cooling also form in two ways: either as a result of warm air moving over a cold surface, that is, by advection, or as a result of heat being emitted from the earth's surface into space, that is, by radiation.

With the exception of sea smoke which occurs only near pack ice or where warm ocean currents flow past very cold lands, for example, northwest Russia in winter, sea fogs mostly form in warm moist air (often of tropical origin) which has come up from low latitudes.

While, on this account, advectional fog is uncommon in autumn over the sea, it is common enough over the land. For what the sea cannot do by reason of its storage of summertime warmth, the faster-cooling land can easily accomplish—especially by night. In fact, you can be practically sure that when a stream of ex-tropical air stagnates over land or slows down to less than 10 miles an hour, the night and early morning visibility will be poor, even if it is not poor enough to be called fog.*

But it is radiation, rather than advection, that gives us most of our fall and winter fogs.

". . . *Mists that roll and rise*"

The development of radiation fogs depends on the cooling of the ground surface at night. As the sea surface does not cool off appreciably by night, radiation fog is purely a land phenomenon: this, of course, does not stop its drifting out to sea once it has formed. Although it does occasionally occur in unsaturated air, nine times out of ten it will not form unless the air has cooled down to, or slightly below, its dew point. There is no guarantee, however, that fog will form when this has happened. For one thing, there may be too much breeze, or too little. For another, the air may be too clean, that is, deficient in those microscopic solid particles which act as carriers for the water droplets.

How does this sort of fog form? Weather experts would give much to know the complete answer to this question. In the absence of it, they are wont to talk of the strong nocturnal cooling which goes on as a result of the radiative loss of heat suffered by the earth and by the moist surface air, and the subsequent transport, by turbulent mixing, of the cooled saturated air to the overlying layers from which upward escape is impossible because of the formation of a temperature inversion

* In official parlance it is proper to speak of "fog" only when the range of horizontal visibility falls below 1 kilometer (roughly 1,100 yards). When the range lies between 1 and 2 kilometers (2,200 yards), it is more appropriate to speak of mist or haze, depending on whether the obscuration is produced by water particles or solid matter such as dust and soot.

at the top of the mixing layer. Which does not take us very far, as anybody can see, when we consider what happens on a windless night. On such an occasion, because there is no turbulence in the atmosphere, the cooling cannot be communicated upward to any extent, and the ground may easily become 10 to 15°F. colder than the air a few feet above it. Now just as condensation of water may take place very freely on the cold walls of a room, when the air is humid, without the moisture in the air being visible, so on a calm night there may be a heavy fall of dew (or hoarfrost, if the temperature is low enough), but no mist or fog.

Or, again, suppose the night is windy; the stronger the wind, the deeper is the layer affected by the turbulence. With wind velocities of more than 15 to 20 miles an hour, this motion becomes so extensive and rapid that the total duration of contact between any portion of the warm air and the cool surface is likely to be so brief that only very little cooling can take place at, or near, the surface; consequently, no fog forms. If the dew point is reached at all, it will not be at the ground level but at, say, 1,000 to 1,500 feet above, for turbulence produces a lapse rate, in the layer of air affected by it, approximating the dry adiabatic rate of 5.4°F. per 1,000 feet. This means that the lowest temperatures are not at the surface, but near the upper limit of the turbulent layer which, depending on the wind speed and the configuration of the land, may be anything up to 1,500 feet above the surface. Accordingly, if there is any deposit of water droplets, it will take the form of stratus cloud, and not of fog.

Somewhere in between these extremes there is an intermediate state in which the moisture supply, the rate of cooling, and the degree of turbulence are so balanced as to ensure that condensation of the water vapor shall take place *near* the ground in the form of mist or fog. It is because this balance of forces is finely adjusted that radiation fog is so irregular in its habits and so difficult to forecast.

What, at first sight, could be more irregular than the fact that ground fogs are often at their worst, not during the night when the temperature is lowest, but shortly after sunrise when the ground and the layer of air immediately above it are beginning to gain more heat than they are losing by radiation? Indeed, quite often when no fog forms during the night at all, it begins to do so as soon as the sun is up. It has been suggested that the soot and other water-loving compounds discharged into the saturated air from innumerable factory furnaces, which are usually fired in the early morning, may have something to do with this. They may, near the towns and big industrial areas. It is also probable that the explanation lies partly in the fact that after sunrise there is an increase of turbulence: this causes the cold saturated air near the surface to condense onto the hygroscopic particles which are present in the overlying layer of warmer but nearly saturated air. However, beyond a certain point, mixing, or turbulence, makes for the dispersal of fog rather than its growth, for it starts to bring down drier air from aloft which swallows up the surplus water as invisible water vapor.

The fog spots

From what we have said, it will be seen that the places most subject to fog are of three kinds: valley bottoms, mountaintops or hilltops, and cold-water lee shores.

A valley bottom, particularly one of gentle gradient, provides an ideal gathering ground for radiation fogs. On a clear, almost airless evening, the cooling process proceeds at a faster rate on high ground than on low, for whereas a given parcel of air suspended at sundown immediately above the floor of a valley is likely to receive some heat from the walls as well as the floor of that valley, the same parcel of air, if elevated to the crest line of the valley, will receive heat from one direction only, namely, from below. Because the cooling process works faster at the upper levels, exposed surfaces lose their heat faster; consequently air directly in contact with them becomes heavier than the "free" air, and because it is heavier it sinks, undercutting and displacing the lighter warmer air adjacent to the ground. Being a fluid, this cooled air behaves like water and goes on sinking until it "finds its own level." As more air is cooled and sinks, a larger pool of heavy moist air (moist because cooling increases the relative humidity) collects in the valley bottom. Once the valley bottom is shut off from the warmer "occluded" air, it begins to cool at a faster rate than the sides of the valley, with the result that the dew-point temperature of the air is generally reached at the bottom of the valley before it is reached on the upper slopes. Hence radiation fogs customarily start sooner, last longer and, to boot, are thicker in valleys than on higher ground or even on flat open ground.

But nobody who lives in the heavily industrialized valleys of western Pennsylvania needs to be instructed on this point. On a good radiation night, there is practically a 100 per cent risk of some impairment of the visibility in downtown Pittsburgh (haze, mist, or fog—or smog). Pittsburgh is, in fact, one of the foggiest places on the entire continent, with a mean annual expectation of at least 50 days on which the visibility will fall below 1,000 meters (or approximately 1,100 yards).

Mountaintops or hilltops are equally prolific breeders of upslope fog, a species of advection fog. Whereas the cooling of horizontally moving air proceeds slowly under normal circumstances (horizontal temperature gradients over land seldom being greater than 1 to 2°F. per 100 miles), the cooling of vertically rising air is very much faster, gradients being of the order of 1 to 2°F. per 500 feet. This means to say that Gulf air moving up the Appalachians frequently envelops in mist or fog every hill more than 1,000 feet high, while leaving the valley floors clear all the way from Birmingham to Binghamton.

From which it follows that if you are planning an automobile journey for which there are alternative routes, you should go the high road when conditions are suitable for the formation of radiation fog, and the low road when advection or upslope fog is likely. And remember that fog kills more motorists than any other meteorological hazard.

But foggier than any hill or valley is a seacoast flanked by a cool current, and swept by winds that are prevailingly on-shore. Such a coast is the central Californian from Point Conception northward; another is the Cape Cod coast; a third, the southeast coast of Newfoundland. In each case the horizontal sea-temperature gradient between the shore and the open

Fig. 21. Average number of days of dense fog per year. (Courtesy of the Weather Bureau, U.S. Department of Commerce)

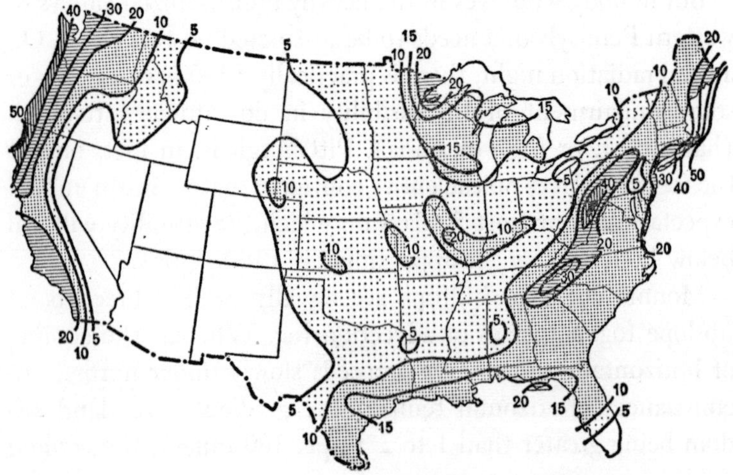

ocean is sharp—sometimes as much as 10°F. in 100 miles. When maritime air masses, especially those of tropical origin, move athwart the sea isotherms, as they must do on approaching the coast, the rate of advectional cooling of their already moist surface layers is accelerated, and provided the turbulence is insufficiently strong to mix the saturated surface air with the drier air aloft, it is only a matter of time before a layer of fog, or mist, forms at the plane of contact. The people living in and near St. John's, Newfoundland, will probably tell us that it takes no time at all! And in the face of the accompanying figures, we would be foolish to argue with them.

FREQUENCY OF POOR VISIBILITY AT TORBAY (AIRPORT FOR ST. JOHN'S, N.F.) EXPRESSED AS A PERCENTAGE OF ALL HOURLY OBSERVATIONS, 1944–1947

Visibility below 6 miles

Jan.	Feb.	Mar.	Apr.	May	June	July	Aug.	Sept.	Oct.	Nov.	Dec.
19.9	21.8	23.0	30.7	30.4	36.3	28.7	28.4	24.8	20.6	33.2	13.8

Visibility below 55 yards (i.e., dense fog)

Jan.	Feb.	Mar.	Apr.	May	June	July	Aug.	Sept.	Oct.	Nov.	Dec.
8.3	8.6	9.3	16.7	14.2	18.0	13.6	9.8	6.6	6.6	12.8	7.0

The figures for the inland airport of Gander are distinctly better, but still far worse than those for any other major international airport on the continent. They, too, show that November, like April in Caroline Southey's well-known lines, has a special genius for wrapping "hill, valley, grove and town" in "low-hung clouds" and "soft gray mist."

FREQUENCY OF POOR VISIBILITY (LESS THAN 6 MILES) AT GANDER, N.F.

Jan.	Feb.	Mar.	Apr.	May	June	July	Aug.	Sept.	Oct.	Nov.	Dec.
9.6	14.2	11.6	16.4	9.6	15.9	12.7	12.1	14.3	12.8	23.6	6.6

Smog . . .

It is not difficult to see why large urban and industrial areas tend to have a bad fog record.

Before a fog can form, the lower layers of the atmosphere must be so far chilled that the normal lapse rate is reversed, that is, the temperature increases, instead of decreases, with height. When this happens, the vertical displacement of air is sharply curtailed, if not eliminated, for the resulting inversion, as it is called, acts as a ceiling that prevents the escape of surface air to higher levels. An inversion has this trapping ability, whether the air below it is foggy or not.

When an inversion is present, the chemical by-products of combustion, such as soot, sulfur dioxide, and carbon monoxide, as well as street dust, particles of paint, rubber, tar, and asphalt, pollen, and all the other contributors of impurity to our atmosphere, must accumulate near their places of origin: they cannot penetrate the ceiling of the inversion, and because of the customary absence of surface wind under such circumstances, they cannot be dispersed horizontally either. Thus, when an inversion of temperature occurs, the concentration of smoke particles in the air of large towns increases rapidly. If the air under the inversion is approaching saturation point, these particles will in time acquire a coating of moisture, for during the hours of darkness each particle radiates into the surrounding air its own tiny store of heat and so gets colder, chilling the damp air in contact with it, and causing the excess of moisture in the cooled air to condense on its outer surface. Once formed, these droplets are likely to increase in size by overspending during the night the income of short-wave radiation received during the day, which results in their becoming still colder, that is, in their being able to condense still more of the ambient water vapor.

The end product of this cumulative process, which grows by its own increase, is too well-known to need description. Apart from rendering the fog dark-colored and exceedingly dirty, these suspended impurities act as a barrier to the penetration to the earth of the sun's rays—an even more effective barrier than is offered by ordinary fog particles, for smoke particles that have risen to the top of the inversion absorb the incoming solar rays, getting appreciably heated by them and augmenting the temperature of the air in their vicinity, and thereby strengthening rather than weakening the inversion. Because of this, a smoke fog, or smog—its more usual name in these days—is hard to budge once it has become well established over a large industrial center; and the longer it lasts, the higher the content of toxic impurities, with their attendant hazards for the smog-bound.

When an inversion builds up over a heavily industrialized area in unsaturated air, few of the rising impurities succeed in entraining droplets of water. Consequently, such obscuration of the atmosphere as occurs is the product, almost exclusively, of the accumulation near the top of the inversion layer of solid particles. While the vertical visibility will be impaired by these particles, horizontal visibility is likely to remain better than it would be in a smoke fog. During the November, 1953, spell of smoke haze, or smaze as the economy-worded journalists preferred to call it, the concentration of "particulate matter" in the New York region at the breathing level was between seven and ten times greater than it customarily is at that time of the year: whereas the metropolitan air is in the habit of carrying half a ton of dust, soot, etc., to the cubic mile, its load then rose locally to between 3½ and 5 tons per cubic mile. Though there was nothing lethal about such a concentration, it produced a remarkable crop of persons suffering from throat irritation, burning eyes, headaches, nausea, loss of appetite, not to mention fright for, as is not unusual with the unusual, some people preferred to believe that the phenomenon was the work of an adversary.

Before now, alas, there have been "killer" fogs. The smoke fog that enveloped Greater London from December 5 to 9, 1952, is thought to have been directly responsible for the deaths of not less than 4,000 people. In a report published in *The Lancet*, the journal of the British Medical Association, Dr. William P. Dowie Logan, one of Britain's leading medical statisticians, claims that during the first twenty-four hours the number of deaths in the affected area reached 400, or about twice the rate before the fog began, that it reached 600 on the second day, and exceeded 900 on each of the third and fourth days, and was still nearly 800 on the fifth day, during which the fog lifted. Old and young were affected. The mortality rate of newborn infants almost doubled, and that of infants between 1 month and 12 months more than doubled: in the forty-five years and over age group, the rates were still higher, being especially high among sufferers from bronchitis and pneumonia. Another investigator, Dr. Ernest T. Wilkins, head of the atmospheric-pollution section of the Department of Scientific and Industrial Research, claims that 8,000 more people died in the following months from aftereffects of the fog.

The only other occasions when the death rates in the London area were of this order were at the height of the cholera epidemic of 1834 and during the influenza epidemic of 1918–1919.

So far, American cities have been spared the horrors of such an experience. Admittedly, the Donora, Pennsylvania, smog of 1948 was bad enough, but it is doubtful if it was directly responsible for more than twenty deaths. But we may not always be let off as lightly.

It is true that we do not have to compete with the problem

of the domestic open coal-burning fire (perhaps the biggest poison producer in metropolitan England), but we have all the other ingredients of the Londoner's lethal fog to contend with —and as far as one of them is concerned, namely, carbon monoxide, any of our big cities can claim the doubtful distinction of outproducing London, whose automobile exhausts produce a mere 2,000 tons of the poison daily. (The corresponding production for New York is nearer 10,000 than 5,000 tons, and is increasing all the time.) It is also true that a good many people in this country are directing a great deal of thought to the problem of smoke abatement, and that they may in time learn to take the color out of smog, and so give us cleaner towns. However, the problem goes deeper than that—even smokeless fuels can give off poison gases. Indeed, one of these poisons, sulfur dioxide, stands a bigger chance of working havoc in a "clean" than in a dirty atmosphere, since under the action of sunlight it reacts with oxygen to form sulfur trioxide which, in turn, combines with water vapor to form a mist of dilute sulfuric acid! Perhaps it's that, rather than the cigarettes, that is responsible for the lung cancer we hear so much about these days. Be that as it may, the advertising people are already telling us that it's not the cigarette smoke, but the city smog! *

. . . *And its cure*

Unfortunately the smog problem shows many signs of getting worse rather than better, since with every passing year our lives are becoming more mechanized and, consequently, more dependent on the goods of industry and our cities bigger and so more productive of the toxic ingredients of fogs; at the

* One London health officer has recently gone on record as saying it is possible that the connection between cancer deaths and lack of sunshine could be either that a smoky atmosphere predisposes to lung cancer, or that sunshine is important in its prevention.

same time, our autumns and winters show signs of getting milder and so capable of giving us stronger temperature inversions.

It is, of course, simple enough to prescribe solutions to the problem, at least the more noxious aspects of it. All we have to do is to trap the impurities before they leave the smokestack or the exhaust pipe. But that costs money, which many corporations do not seem to have, and involves legislation, which many communities do not seem able to pass or willing to enforce. Where money and legislation have been forthcoming, notable progress has been made. In the late thirties, St. Louis, Missouri, enacted a series of smoke-elimination laws prohibiting the use of certain types of soft coal. These laws have been rigorously enforced with very evident success: during the fall of 1953—one of the smoggiest on record over the eastern half of the country as a whole—the visibility in downtown St. Louis was only once seriously impaired.

Los Angeles County has been grappling with the same problem almost as long and claims to be "holding its own," notwithstanding the establishment of more than a billion dollars' worth of new industrial plant in the six-year period 1948–1953, during which most of the remedial measures (costing more than 50 million dollars!) have been taken. But the patient is going to give the doctors a lot more trouble before they can pronounce a cure. It's just too bad that the founders of Los Angeles didn't know more about meteorology. Every other big city in this country can rely on getting a shower of rain to wash away its smog from time to time, but Los Angeles only gets a total of 15 inches per annum, is frequently without measurable rain for four to five months on end, and during the greater part of its annual drought season is canopied by one of the most unaccommodating inversions to be found anywhere on the earth.

Granted that brains, money, and legislation will eventually

take the tears out of smog, will they also be able to take the fear out of fog? Even disperse it? As far as fear goes, radar has already done much to eliminate it. Ships that pass in the night of fog can, thanks to their radar scopes, "see" as clearly as in the broadest daylight: and air-ground control and other homing devices allow aircraft to make blind landings with no less precision. But fog-bound ships fall behind their schedules, fog-bound airports cancel their services, and, worse, accidents attributable to fog, whether on land, sea, or in the air, still trouble our headlines.

As for the possibility of dispersing fog, it seems that the only real problem here is one of cost, for given enough heat, any fog can be dispersed—temporarily at least. During World War II, when round-the-clock aircraft patrols were frequently necessary, many a British runway was kept open in thick weather with the help of gasoline. The device employed was simple. It consisted of using a series of perforated pipes, laid along the edges of a runway, through which gasoline vapor could be sprayed and then set afire. The intense heat generated by the resulting flames evaporated the excess moisture in the air and so "burned off" the fog. The cost, however, was considerable. Fifteen million gallons of gasoline was consumed over a period of two and one-half years in bringing in 2,500 fog-bound planes. Needless to say, few commercial airlines could afford to expend 6,000 gallons of gasoline per plane per landing.*

More recently, Drs. Irving Langmuir and Vincent J. Schaefer of General Electric's Research Laboratory at Schenectady have demonstrated that stratus cloud (alias fog) can be dispersed

* In this country Los Angeles has experimented with a fog-clearing technique based on the British prototype, but then Los Angeles has oil derricks almost on its airport—an arrangement that reflects great credit on the city fathers and no small sense of propriety on the part of the oil companies. (Since they are among the biggest producers of smog, what could be more fitting than that they should seek to get rid of it—and by means of "the hair of the dog that bit them"?)

more simply and very much more cheaply by means of the so-called seeding technique. On March 6, 1947, they sprayed a layer of stratus cloud with a few dollars' worth of dry ice from an airplane. Looking down on the cloud they observed that almost immediately a deep groove was produced along the top of the seeded area and that later the sky cleared over an area some twenty miles long by five miles wide, even though there were no other breaks in the overcast in any direction. Further tests on stratus clouds produced similar results and encouraged the hope that, for the price of a few pounds of dry ice or some other nucleating agent, such as silver iodide, any pilot could clear himself a large enough patch of fog to make a contact landing. But it seems that, to realize this hope, the pilot needs to have a Langmuir or a Schaefer on board to help him, for if he should choose the wrong cloud patch, or "overseed" the target area, he might actually finish up with more fog instead of less.

Buttressed by their quite spectacular successes and nothing deterred by their failures, some cloud physicists are now asking what is to stop them from doing away with troublesome fogs altogether, merely by applying the seeding technique to moist air in advance of condensation. And the idea has great merit, as any luckless Londoner would be quick to concede, but *please,* Dr. Langmuir, leave us at least

A *wisp of fog betwixt us and the sun,*

for while there may no longer be much to be said for the feeling of fog in our throat, we confess that we still share Robert Browning's liking for the mist in our face.

High-flying saucers and low-lying fogs

Inversions are inveterate troublemakers. Not only do they work great havoc with our cities by conjuring up smog and smaze, they also conjure up optical illusions that work scarcely less havoc with the citizens.

When the normal density gradient of the atmosphere is disturbed by the intrusion of a layer of warm air between two colder layers (or vice versa), or by the exceptional heating up of the surface layer, the refractive condition of the atmosphere is likewise disturbed, with the result that light rays are "bent" as they pass from one layer to the next—much as they are when they pass from air to water or through a prism. Every motorist is familiar with one optical effect of this bending process, for it is responsible for the "heat" mirage commonly observed on a highway in summer. What the motorist sees then is not the road but the sky reflected in the surface. Sometimes the bending, or refraction, is so clear cut that it would almost appear as if a mirror had been interposed at the plane of discontinuity. However, in this case, which is sometimes referred to as an "inferior" mirage, no inversion is involved: on the contrary, the vertical lapse rate is exceedingly steep.

Less common, but far more productive of newsworthy optical phenomena, is the mirage which forms when an inversion, or more than one inversion, is present. This type, sometimes referred to as a "superior" mirage, has the effect of bringing into view objects normally beyond the range of surface vision. In order to stage such a mirage, Nature must first produce a strongly heated land surface, and then conjure up a light breeze which will transfer, without dissipating, the heated layer of air to a noticeably cooler surface (usually water). The consequent chilling of the underside of the heated layer produces the inversion. When this happens, all kinds of optical illusions are possible; lakes, woods, rivers, roads, dwelling houses, indeed whole townships that lie beyond the horizon are lifted "bodily" into mid-air; the observed times of sunrise and sunset may differ by as much as 2 minutes from the times given in almanacs, and, by night, new "stars" swing into the astronomers' ken and "unidentified aircraft" into the observers' radar scope.

It is not without significance that a considerable percentage of the corroborated "saucer" stories can be traced to parts of North America and to times of the year in which inversions capable of producing superior mirages are known to have been present. This is not to say that all the Air Force's unidentified flying objects are merely reflections of motorists' headlamps, but merely that some of them could be—including, perhaps, those seen flying across the night sky in formation. The accompanying diagram may help those of us who have forgotten our physics of light to see how such a phenomenon could arise.

The Civil Aeronautics Administration has a much more complicated explanation of some of the "blips" that impair the vision of the radar expert, but this, too, involves inversions. It

Fig. 22. Refraction of light sources by inversion plane.

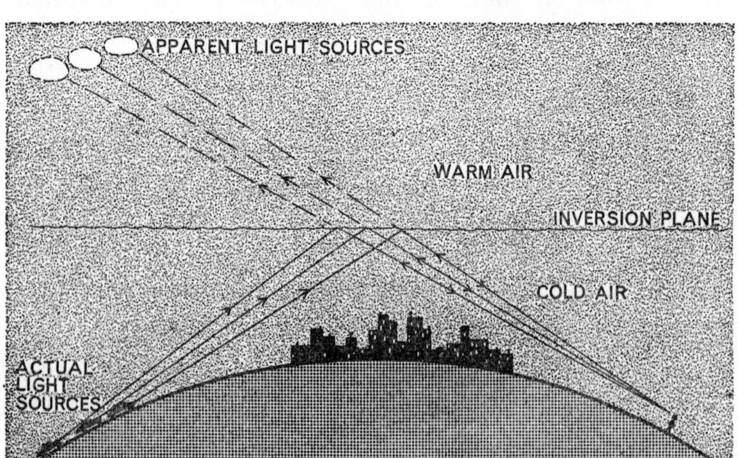

appears that radar echoes or reflections can be received from moving parcels of air that are of a different density from the air in their immediate environment. Such parcels may represent the vestiges of a cold stratum of air sandwiched between two warm ones, or vice versa. These parcels will travel with approximately the speed of the air in which they are enveloped, which speed may be anything up to 200 miles an hour—even more. While they may not always be of sufficient density to produce direct reflections (or returns as they are called in radar language), they are often able to bend the radar beam downward to give a ground return. Horizontal movement of these parcels would, according to a 1952 report by the CAA, produce a movement twice as great in the image being received on the radar scope, and in a parallel direction. This ties in with the fact that when the speed of targets on the radar scope was divided by two, their motions corresponded closely to the reported wind directions and velocities at certain altitude levels. In nearly all cases, the temperature inversion levels were at or adjacent to those altitudes.

All of which should help us and the Martians to sleep better o' nights. (Maybe *they* have their inversion worries, too.)

Driest month?

It is a striking testimony to the inconstancy of our climate that, over considerable tracts of North America, any of the twelve months may emerge as the wettest or the driest in a particular year. We once had occasion to look into the incidence of dry and wet months for Montreal and found it to be as follows over a seventy-one-year span of observations:

	Jan.	Feb.	Mar.	Apr.	May	June	July	Aug.	Sept.	Oct.	Nov.	Dec.
Wettest month	4	5	8	1	4	6	7	8	10	7	4	7
Driest month	1	4	7	9	11	6	4	8	6	9	2	4

We suggest that somewhat comparable figures could be produced for at least half the observing stations in the United States.

At the same time, in most parts of the Union there is a much greater chance of certain months being the driest, or wettest, of the twelve than of others. In fact, this is even true if we take the country as a whole (admittedly a rather "unclimatic" thing to do, since it is made up of many highly differentiated climatic zones). The accompanying table shows the mean monthly location of the wettest and driest months over the forty-eight states.

Number of states in which each month of year is normally	(1) the wettest of the twelve and	(2) the driest
January	4	5
February	0	12
March	5	0
April	0	0
May	8	1
June	9	1
July	12	3
August	3	2
September	0	0
October	0	7
November	0	11
December	1	0 *

* The observant reader will note that the sum of these columns is not 48, but 42: the reason for this is that in the weighted averages we employed, Maryland was grouped with Delaware and New England was treated as a single state.

The marked tendency for mid-fall and midwinter to be drier than the rest of the year is immediately apparent.

The prominence of February among the dry months is due in large measure to the fact that the month is two to three days shorter than its neighbors: actually, the mean *daily* precipitation reaches its lowest monthly value in February in only six of the forty-two areas listed. (This still makes it one of the four driest months of the year—and certainly not the "dike filler" it is reputed to be.*) The claims of October and November to be the driest month of the year are more substantial. On the face of it, November would appear to be the drier of the two, since in eleven areas (representing twelve states) of the forty-two we have listed, it is the driest month of the year, whereas October is the driest in only seven areas (representing seven states). On the basis of mean monthly precipitation, November is drier than October, for, according to figures compiled by J. B. Kincer, one-time Chief of the Division of Climate and Crop Weather, in the U.S. Weather Bureau, the mean November precipitation over the Union as a whole is 2.02 inches, as against 2.06 inches for October. However, since October has an extra day, this means that the average *daily* precipitation is actually somewhat lower in October than in November, namely, 0.0664 inch as against 0.0673 inch. Which, very approximately, is just another way of saying that the odds on the month of November being the driest of the twelve are just about as long (or short) as the odds on a given *day* in October being the driest of the 365. But I am no statistician: most statisticians are no meteorologists, and most meteorologists are no good at gambling anyway.

* The fact that the dikes and rivers are frequently full in February, notwithstanding, can perhaps be attributed to the slow rate of evaporation prevalent at that time of the year. The wetness of the surface of the earth depends largely on the excess of precipitation in any period over and above what can be evaporated or readily run off during that period. Whereas the rate of evaporation in summer is usually sufficient to remove in short order any temporary surplus of surface water, in winter the average precipitation over many parts of the continent is twenty to thirty times greater than the evaporative power of the air. Even so, the poorest month for evaporation is generally not February, nor even January, but December.

Dry spells and droughts

Whereas a dry spell can occur almost any time of the year, a drought * is more likely to occur in some seasons than others.

At first sight it may seem odd that the fall is a drought breeder. After all, plant moisture requirements are then very low, the worst of the year's heat is over, evaporation rates are down, and it is the "season of mists," dews, and fogs—all of them indicators of a moist atmosphere. The effect of these factors, however, is more than offset by others, such as the generally low ground-water level at the end of the summer (even in a wet summer it is rare for precipitation to make good the moisture losses sustained through evaporation, absorption by plants, and runoff); the characteristic dryness of large parts of the country in the fall, for this means that the earth is less able to "cushion" the shock of a prolonged dry spell; and the prevalence of high-pressure systems, sometimes dominating the entire continent at that season. This last factor is without question the most important of the three, for while, as we have seen, rain can fall when the pressure is high, the chances of heavy, continuous, and widespread rain occurring under anticyclonic conditions are very poor. It is no coincidence that all the great deserts of the world are located in areas of permanently, or semipermanently, high pressure. Nor is it any co-

* A drought in the United States is usually defined as a period during which the dearth, or absence, of precipitation is seriously injurious to vegetation. Meteorologists have never been able to agree on a more specific definition, largely because the degree of injury which a prolonged dry spell can do to plant life depends on several things besides the accumulated deficit of rainfall: it depends, too, on the prevailing temperatures, amount of wind movement, character and condition of soil (for example, how well, or ill, supplied with moisture it was to begin with), rate of evaporation, cloudiness, and stage reached in the plant-growth cycle. Another complicating factor is that what would constitute a drought agronomically in one part of a state would not necessarily do so in another part.

incidence that every time we get a national dry year (that is, a year in which the rainfall over the country as a whole is subnormal) the Pacific high is in an "empire-building" mood and adds the Great Basin and adjacent cordilleras to its maritime domains. Now it happens that pressure over the Great Basin region normally reaches its seasonal peak in November.

The connection between this November high and the national rainfall is very clearly demonstrated in the accompanying graphs constructed by Dr. I. R. Tannehill, who has made a more intensive study of American droughts than any other climatologist, dead or living.

In the ten years (between 1886 and 1944, the period covered by the graphs) when the November pressures at Salt Lake City in the heart of the Great Basin were highest, the national precipitation for the month of November averaged 37 per cent below normal; at St. Louis, Missouri, for instance, the mean precipitation for the month in those years was 1.49 inches, as against 2.39 inches for the fifty-nine-year period. On the other hand, in the ten years when the November pressures at Salt Lake City were lowest, the national precipitation for the month

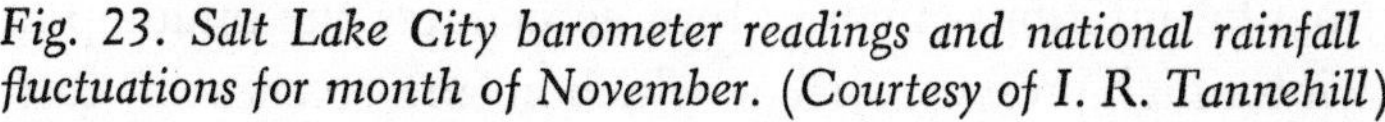

Fig. 23. Salt Lake City barometer readings and national rainfall fluctuations for month of November. (Courtesy of I. R. Tannehill)

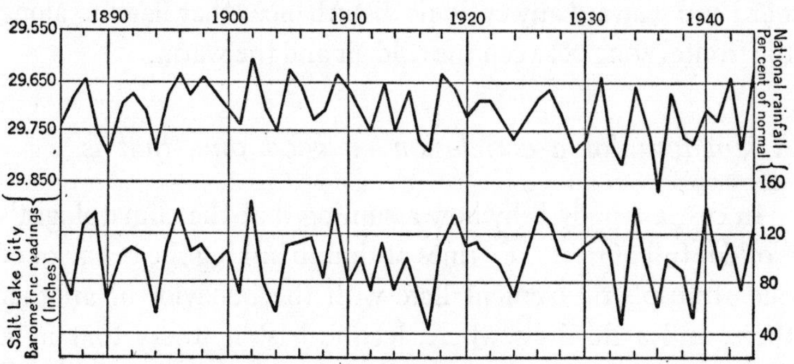

was 20 per cent above normal; in those years the precipitation at St. Louis averaged 3.02 inches, that is, twice what it was during the "high-pressure" Novembers.

It may well be asked why an expanded Pacific high should play such a crucial part in the nation's precipitation economy. There seem to be at least two strong contributory causes. Firstly, the air in the Great Basin extension of the high is relatively dry, having lost most of its precipitable moisture in climbing over the coastal Sierras. Secondly, the high pressures which build up over the Basin and, often, over neighboring parts of the Great Plains have the effect of blocking the free northward flow of warm, moisture-laden air from the Gulf of Mexico and the southward flow of cold air from the Canadian arctic, the interplay of which has so much to do with the generation of our mid-latitude cyclones—our main rain bringers. This blocking action is sometimes reinforced as the result of a temporary union of the Great Basin high with the Bermuda high, whose "behavior patterns" sometimes show a striking similarity to those of the Pacific high. A third contributory cause may be the fact that the inability of warm air masses to penetrate very far north under such conditions hastens the cooling off of the continental interior, which in turn accelerates the build-up of the winter high-pressure system, which in turn steers away eastward and seaward any cyclonic disturbances that flare up along the frontal zone between the cold air and the warm.

A *kingdom for a correlation—a good one, that is*

In case anybody is by now assuming that the climatologist's world is full of neat little rules of thumb linking the behavior of one atmospheric element here with the behavior of another there, and a third elsewhere, let me hasten to say that it is. The only trouble about nearly all of them is that they don't tell you very much: and there's little or nothing you can do with them when you've got them. If only we could find a correlation between, let us say, the pressure at Salt Lake City in November and the rainfall at St. Louis six months later, or between this November's weather in Texas and next November's prospects in Washington!

The search for correlations of this kind is unceasing and probably engages the thinking of more climatologists than any other single topic. Like the sourdough who has spent a lifetime looking for gold and found a dime's worth, many a climatologist has spent years "panning" his way through mountains of dusty statistics, smoothing endless curves, and constructing interminable mathematical series, in the hope of "striking it rich." And the stakes are high enough, to be sure. Six months' foreknowledge of rainfall distribution and amount would be worth a king's ransom to the ranchers of Colorado, the cotton growers of California, the truck farmers of New Jersey, and for that matter, the lobbyists on Capitol Hill.

These correlation seekers argue that, as the atmosphere is a unit, marked deviations from the normal over one large area must be compensated for, either simultaneously or subsequently, elsewhere, and that major deviations are probably expressions of slow oscillations, or rhythms, and can therefore be expected to have terrestrial antecedents stretching back weeks, months, or even a year and more, into the past. A few such correlations have indeed been established. It is well known, for instance, that the mean pressure of the atmosphere in the Icelandic region varies inversely with that in the region of the Azores in winter, which means that when the Azores high is abnormally well developed and the weather correspondingly sunny and settled, the weather along the northern sea lanes of the Atlantic is more stormy than usual. Nobody quite knows why, and, even so, the prognostic value of the correlation is really no greater than that between pressure in the Great Basin and rainfall in the Great Plains. Of rather more practical interest are correlations of the type demonstrated by Dr. G. F. McEwen of the Scripps Institution of Oceanography at La Jolla, namely, between the rainfall curve of a given season in Southern California and the sea and air temperatures of the preceding months, and between both of these and changes in the pressure gradient off the Pacific coast. The late Sir Napier Shaw established an even more spectacular correlation between the amount of rain falling in Java between October and March and the pressure at Bombay in the following April to September; it is just too bad that the converse was not found to apply, for what worries the 360 million Indians is not so much the pressures as the rains they are likely to get between April and September. More recently another British climatologist, C. E. P. Brooks, has proved that a relation exists between the state of the polar ice field and the weather subsequently experienced in the British Isles, a relationship which is entirely reasonable on physical grounds, but which, like the others, is so loose-jointed that it seldom stands up to the test of application. Forecasts based on these relationships have often proved worthless.

The road to fame and fortune as a correlation maker is still wide open: but most of those who walk it die poor and unsung.

Climatic rhythm

Not all the results of statistical investigation are negative, however. It is true that they provide very little support for the theory that the weather runs to a schedule, giving, year after year, the same kinds of weather in the same places at the same seasons, and still less for the belief that it is geared to the moon. At the same time, they make it clear that there is both form and pattern—rhythm, in fact—behind the seemingly inconsequential behavior of our weather: that there are periods of time in which the climate swings back and forth as though it clung to the butt of a giant pendulum or "throbbed in a cosmic pulse."

The idea that climate swings back and forth is far from new: it is certainly as old as Plato, probably older. But the discovery of climatic cycles and the measurement of their "beat" are comparatively modern achievements, and hard-won at that. The evidence is scattered and often obscure: some of it is in cipher, some of it has been well-nigh obliterated by the hand of man, and nearly all of it is capable of being construed in more ways than one. Much of the more recent evidence lies embedded in the archives of observatories whose systematic records go back, in a few instances, more than 200 years. For the remoter past, the evidence has to be looked for in such self-registering phenomena as the growth rings of a tree, which reveal not only the age of the tree but, in the variable width of its annual rings, changes from year to year in growth conditions; in the layers of sediment—varves—deposited every year round the shores of lakes and inland seas; and in the archaeological records of bygone civilizations.

Of the hundreds of postulated weather cycles, by far the best known and most significant is the sunspot cycle. Records which have been kept for over two centuries show that sunspots reach a maximum in number and extent about every 11½ years on the average, the exact interval varying between seven and fifteen years. These sunspots are expressions of exceptional thermal activity. Since the sun is the root cause of all earthly weather, it is reasonable enough to suppose that weather cycles should correspond with cycles of the sun's condition. And this seems to be the case, for an increase in the number of sunspots usually means an increase in the amount of solar radiation, though if the sunspots become too numerous, they cover so much of the sun's face that solar radiation is reduced in spite of the increased activity of the sun. This fact, coupled with the greater opacity and cloudiness of the atmosphere induced by the greater ionization of ultraviolet light at sunspot maxima, probably explains why temperatures for the earth as a whole are lower at sunspot maxima and higher at sunspot minima. However, the relation is not everywhere so direct or obvious as this: for, while the greater ionization of the water vapor in the atmosphere during the sunspot maxima undoubtedly induces abnormal cloud formation and thunderstorm activity in many areas, such as the east coast of Canada and the equatorial zone, it seems to have the opposite effect on others, for example, mid-continental Canada and the arid subtropical zone where temperatures average rather higher during sunspot maxima and lower during sunspot minima. Many other significant correlations with the sunspot cycle have been established. Thus the late H. H. Clayton found that 40 per cent more snow fell in the region of Harvard University around the time of a sunspot maximum than around the time of a sunspot minimum. He also found that two or three times as many icebergs were reported in arctic and antarctic waters at sunspot maxima as compared with sunspot minima.

The existence of a double and also a quadruple sunspot cycle, namely, twenty-two to twenty-three and forty-four to forty-six years, respectively, can be traced in the fossil weather records preserved in the long-lived sequoias of California and in the lake sediments in many parts of the North American continent and elsewhere.

For a time there was thought to be an even more significant thirty-five-year cycle. The existence of this cycle was first suspected in 1626 by Sir Francis Bacon, but it was not until 1890 that the eminent Viennese climatologist, Eduard Brückner, adduced what he believed to be irrefutable statistical evidence of it. According to Brückner, who had examined every weather record he could lay his hands on, temperature and rainfall variations in Europe had a periodicity of 34.8 ± 0.7 years. Each period, or cycle, so he argued, was composed of a cool-humid half and a warm-dry half: the amplitude of the oscillations was small (in the case of temperature, not more than 2°F., and in the case of rainfall, approximately 8 to 9 per cent of the mean value) but recognizable when plotted graphically. And there are parts of Europe where it does appear to be in harmony with the facts. Thus, it fits, or did until recently, the oscillations of the surface level of the Caspian Sea, the advances and retreats of certain Alpine glaciers, and the variation in the dates of opening and closing of Russian rivers, and in the date of the European grape harvest. However, Sir Gilbert Walker has demonstrated that it is not an important factor in the weather fluctuations of the British Isles, and even on the continent of Europe where it originated, more than one authority has described the cycle as being "merely of historic interest."

The big trouble with weather cycles is that, once you start looking for them, it is very easy to make yourself believe that the world is full of them—and it probably is. The late Sir Napier Shaw, who was too good a meteorologist to let his cycles carry him away, believed he had found evidence of no less than 130, ranging in period from 14 months to 260 years. And if we are to accept the evidence of the varves, it seems that even this figure is a gross underestimate, for the annual silt deposits around the shores of Lake Saki in the Crimean Peninsula show rainfall cycles running all the way from 7 to 1,701 years.

What is the cause of all these cycles? Since the sun is the father of us all (for without its energy communicated through its electrons, where would any of us be?), it is tempting to suggest that these cycles must be geared to emanations from the sun's surface, of which "spottedness" is but one expression.

But most of these cycles do not appear to be in harmony with known solar rhythms. This is not to say that the physicists will not sooner or later be able to "square the cycle" of the earth with that of the sun. Meantime some among them are showing an increasing disposition to speak of "the earth's *cosmic* environment" as a factor in the geophysics (which includes the meteorology, of course) of our planet. They are even beginning to hint that the bombardment of the earth's outer atmosphere by electrons from interstellar space may not be without its effect upon terrestrial weather.

So perhaps we shall come to find that the stars in their courses do, after all, fight for us! To say the least, there are some queer resemblances between the periodicity of weather cycles and the lengths of the orbital periods of the planets, particularly in the case of Neptune, Uranus, Saturn, and Jupiter.

When the birds go south again

The uncanny responsiveness of migratory birds to their "appointed times" is an ageless theme with poets, preachers, and philosophers alike. Jeremiah speaks for them all when he laments: "Yea, the stork in the heaven knoweth her appointed times; and the turtle [dove] and the crane and the swallow observe the time of their coming; but my people know not the judgment of the Lord." * While this is no book of poetry, preaching is out of place, and philosophy is *terra incognita,* we trust we share something of Jeremiah's wonderment in the face of mystery. And mystery still invests almost every phase of the study of bird migrations. How does the swallow find its way from a farm in Israel to a farm in Natal in its first autumn, and find its way back the following spring to the place where it was born? And why should it want to do so? (It is, of course,

* Jeremiah 8:7.

absurd to suppose that a swallow needs to go all the way back to Israel to find the food it requires, let alone a suitable nesting place.) Or, to come nearer home, why does the golden plover travel from Nova Scotia to the mainland of South America every fall or the arctic tern travel still farther, all the way from the shores of Baffin Bay to the South Atlantic?

It seems that not even the ornithologists have answers to all these questions. However, there's one question they are well on their way to solving, and that is the role of the weather in bird migrations. They have long known that there was an approximate relation between the southward retreat of the isotherms and the southward progress of the fall migrants, and similarly with the northward advance of the isotherms in the spring. But the extent to which individual migratory flights are regulated by synoptic conditions, and notably by the wind—this is something that has only recently become apparent. As the result of cooperative effort between meteorologists and ornithologists, we now know, for example, that over the eastern half of the United States and in eastern Canada fall migrations are most likely to occur when those regions are invaded by south-moving air masses of polar origin, and most unlikely to occur when a pronounced flow of warm air northward and northeastward from the Gulf of Mexico is set up.*

We also know that many of the migrants are willing, seemingly, to go thousands of miles out of their way in order to make use of a favorable wind. What strikes the meteorologist most about the normal flight path of the arctic tern, for instance, is its obvious employment of the tail winds of the North and South Atlantic. Thus, the flight path from the Baffin Bay area to south Greenland lies in the zone of northwesterly winds;

* It is only fair to say, however, that *some* bird movement goes on almost continuously—night and day—during the migrating season, whatever the weather.

from south Greenland to western Europe, in the zone of the prevailing westerlies; from western Europe to northwest Africa, in the zone of northerly and northeasterly winds; while the recurving of the flight path to eastern South America closely follows the trajectory of the easterly trade winds, which in the northern fall and early winter are likely to be found as far south as 35°S along the east coast of South America. South of that parallel, northerly and northwesterly winds prevail offshore and so give the arctic tern yet another tail wind with which to complete its migration to the South Atlantic. The flyways of the Pacific golden plover, the greater shearwater, the Greenland wheatear, and a hundred other fall migrants are capable of a similar interpretation.

All of which suggests very strongly that birds are interested in what has now come to be called "pressure-pattern" flying—that is, flying on a course and at an altitude where the winds, which are a function of the pressure pattern, offer the greatest help. If powerful modern aircraft, for reasons of economy and safety, practice pressure-pattern flying, need we be surprised that birds which are much more sensitive to air resistance are also disposed to do the same?

December

"When winter comes . . ."

Ask almost anybody when winter begins, and he will tell you round about December 21 or December 22, the time of the winter solstice, that is, when the noon sun is overhead at the southern tropic and consequently at its lowest altitude in the northern heavens. But to fix a climatic period from astronomical data is just about as appropriate as trying to tell the time of day by the number of people riding the subways: there is a connection between the two, but it varies from place to place and from season to season.

Those who do not settle for the solstice are likely to follow the conventional division of the calendar—to which leaders of fashion, sports columnists, transportation bosses, and insurance brokers are wont to give their consent—and insist that winter begins the first of the month. But they, also, would be in error from a strictly climatological standpoint—and that, after all, is the only rational standpoint from which to approach the question.

Assuming that the year is divisible into four equal seasons (a highly erroneous assumption for some parts of the continent, as we shall see), and that winter is the coldest of the four, which, of course, it is, then the most obvious way of fixing the onset of winter is by fixing the average date on which the coldest thirteen-week period of the year commences. By doing this for a large number of observing stations we find that the date differs widely from one part of the continent to another. Along the Rio Grande border it is already winter, in a normal season, by November 25: in northern Michigan the coldest quarter does not get under way much before mid-December, and in Baffin Island not before Christmas—though the mean daily temperature there has been well below freezing point for all of three months by then!

If, instead, we take as our criterion the average date on which the air temperature falls below freezing point (32°F.), we get an entirely different picture. On this basis, winter comes to the Arctic Archipelago around the end of August or beginning of September—that is, at a time when most of us are either on our summer holidays or seeking the solace of the

Fig. 24(a). Beginning of winter, as measured by the date of the start of the coldest 3 months of the year.

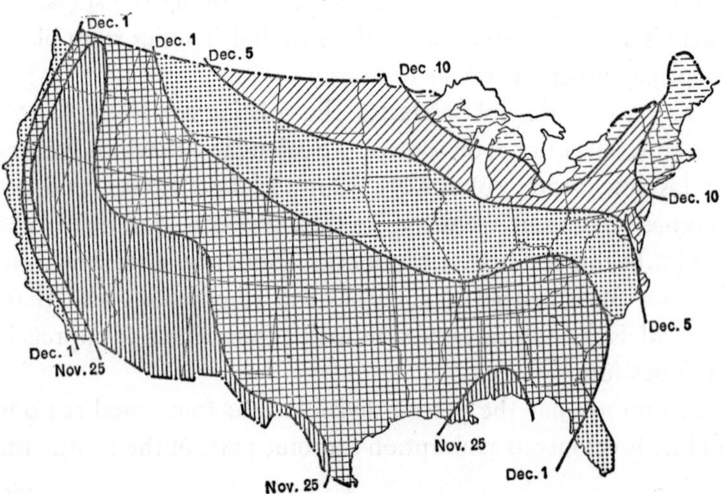

nearest air-conditioned bar. In northern Quebec, the corresponding date is October 1 or thereabouts; in North Dakota, November 10. In regions as far apart as Long Island, southern New Mexico, and eastern Washington, the "freeze" does not normally arrive before mid-December. In fully one-third of the Union, as can be seen in the accompanying map, it never arrives—at least not as a matter of course. This, perhaps, is the most striking feature of the map and, at the same time, its chief disqualification for the purpose in hand; for, as anyone will tell you, it isn't summer all the time in Florida and Southern California.

A third, and possibly the least equivocal basis for identifying the onset of winter is the rest period. After all, that is what winter essentially *is*, in the seasonal round of Nature's activity.

In winter, growth processes in plants and animals are, to say the least, at a low ebb. The sap ceases to run, the grass withers, and the flowers fade; even buds that earlier gave promise of

Fig. 24(b). Beginning of winter, as measured by the southward advance of the 32°F. isotherm. [Figs. 24(a) and (b) courtesy of Professor S. S. Visher]

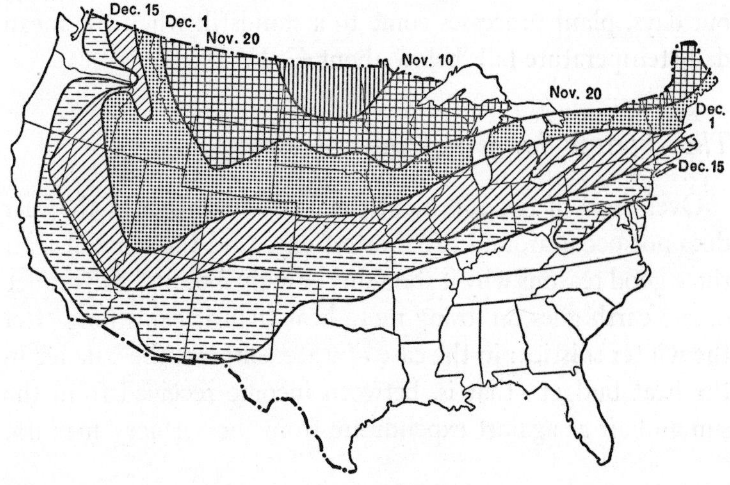

bloom shrivel and fall; toads seek the warmth of the subsurface and slip away into a coma; many of the small mammals, having eaten their fill of the harvest, hole up in the earth safe from the bleak midwinter winds. But for many living things winter means more than lowered metabolism and suspended animation. For those plants and animals and insects that cannot protect themselves against windchill, dearth of food, and enemies, it means death. With the lengthening of the meridional shadow and the concomitant decline in solar radiation and air temperature, their days are numbered. What the critical values of these variables are for the myriad forms of life, science has yet to disclose, and may never fully disclose, for it seems probable that every kind of living thing—and there are millions, if not billions, of kinds in the aggregate—has its own environmental requirements, and that no two are precisely alike. One doesn't have to be a naturalist to realize that "winter" for a squirrel does not begin, or end, the same day as it does for a toad or a field mouse.

In the circumstances about the only thing we can do is to fall back on the rather rough and not so ready rule of thumb that, in the mid-latitudes of the earth where most of us pass our days, plant processes come to a standstill when the mean daily temperature falls below about 43°F.

The shortest day is not the coldest

Over most of the continent the coldest weather of the year does not occur around the shortest day. And there are at least three good reasons why it shouldn't. Firstly, because the surface of the earth goes on losing more heat than it gains long after the winter solstice: in the case of water surfaces the balance in the heat budget (that is, between income received from the sun and air as against expenditure from the surface) may not be struck until March. Secondly, there is the increasing cold of the far north. Receiving absolutely no heat directly from the sun—north of 70°N the sun is not seen from November 16 to January 18, and north of 80°N it is not seen from October 19 to February 22—this region continues to lose such residual heat as it has by radiation to the cloudless skies above it: in consequence the pools of cold air that accumulate over the region and sporadically spill southward get progressively colder until the longer winter night is over. Thirdly, there is the influence of the great continental snowfields themselves. As the winter advances, the snow cover increases in depth. This leads to a lowering of the surface temperature: snow is one of the best insulators in the world; it can stop the upward conduction of heat from the earth below as readily as it can reflect back into the air the incoming heat from the sun. Accordingly, winds originating over snow- and ice-covered terrain tend to be colder in January and February than in December before the snowfields have had a chance to get established.

The odds on a white Christmas

Although Christmas-card artists are getting better, about one in every three of them still insists on playing a variation on the threadbare theme of frost, icicles, and snow. Among the trimmers of trees and the writers of popular lyrics, the ratio is considerably higher, no matter whether their field of operations is Miami or Montreal, Dallas or Dawson City. At times it would almost look as though respect for the traditional properties—and proprieties—of Christmas increases with distance from them. You find it even in the Belgian Congo: the fir trees that deck the hotels in Léopoldville may be imported, the snow synthetic, and the yule log unnecessary, but they make everybody happy, including the Africans.

However, the regrettable truth of the matter is that over fully three-quarters of the United States of America the odds on your waking up to a white Christmas are so long as to be incapable of calculation. Places as far apart as St. Petersburg, San Antonio, and San Diego have never seen snow at Christmas, and are not likely to. San Diego, in fact, has only once had a measurable snowfall in the entire history of its weather station. Farther north the odds get shorter, since the annual snowfall and the number of snowy days increase and the snow season starts earlier. All the same, to find snow at Christmas along the Pacific coast at sea level may mean a trek of a couple of thousand miles all the way to Alaska—and there is a very good chance that when you got there you could only find it with the aid of binoculars. In the central lowlands the search would probably take you as far north as St. Louis, Missouri, if not to the Great Lakes. On the east coast you would almost certainly have to go as far as New York City, perhaps farther, since in recent years a white Christmas in the metropolitan region has been the exception rather than the rule. There have been only fourteen occasions in the past fifty years * when the city streets were covered with snow on the morning of December 25, and only seven occasions when snow fell in measurable quantities on that day: on the other seven occasions, the snow was a hangover, and undoubtedly looked like it. The last eighteen years of the fifty failed to show a single measurable snowfall on Christmas Day. (It is only fair to add that the great blizzard of December, 1947, when 32 inches fell in 22 hours, missed Christmas Day by a mere five and a half hours!)

To be absolutely sure of finding "a picture-card" Christmas, you would need to go north of the border—even north of Montreal and the Laurentians, both of which have had at least one

* Down to 1953.

green Christmas since 1945, to the unconcealed dismay and pecuniary embarrassment of their innkeepers. Alternatively, you would need to climb a mountain—something of the order of Mount Washington which, notwithstanding the modern trend toward later and lighter snowfalls, still manages to get some snow as early as October and to keep on getting it until the following May or June. In the high Sierras, you would probably do even better, for in a "good" winter, such as the winter of 1951-1952, the accumulation near the Donner Pass, for instance, can already be as much as 12 *feet* by late December (and up to 20 feet by the end of February). But even the Sierras do not seem to be getting the winters they did.

All things considered, it would look as though 50 million red-blooded American children, to say nothing of their tradition-loving fathers and mothers, had better settle for a white-tinsel and cotton-wool Christmas. And the song writers had better begin to dream up some nice words to rhyme with "green," because the way things are going, that's the kind of Christmas most of their fans are in for.

Those good old-fashioned winters

If there's one point on which most people agree when they talk about the weather, it is that things were very different when they were young. But the moment you probe them for the nature of the differences and their magnitude, you are likely to be faced with considerable disparities of opinion. Memory is a capricious mistress at the best of times: where the weather is concerned she is positively tantalizing. How well we recall some kinds of weather—that day in December, for instance, when we played golf in our shirt sleeves, or that particular July 4 when it did everything but snow! But of other peoples' equally "unusual" days we can recall nothing, and for no better reason, it seems, than the fact that we didn't happen to be playing golf then, or to be troubled with rheumatism. So, much as folks may admire your memory, never rate its ability on a par with that of the U.S. Weather Bureau, which never forgets anything—and, what is more, can quote chapter and verse for everything it remembers.

What, exactly, has been happening to our winters? Are they merely fluctuating on a short-term basis in keeping with Dame Nature's notoriously unsteady gait, or are they undergoing a major long-term change, the true dimensions of which are masked by the more readily sensed day-to-day, month-to-month, and year-to-year changes?

That there have been cumulative climatic changes of the first magnitude in the distant past is apparent to anyone who has ever studied geology, archaeology, history, or geography. Twenty-thousand years ago or thereabouts, half of the entire North American continent was buried under a sheet of ice and a great deal of the rest was buried under its melt waters. Displaced ice-transported boulders, moraines, furrowed rocks, and tundra-type animal and plant remains in our subtropical Southwest are but a few of the unassailable evidences that the climate of this continent was radically different then from what it is today. But what of the recent past—of changes in our own lifetime? Admittedly we cannot point to anything comparable in magnitude with the warming up which must have taken place after the final recession of the great continental ice sheets, but by piecing together the various fragments of statistically reliable evidence we shall, I believe, find it difficult to support the view that the winters of a large part of the continent are as severe, and/or as long, as they were in the days of our grandfathers. For consider the following facts:

In Montreal, Quebec, subzero temperatures have been only half as common in recent years as they were at the end of the nineteenth century, the mean temperature for March has risen nearly 4 degrees, and the snowfall which averaged 130 inches in the 1880s now seldom exceeds 100 inches and averages nearer 80 inches. In the Boston region the mean winter (December, January, and February) temperatures have risen 3½°F. in the last hundred years; in the last fifty years the average duration of the snow cover has declined by about seven days, and the seasonal frequency of days with maxima no higher than 32°F. and minima no higher than zero have shown similar declines. In Washington, D.C., during the twenty-year period ending with 1892 there was a total of 354 days with freezing temperatures during the spring months; for the twenty years ending with 1933, the corresponding total was 237.

Of course, it is nearly always possible to find alternative explanations of individual differences. Thus, some meteorologists contend that the amount of hot air which escapes from our all-too-generously heated factories, offices, and houses is enough to raise the ambient temperature, at least in our cities, by at least 2°F., and that that, in turn, is enough to turn a good deal of the winter precipitation that would normally fall as snow into rain. Others see in these differences nothing more than the random series of the statistician, the kind of chance distribution that causes a gambler to throw double sixes three times in a row. I confess that I am not too impressed by such arguments. And I doubt whether the birds which frequent my garden are impressed by it either, for since about 1920 there has been a noticeable increase in the number of species of birds wintering in the northeastern states. Among those which are now to be found north of their traditional range are the cardinal, the Carolina wren, the turkey vulture, the blue-winged warbler, and the tufted titmouse. And the same applies to several species of mammals, including the opossum. Admittedly, the changes in range could be more the result of stimulation of plant growth, and so of insect population, consequent upon temperature changes than the result of the changes themselves (since it is well known that the climatic tolerance of birds and animals is considerable), but that merely forces us to ask what stimulated the plants and minds to grow more vigorously and abundantly. Whatever the full answer, it is difficult to believe that greater warmth is not a part of it. Certainly plants, especially those growing near their ecological borders, have no such tolerance as those birds and animals that batten on them. As a matter of fact there is no lack of evidence that the plant zones of this same region have been advancing poleward. In northern Quebec larches and birches are growing faster than they did thirty to forty years ago and are beginning to colonize new ground—north of the timber line. And did not we hear recently that Tennessee cotton was flourishing in a Linden, New Jersey, backyard?

But let us not draw any hasty conclusions from all this. There is good reason for believing that more winters are mild throughout the eastern and northeastern half of the continent than was the case fifty, or one hundred, years ago: equally, there is reason for believing that the incidence of really severe and snowy winters is lower now than ever. Even so, a "good old-fashioned winter" is by no means a thing of the past. The lowest temperature in sixty-five years' observations at Blue Hill Observatory, near Boston, was recorded as recently as February, 1934, and the snowiest winter in its entire history more recently still, during the winter of 1947–1948.

Furthermore, before we try to make short work of those who are contrary-minded on this matter, it is always as well to find out where they come from. Generally speaking, temperature records for places in the western half of this continent do not reflect the upward trend as strongly as those located within a thousand miles or so of the Atlantic Ocean.

And, again, it seems that our grandfathers had the same idea about *their* winters as many of us have about ours. Writing 100 years ago (1853) in the *Colonial Magazine*, a Canadian journalist informed his readers that

> it appears that Canada has already relaxed some of its former rigors, and is in a state of continued mitigation. Since a portion of its forests have been cleared, its swamps drained, its villages and settlements established, the Indians inform us that the frosts have been less severe and frequent—that the snows fall in smaller quantities, and dissolve sooner.

If the Indians were right, we wonder what on earth people 100 years hence will have to put up with, for by then all the swamps will surely have been reclaimed, the forests will be smaller—alas—than they are today, and the cities larger.

South for sunshine

Even though the winters may not be what they used to be, there's still much to be said for taking a "summer" vacation

Fig. 25. Average number of hours of sunshine per winter day. (Courtesy of the Weather Bureau, U.S. Department of Commerce)

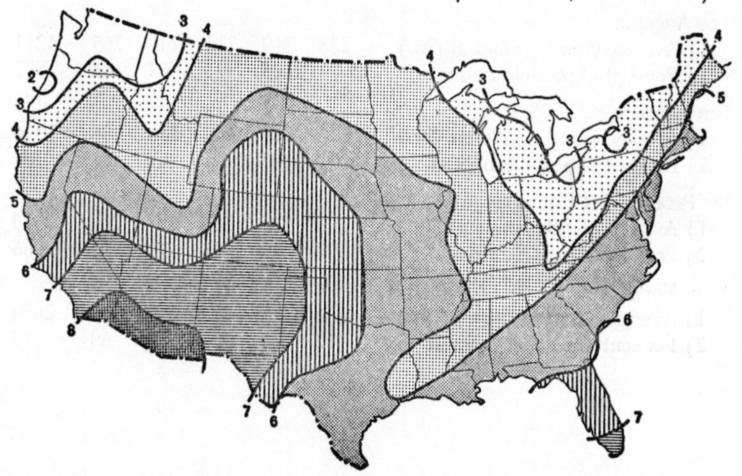

around the turn of the year. For one thing, it enables you to get two summers for the price of one, since every state in the Union has a recognizable summer. And for another, you can acquire all the evidences of a summer holiday without being scorched alive, bitten to death, and dehydrated by excessive perspiration, for whether your destination be Florida, Southern California, Arizona, or New Mexico, you will find sunshine. Maybe you won't always find as much as the chambers of commerce say there is, but you are certain to find some. Of this the official Weather Bureau statistics leave us in absolutely no doubt. Here, for instance, are the sunshine figures for five resort centers for each of the months from December through April. The figures for New York City are also given for purposes of comparison.

	Dec.	Jan.	Feb.	Mar.	Apr.	Average per year
Miami:						
1) Average monthly amount (hr.)	215	217	231	276	284	2994
2) Per cent of possible amount	66	65	72	74	74	67
Phoenix:						
1) Average monthly amount (hr.)	240	238	246	303	341	3779
2) Per cent of possible amount	77	75	79	81	87	84
Los Angeles:						
1) Average monthly amount (hr.)	228	219	211	247	265	3211
2) Per cent of possible amount	73	68	68	67	68	72
San Diego:						
1) Average monthly amount (hr.)	226	215	209	250	266	3046
2) Per cent of possible amount	73	67	67	67	68	69
St. Petersburg (Tampa):						
1) Average monthly amount (hr.)	190	193	207	263	286	2933
2) Per cent of possible amount	59	59	65	70	74	66
New York City:						
1) Average monthly amount (hr.)	150	152	183	218	239	2634
2) Per cent of possible amount	52	51	59	59	60	59

What Florida has on California—and vice versa

We suspect that, if the truth were known, most of the people who talk so nostalgically about the "old-fashioned winters" of fifty years ago haven't the slightest desire to see them return and, furthermore, that they would prefer to do most of their talking about them in the mellow warmth of the southern sun. Nor is it only the aged among us who prefer to have their winters piped to them by television. Judging by the people you meet on the streets of Palm Beach and Palm Springs, the appeal of winter sunshine knows no distinction of age. And every year the appeal grows stronger. In the period 1920–1950 the population of Florida increased by 182 per cent, that of California by more than 200 per cent, while the population of the United States as a whole increased by only 42 per cent. During the same interval the population of the southernmost part of each state—that is, the least wintry part—grew even faster: Dade County experienced more than a tenfold increase; the population of Los Angeles County grew from less than 1 million in 1920 to over 4 million in 1950; and that of San Diego County grew from just over 100,000 to more than half a million.

Even though we are well aware that personal opinion concerning the relative merits of Santa Barbara and St. Petersburg, Los Angeles and Miami, San Diego and Key West tends to derive its strength more from the accident of birth, education, marriage, occupation, and inheritance than from the examination of U.S. Weather Bureau data, we should be failing in our duty to their respective chambers of commerce were we not to draw attention to some of the climatic differences between these places. If we do so without comment, it is not because we have no preferences of our own, but merely because we think it improper to express them in print.

	Average rainfall amounts (inches)				Average temperatures (°F.)				Average length of growing season (days)
	Dec.	Jan.	Feb.	Mar.	Dec.	Jan.	Feb.	Mar.	
Santa Barbara	2.94	4.25	4.16	3.34	55.1	53.4	54.7	55.8	331
St. Petersburg	2.22	2.25	2.97	2.62	64.4	63.6	64.5	68.0	348 *
San Diego	1.84	1.97	2.22	1.59	56.2	54.7	55.3	56.7	365
Key West	1.70	1.78	1.48	1.54	70.5	69.7	70.9	73.1	365

	Highest recorded temperatures (°F.)				Lowest recorded temperatures (°F.)				Average number of days with rain			
	Dec.	Jan.	Feb.	Mar.	Dec.	Jan.	Feb.	Mar.	Dec.	Jan.	Feb.	Mar.
Los Angeles	89	90	92	99	30	28	28	31	6	6	6	6
Miami	91	85	88	92	30	29	27	34	7	9	7	7

	Average daily high temperature (°F.)				Average daily low temperature (°F.)				Average cloudiness (per cent)			
	Dec.	Jan.	Feb.	Mar.	Dec.	Jan.	Feb.	Mar.	Dec.	Jan.	Feb.	Mar.
Los Angeles	67	65	66	67	48	46	47	49	37	44	47	46
Miami	75	75	75	77	63	62	61	64	53	53	48	48

* For Tampa.

Smog statistics are hard to come by: the Miamians claim that they do not have any and, in evidence, adduce the fresh pink color of their lungs and the good looks of their grapefruit. The Angelenos, on the other hand, are rumored to have dirty gray (if not pitch-black) lungs, to be buying up sun lamps in a big way, and to be having difficulty in telling the difference between a local-grown orange and an imported tangerine.

Of course, Florida has devastating floods, debilitating humidities, hair-raising thunderstorms, and house-razing hurricanes *—but not in December. It also has nice warm seas—and in December!

* It seems that even the hurricanes are regarded by the natives with pride, albeit tinctured with anxiety, for they spend no small part of their time looking for them on the weatherman's chart, pouncing eagerly on the slightest synoptic anomaly, even though 1,500 miles away, and endowing it with all sorts of ominous properties it does not have.

The role of the Gulf Stream

Exactly what the people of southern Florida owe to the Gulf Stream nobody has ever been able to calculate, but it's probably less than they owe to Henry M. Flagler's railroad and the trade winds. The one thing they certainly owe to it is the warmth of the surf, for the Gulf Stream has its "head waters" in the perennially warm seas of the Caribbean and Gulf of Mexico—seas which, even in midwinter, maintain a temperature between 70 and 75°F., and lose little of their warmth en route to the Florida Straits. The normal sea temperature off southern Florida in December is between 73 and 75°F. However, warm sea does not necessarily mean warm land. True, the air immediately over the Gulf Stream is quick to acquire, by conduction and turbulent mixing, heat from the Gulf Stream, but the bulk transfer of that heat to the adjacent mainland calls for advection, that is, for an onshore wind.

Fortunately for Mr. Flagler and his contemporaries, the "Gold Coast" of Florida lies year round in the lap of the trade winds. These winds begin life in mid-Atlantic on the equatorial side of the semipermanent Bermuda-Azores high, in a region of warm water, and they may spend anything up to ten days in transit to the American continent. Consequently, even without the Gulf Stream they would reach the east coast of southern Florida as conspicuously warm winds. What the Gulf Stream does is to serve as a heat booster to the trades, increasing their surface temperatures by a mere couple of degrees or so.

Accordingly, it is the trades rather than the Gulf Stream that put the "gold" into the Gold Coast. If you doubt it, take a walk through the main shopping section of Palm Beach or Miami on a day when the trades have been temporarily ousted from their beat by a land wind, or even by a northwesterly wind, that is, one blowing parallel to the coast. The Gulf Stream is there all the time—never more than a few miles out to sea and never less than a tepid 65° to 70°F.—but the people aren't.

If the prevailing winter winds were onshore all the way up the east coast, things might be very different, not only for the northern half of Florida,* but for Virginia Beach, Atlantic City, Jones Beach, and a hundred other resort centers: for that matter, they might even be different for Miami! For with daytime air temperatures averaging 65° to 70°F. at Christmas along a thousand-mile stretch of seaboard, there would be a great many more competitors for the tourist's dollar: the Gold Coast might even have to devalue its currency. Maybe it's time the Miamians erected a shrine to the trade winds—just in case.

What an onshore prevailing wind and a large body of relatively warm water can do, in combination, for the climate of a country is clearly seen by comparing the mean winter (January) air temperatures, latitude for latitude, on both sides of the Atlantic:

	Mean temperatures (°F.)	
Latitude	American side	European side
30°N	57	59
40°N	32	50
50°N	21	43
60°N	–9	35

All these European figures represent what climatologists call positive thermal anomalies, plus departures from the temperature norm along a given parallel of latitude. The largest anomaly occurs off the coast of northern Norway, where in midwinter air temperatures are 47 degrees higher than the

* From about Vero Beach northward, the frequency of easterly—onshore—winds falls off quite sharply; in the vicinity of Jacksonville the trades are practically confined to the three months of September, October, and November.

average for the latitude (approximately 70°N). In every case these anomalies are the result of the fact that the prevailing winds over the North Atlantic in winter are westerly (southwest—northwest), that is, offshore on the American side and onshore on the European. The fact that during part of their long sea traverse they may parallel the track of the Gulf Stream is an important, but secondary, consideration, because the main source region of these winds is not the Gulf Stream but the stagnant warm-air regions of the doldrum belt and Bermuda high.

It is wind direction, therefore, rather than sea temperature that holds the key to the climate of southern Florida in winter. There is, however, one way in which the Gulf Stream may exert an indirect influence on the climate of the adjacent land even when the wind is blowing offshore. In the opinion of a number of meteorologists, an increase in the temperature of the Gulf Stream off our eastern seaboard tends to intensify the northerly and northwesterly wind circulations in the rear of passing depressions. This, in turn, has the effect, so they tell us, of intensifying the coldness of the winters by giving the subzero air from the arctic less time to warm up on its way south. If they are right, then quite obviously it is not the kind of result envisaged by the promoters of the scheme, laid before Congress some years ago, for warding off the cold Labrador Current from the New England coast and deflecting the Gulf Stream *inshore!*

"Green Christmas—fat churchyard"?

All the world over the two most common topics of conversation are God's weather and man's health: and running them a close third is the effect of the one upon the other. As far as we can tell it has ever been so, and not without reason: of all the influences, known and surmised, that bear upon the well-being of mankind, mental as well as physical, none has been so universally acclaimed as the weather.

The relationship has been variously expressed. Virgil in his *Georgics* put it thus:

. . . when the changeful temper of the skies
The rare condenses, the dense rarefies,
New motions on the altered air impress'd
New images and passions fill the breast.

Cicero has a somewhat similar point of view:

The minds of men do in the weather share,
Dark or serene as the day's foul or fair.

On the physical level Giraldus Cambrensis, who flourished about A.D. 1200, advanced the view that western Europe with its stormy, damp weather is more healthy than the Orient.

> In those [oriental] countries . . . the heavens terrify you with their thunders, and flash their lightnings in your eyes. The blazing sun allows you no rest. If you eat too much, death is at the gate: if you drink wine undiluted with water, death is at the gate. [On the other hand, he continues] We [in Ireland] sleep secure in the open air . . . we fear no wind piercing us with cold, prostrating our strength with heat or carrying pestilence in its blast. The air we breathe and with which we are surrounded, lends us its beneficent and salutary support.*

Another medieval writer, Giovanni da Fontana, went as far as to declare that in Ireland men grow so old that they ask to be taken to some less salubrious climate in order to be able to die. And it seems that their request has been answered, for in the New World the Irish have had no difficulty in dying—though, truth to tell, they are not alone in this ability.

* *Topographia Hiberniae*, Vol. I, pp. 26–27. English translation by T. Foster, London, 1863.

Whether or not we incline to the prejudices of Giraldus and de Fontana (and the more the matter is studied statistically, the nearer to the human optimum would the climate of Ireland appear to be), it is hard to escape the conclusion that death rates vary with the temperature. In a study of daily deaths in New York City during the June, 1952, heat wave, the Health Department reported as follows:

Average number of deaths, per diem, June 1–24 (*i.e.*, before heat wave began)	213
Average number of deaths, per diem, June 25–27 (when thermometer soared into the 90s)	376
Average number of deaths, per diem, of people sixty-five years of age and over, June 1–24	103
Average number of deaths, per diem, of people sixty-five years of age and over, June 25–27	210

A similar study of the August, 1948, heat wave showed a 300 per cent increase in the metropolitan death rate.

It seems, though, that the tendency for more people to die when the thermometer takes a sharp upward turn is not confined to the summer season. Thus, the late Ellsworth Huntington, American geographer and explorer, found that even in winter about 10 per cent more people died in the New York region following a two-day rise of temperature of the order of 16°F. than on days with a corresponding drop of temperature, and that even in the severest cold spells the life expectation of New Yorkers was greater than in the most pronounced mild spells.

Whether it is the warmth that kills us, or the shock given to our systems by its sudden arrival, or the greater water content of the warm air, or the lower pressures which accompany it, or the bacteria and viruses that find in such air a congenial environment for their operations, these investigations do not disclose. The thing that is established by them, and confirmed by those of many other workers in the same field, is that unseasonable warmth (of which a green countryside is the traditional sign, par excellence, in middle latitudes) is no kind of present for Christmas Day—except, perhaps, for the morticians among us.

Lest we should be accused of an unhelpful obsession with mortality, we hasten to assure our readers that the population of New York City continues to grow, in spite of all the pestilences that walk in darkness, the destructions that waste at noonday, not to mention the terrors by night and the arrows by day. After all, the odds are 20,000 to 1 in your favor.

It's been a good year—almost everywhere!

We suspect, however, that even green Christmases have their saving graces. They may not greatly please the innkeeper of Lake Placid, or the woodsman eager to get moving with his lumber, or the manufacturer of snowshoes, but they do not come amiss to the southbound vacationist, the hydroelectric engineer for whom an early freeze means a heavier-than-usual drain on his water-storage facilities, or the Pennsylvania farmer who finds himself behind with his plowing.

We suspect, furthermore, that every other lamented departure from meteorological normalcy—and how many there are in a twelvemonth!—is likewise to be regarded as an occasion more for gratitude than anxiety, let alone for a committee of investigation. We may not understand, or like, the "extravagance" of the physical universe any better than Job's misnamed comforters, but the explanation of it proffered by one of them, Elihu, is still worth pondering: "He causeth it to come, whether for correction, or for his land, or for mercy." * In matters of weather, most of us are more interested in mercy—

* Job 37:13.

sunshine for our golf, good visibility for our hunting—and in land—rain for our raspberries, warmth for our corn—than in correction. Of that we would be spared, if, indeed, we haven't had enough already, what with being fined by frost for growing fruit in the wrong places, imprisoned by dust storms for abusing the hospitality of pasture and plowland, and thrashed by rampaging rivers for having destroyed the protective cover of our watersheds.

But though we may not be able to rise to gratitude, at least we should be slow to sink to slander, for if we had but the wit to see it, we should find that "abnormal" rains, "unusual" drought, "phenomenal" cold, and "record-breaking" heat were part of the price—not exorbitant at that—we pay for our apprenticeship in the art of living with the good American earth, and that any skill we may have acquired in the art is largely the result of learning to wrestle with them. (Perhaps it is our preoccupation with such matters—with spreading tables in the wilderness, with making deserts blossom as the rose, and with storing rain and crops in the months of plenty against the day of scarcity—that is responsible for our habitually aggrieved attitude towards the weather.)

Far from being either wasteful or wanton, I believe that the ordering of the meteorological realm, including the not infrequent semblances of disorder, is providential and, so, a matter for reverence; and that what we cannot explain or find it in our hearts to commend, we should at least refrain from reviling.

But, it may well be asked: what merit can there be in an arrangement whereby some parts of the North American continent are almost perennially in the grip of cold and drought, while others daily wilt from exposure to high temperatures and higher humidities? And what conceivable good is there in having the resources of heat and moisture distributed so unevenly, and with such small regard, apparently, for human needs?

As a wartime meteorologist, I had occasion to make a quite intensive study of weather conditions in what has come to be known technically as the intertropical front, but what for most of us, sailors and landsmen alike, will doubtless continue to be thought of as the doldrum belt. The longer I examined this region, the more I came to realize that here, where the Ancient Mariner found himself becalmed, with neither

. . . breath nor motion
As idle as a painted ship
Upon a painted ocean

is the powerhouse that drives the weather not only of the tropics but of almost the entire world, and that it does this by the simple, if seemingly prodigal, device of charging the surface layers of the atmosphere with so much heat and moisture that they become unstable and rise into the upper atmosphere, where they take flight poleward, carrying their precious cargo to middle- and high-latitudes. Seen in this context the exceedingly heavy rains and irksome humidity of the low tropics are inescapable by-products of a lifting mechanism without which life in North America could barely be sustained. Those who may be disposed to doubt the actuality, let alone the wisdom, of this arrangement would do well to study the weather forecaster's daily synoptic charts—almost any day's charts would do. Even in December it is not uncommon for large areas (up to 30 per cent) of extratropical North America to be occupied by air masses that originated in or near the intertropical convergence zone. In summer as much as two-thirds of North America may be under the control of the tropics, and tongues of tropical air may then penetrate as far north as the Arctic Circle. Closer inspection would show that probably not less than three-fourths of the rain falling on North American soil on any given day is the gift of tropical maritime air. We would even hazard that between 75 and 80 per cent of all the moisture evaporated into the atmosphere and subsequently precipitated back in the form of rain, snow, hail, and sleet has a tropical origin.*

Again, I do not think it would be difficult to show that without the so-called arctic wastes, the climates of the Middle West, the Great Lakes and St. Lawrence lowlands, New England, and, in fact, most of the inhabited regions of North America, would be much less satisfactory for agriculture as well as less stimulating to mind and body. In the winter the cold waves which from time to time advance upon us out of the Canadian north bring the chill weather which tones up the body, toughens the constitution, and, so the farmer will tell you, cleanses and fertilizes the soil, killing off many unwanted parasites. These cold waves also have a hand in bringing the snow: their very dryness makes them greedy of the moisture which abounds in the lakes, rivers, grasslands, and forests of our central lowlands, and which can be released subsequently by uplift against a mountain range or in the melee of a cyclonic conflict.

I believe that it could equally be shown that the climatic fluctuations which have been so conspicuous a feature of the earth's history, and which are still under way, ought to be regarded as a boon to humanity. At first thought, temperature increases of the order of 2 to 3°F. may seem trivial, and to have

* It is not without interest to note the difference in amounts of rain that have been observed to fall in tropical air masses and extratropical air masses. Falls of over 20 inches in one day have been reported in the former (26.12 inches is the record for the United States), whereas falls of even 2 to 3 inches are uncommon in the latter.

little more than nuisance value. But nothing could be further from the truth. The results of the current fluctuations are of great account to many people. Forty years ago west-coast Greenlanders used to live by hunting seal and walrus; now they live by fishing for cod which, because of the warming up of the northern waters, are found in abundance as far north as 73°N. (At the beginning of the century they were seldom found north of Cape Farewell.) The waters of Hudson Bay and Hudson Strait are now ice-free for several weeks longer, on the average, than they used to be, with consequent extension of the navigation season at Fort Churchill, and brightening of its commercial prospects. No less substantial changes, ecological and economic, have taken place in the European sector of the arctic. If things go on in this way, who knows but what palm trees will one day be growing on Coney Island, and Bostonians speaking with a Southern accent?

Seriously, though, is it not a matter for heartfelt thanks that, at so critical a time in human history, the climate of an area covering no less than one-third of the entire land surface of the earth (in Canada alone the area affected is more than one million square miles) should, its vagaries, uncertainties, extravagances, and downright devilment notwithstanding, be getting more, rather than less, genial? In a world that is already hard pressed to find food for its 2½ billion inhabitants, anything that gives promise of adding to the tally of its living space is surely a major contribution to the happiness of its people, and to the strength of its defenses against the timeless evils of hunger, malnutrition, and war.

And every year that gives us a chance to work toward such an end is a good year.

Epilogue

Praised be my Lord
For our Brother the Wind
And for Air and Cloud,
Calms and All Weather.

—ST. FRANCIS OF ASSISI

Index

About the Author

Dr. George H. T. Kimble was born and educated in England, receiving his B.A. and M.A. degrees at King's College, London. After graduating, he taught geography at the University College of Hull and then at the University of Reading.

During the last war he was a lieutenant commander, engaged on invasion weather projects, in the British Naval Meteorological Service. Among the reports prepared by him were some which helped determine the date of the D-day invasion by the Allied forces. Dr. Kimble was later sent around the world to study the various forecasting techniques employed in the tropics by meteorological agencies.

Released from the British Navy in 1945, he went to McGill University in Canada as chairman of the newly established department of geography and director of the meteorological observatory. He also established the now internationally known McGill Summer School of Geography.

In 1948, Dr. Kimble received his Ph.D. in geography (summa cum laude) from the University of Montreal. In June of 1950, he became the director of the American Geographical Society of New York, the oldest organization of its kind in the United States. He resigned from that organization in 1953 to direct the Survey of Tropical Africa which is being sponsored by the Twentieth Century Fund.

One of the outstanding geographers and meteorologists, Dr. Kimble is the author of a number of books in his field, including *Geography in the Middle Ages, The World's Open Spaces, The Way of the World,* and *The Weather,* which has sold over 200,000 copies.

In addition to holding the office of secretary-treasurer of the International Geographical Union, Dr. Kimble is a member of the United States National Committee of that body, a Fellow of the Royal Geographical Society and of the Royal Meteorological Society. He is also a member of the Association of American Geographers, the History of Science Society and the American Meteorological Society.

He is married, has two children, and lives in Alpine, New Jersey.

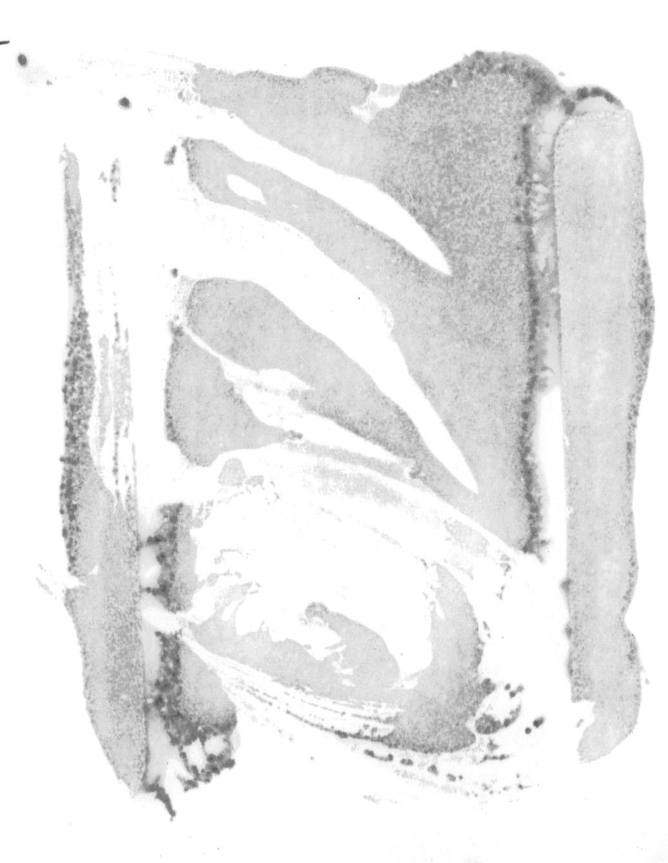